I WILL ALWAYS PLACE THE
MISSION FIRST.

I WILL
NEVER ACCEPT DEFEAT.

ADAPTIVE TEAM LEADERSHIP

I WILL NEVER QUIT.

MSL 301
REVISED EDITION

I WILL NEVER LEAVE
A FALLEN COMRADE.

Custom Publishing

New York   Boston   San Francisco
London   Toronto   Sydney   Tokyo   Singapore   Madrid
Mexico City   Munich   Paris   Cape Town   Hong Kong   Montreal

Printed in the United States of America

10 9 8 7 6 5 4 3 2 1

2008420016

RG/RH

Pearson
Custom Publishing
is a division of

www.pearsonhighered.com

ISBN 10: 0-536-56319-5
ISBN 13 978-0-536-56319-4

CONTENTS

INTRODUCTION

Key Points

1 **Overview of the BOLC I: ROTC Curriculum**

2 **Military Science and Leadership Tracks**

3 **MSL 301 Course Overview: Adaptive Team Leadership**

4 **The Role of the MSL III Cadet**

5 **Academic Approach**

6 **How to Use This Textbook**

7 **Cadet Resources**

Leadership is intangible, and therefore no weapon ever designed can replace it.

General of the Army (GOA) Omar N. Bradley

Overview of the BOLC I: ROTC Curriculum

Being an officer in the US Army means being a leader, a counselor, a strategist, and a motivator. Officers must lead other Soldiers in all situations and adjust to environments that are always changing. To prepare prospective officers to meet this challenge, the Army ROTC program is designed to develop confident, competent, and adaptive leaders with the basic military science and leadership foundation necessary not only to lead small units in the Contemporary Operating Environment (COE) but also to evolve into the Army's future senior leaders.

The ROTC program is the first, or pre-commissioning, phase of the Army's Basic Officer Leader Course (BOLC). The goal of BOLC is to develop competent and confident leaders imbued with a warrior ethos, grounded in field craft, and skilled in leading Soldiers, training subordinates, and employing and maintaining equipment. BOLC is designed to ensure a tough, standardized, small-unit leadership experience that flows progressively from the pre-commissioning phase (BOLC I, one source of which is ROTC) through the initial-entry field leadership phase (BOLC II) to the branch technical phase (BOLC III). This progressive sequence will produce officers with maturity, confidence, and competence who share a common bond—regardless of whether their branch is combat arms, combat support, or sustainment—and who are prepared to lead small units upon arrival at their first unit of assignment.

The basis of the Army ROTC curriculum is the BOLC common core task list, which represents the foundation of competencies a second lieutenant needs upon arrival at his or her first unit. ROTC Cadets receive education and training in each of the BOLC I common core tasks, as do officers produced by other commissioning sources (the United States Military Academy and Officer Candidate School). Then, in BOLC II and III, all second lieutenants, regardless of commissioning source, participate in more-advanced, field- and branch-oriented education and training events that are part of the BOLC II and III common core task lists.

Like the BOLC model, ROTC's Military Science and Leadership (MSL) courses are sequential and progressive; that is the content and expectations placed on you as the student increase as you progress through the ROTC Program. As you may recall, the academic rigor of your MS II year was greater than that of your MS I year. Your MS III year will be far more challenging and involved than your MS I and II years combined.

As was the case with your MS I and MS II ROTC curriculum, your MS III courses are organized into five tracks: the Leadership Track, the Personal Development Track, the Values and Ethics Track, the Officership Track, and the Tactics and Techniques Track. The MSL III and IV years will treat each MSL track in greater depth in order to teach you all the knowledge, skills, and attitudes essential for commissioning, success at BOLC II, and the establishment of a sound foundation for a career as a commissioned Army officer.

In addition to classroom instruction, your MS III year will provide you with multiple opportunities to apply military science and leadership concepts in field environments, including leadership labs, battalion or joint field training exercises (FTX), and any battalion STX training that your PMS may direct. As a contracted Cadet, you must participate in physical training (PT) to build your fitness ethos and maintain Army Physical Fitness Test (APFT) standards. Crucial to the ROTC program is Cadet attendance at the Leader Development and Assessment Course (LDAC), normally between the MSL III and MSL IV years. The primary focus at LDAC is to evaluate each Cadet's officer potential in a collective garrison and field training environment. The secondary purpose of LDAC is to validate specific skills taught on campus and to impart selective individual and collective skills.

Military Science and Leadership Tracks

Each of the five learning tracks in the Army ROTC military science and leadership curriculum has subcategories that are reiterated and developed progressively through the MSL courses. The US Army has long recognized the importance of the effective leader who fully embodies the leadership ethos, who is fully committed to being a lifelong learner of leadership as a process and journey rather than a destination, and who has the professional acumen to put this leadership into action in an effective, value-added manner regardless of the challenge of the situation faced in the fast-paced, ever-changing COE.

Leadership

- *Leader Attributes* from FM 6-22 are used throughout the curriculum as a graphic organizer for developing a basic knowledge of leader dimensions. The implicit focus throughout the curriculum is on the importance of personal discipline in becoming a leader of character, a leader with presence, and a leader with intellectual capacity.

- *Core Leader Competencies* are centered around what an Army leader does. These competencies are defined and illustrated as they apply to direct (tactical), organizational (operational), and strategic levels of leader responsibility. The course of study as a whole is designed to challenge and develop the leader's ability to lead (demonstrate competence, communicate, and motivate), develop self and others (adapt, learn, and mentor), and achieve (prioritize, plan, and execute).

Personal Development

- *Character* development is an implicit aspect of the ROTC curriculum. Cadets are challenged throughout the course of study to recognize and model the Army Values of loyalty, duty, respect, selfless service, honor, integrity, and personal courage; to empathize with their peers, subordinates, and others; and to live the Warrior Ethos.

- *Physical Presence* is foundational for Army leader development. Every Cadet who seeks to become an officer must be able to demonstrate an exceptional level of physical fitness, composure, confidence, and resilience.

- *Intellectual Capacity* has always been and continues to be an imperative characteristic for officers serving in the US Army. Those serving in the contemporary operating environments of Iraq and Afghanistan are learning firsthand the value of mental agility and innovation to Army leadership. Vignettes and case studies from these environments are used to challenge Cadets to examine non-linear situations, to hone their judgment, and to increase their tactical, technical, cultural, and geopolitical knowledge.

Values and Ethics

- *Army Values.* While it is important for Cadets to be able to articulate the seven Army Values, it is even more imperative that they be able to demonstrate these values in their daily interactions with others. Values form the foundation for Army leadership.

- *Professional Ethics.* In addition to the Army values, military codes and regulations govern ethical behavior and decision making. Cadets apply the ethical decision making process during case studies and historical vignettes.

- *Warrior Ethos* is embedded in case studies and historical vignettes throughout the curriculum. Cadre members discuss the four basic principles of the Warrior Ethos whenever possible. Cadets apply the Warrior Ethos to increasingly complex situations as they progress through the ROTC program.

Officership

- *Military Heritage.* Cadre members teach and model military heritage through daily performance and contact, lab exercises, ceremonies, and interpersonal interactions throughout the ROTC curriculum.

- *Military History.* Cadets review vignettes and case studies, which provide opportunities for critical reasoning in evaluating tactics, leadership styles, problem solving, and decision making.

- *Management and Administration.* Cadets learn Army programs, policies, and procedures related to areas such as organization, human resources, management, administration, training, and facilities in order to support Army operations.

Tactics and Techniques

- *Tactical operations* are *the* major focus of the two MSL III courses. Cadets are expected to shift from mastering an understanding of tactical operations to mastering these operations through in-depth study and experiential leadership opportunities. During labs, Cadets are expected to develop and demonstrate a proficient understanding and ability to perform basic land navigation, troop leading procedures, and squad tactical operations.

MSL 301 Course Overview: Adaptive Team Leadership

MSL 301 challenges Cadets to study, practice, and evaluate adaptive leadership skills as they are presented with the demands of preparing for the ROTC Leader Development and Assessment Course (LDAC). Challenging scenarios related to small-unit tactical operations are used to develop self-awareness and critical-thinking skills. Cadets receive systematic and specific feedback on their leadership values, attributes, skills, and actions. Cadets must meet the following objectives:

Apply the Army Leadership Requirements Model while leading teams.

- Apply the Army Leadership Requirements Model—leader attributes and core leader competencies—in tactical situations
- Compare and contrast different leadership styles and their effects on team dynamics
- Apply effective oral and written communication skills in Army operations
- Counsel subordinates on performance.

Apply tactical principles and doctrine to Army operations.

- Conduct troop leading procedures
- Analyze terrain in practical situations
- Navigate from one point to another
- Apply principles of squad tactics in offensive and defensive operations
- Conduct a risk assessment.

Analyze personal readiness to enter LDAC in key areas of flexibility, character, adaptability, and fitness.

- Conduct a self-assessment in personal development areas
- Develop a readiness plan in preparation for LDAC
- Identify battle fatigue risk factors and leader actions to offset them.

The Role of the MSL III Cadet

LEADS. As a potential Army officer, you will be challenged to study, practice, and evaluate adaptive team leadership skills as you are presented with the demands of the ROTC Leader Development and Assessment Course. Increasingly complex scenarios related to small-unit tactical operations are used to develop self-awareness and critical-thinking skills. You will receive systematic and specific feedback on your performance as a battalion staff officer by your cadre, just as commissioned officers serving on staffs receive counsel and feedback from their raters.

DEVELOPS. Learning the skills required of a competent officer and leader demands that you participate actively in learning through critical reflection, inquiry, dialogue, and group interactions. MSL 301 will teach you competency-based leadership described in FM 6-22 as it relates to your responsibility to earn your commission and to develop junior Cadets to become future Army lieutenants. Based on your understanding and experience of adaptive team leadership, you will work to identify activities (such as club leadership, sports teams, event planning, or other extracurricular activities) in which to practice adaptive leadership skills. You are also encouraged to continue in your own leadership roles beyond ROTC. Everyone is responsible for contributing to the success of the learning experience.

ACHIEVES. Extensive small-group discussions and exercises are embedded throughout the MSL 301 course. MSL III Cadets are encouraged to work together as a team and with their instructors in modifying assignments, suggesting agendas, and raising questions for discussion. Collaborative learning is enhanced when Cadets describe adaptive team-leadership lessons learned from lab and FTX experiences.

Academic Approach

The MSL curriculum is outcomes based and designed to focus on Cadet learning, rather than on any specific subject matter. Focusing on the Cadet requires student-centered objectives and conscious attention to how Cadets react to the instruction received. For effective instruction, Cadets need the opportunity to apply the knowledge received from instruction received by experienced Cadre. Too often, academic instruction is limited to the delivery of information, either through reading assignments, lectures, or slide presentations. Active, student-centered learning, in contrast, is founded on the belief that interaction is central to the learning process. Learning occurs during class in the same way it does outside the classroom: through unstructured and structured experiences in which the Cadet interacts with cadre, with the instructional material, and with other Cadets. Helpful synonyms for ROTC's student-centered approach to learning are experiential learning, direct experience, discovery learning, experience-based learning, and participatory learning. All of these approaches center around five basic steps:

1. Readiness for and openness to the experience.
2. The experience itself.

3. Reflection upon the experience.
4. Analysis, application of theory, or additional explanation of information to clarify the relationship between theory and actions, with an understanding of lessons learned regarding needed changes.
5. The opportunity to re-experience (practice in new situations/practical exercises).

The onus must first be on the Cadet's pre-class preparation. Cadets must come to class with a foundation of knowledge from their pre-class readings. This allows the cadre to apply the Socratic model of reflective learning during the 50 minutes of classroom instruction. During this limited contact hour, the cadre can focus on explaining the concepts or material that needs clarifying.

Helpful synonyms for ROTC's student-centered approach to learning are experiential learning, direct experience, discovery learning, experience-based learning, and participatory learning.

How to Use This Textbook

The readings in this textbook have been compiled to prepare the Cadet to participate actively and productively in MSL classes and labs. The chapters are divided into the five MSL curriculum tracks as follows:

Leadership Track

Personal Development Track

Values and Ethics Track

Officership Track

Tactics and Techniques Track

To be most effective, MSL class sessions are best sequenced to coincide with Leadership Lab schedules, which may vary from campus to campus due to weather, academic calendars, and other local variables. Thus, class sessions may not necessarily follow the same sequence as textbook chapters. Cadets must follow the reading assignments given by their instructors to ensure they are adequately prepared for each class session.

The first page of each chapter orients the Cadet to the key points to be covered in the reading assignment. At the end of each chapter, learning assessment questions serve as "checks on learning" for the Cadet to ensure he or she understands the key points of the chapter. Additionally, vignettes, scenarios, case studies, and critical-thinking questions are dispersed throughout the chapters to help the Cadet build critical-thinking skills and to apply the coursework to real-world situations. The learning assessment questions at the end of each chapter are aligned with the learning objectives for each coinciding lesson.

Cadet Resources

Cadet Textbook. This textbook contains the readings that support the MSL 301 course, Adaptive Team Leadership.

Blackboard (Bb). The Blackboard course web site, **http://rotc.blackboard.com**, contains MSL course materials.

CONCLUSION

The Basic Officer Leadership Course (BOLC) common core task list forms the foundation of competencies a second lieutenant needs to know upon arrival at his or her first unit. Today's Army officer develops through a progression of BOLC sequential learning programs designed for pre-commissioning (BOLC I), common tactical training that is focused on warrior tasks and battle drills (BOLC II), and basic branch-specific training (BOLC III). The ROTC program is the implementation of BOLC I in a university setting. Today's ROTC Cadet represents the future leadership of our great nation. Such responsibility must be carried by officers well versed in the principles and practices of effective leadership, military operations, and personal development. A future officer must be a leader of character, of presence, and of intellectual capacity—a professional who is able to think critically and ready to lead Soldiers in the Contemporary Operating Environment (COE). The MSL III year of ROTC forges this officer through a challenging curriculum of leader development, Army operations, and personal development in preparation for the culminating test during the Leader Development and Assessment Course (LDAC).

Although this course prepares you for this challenge, it is your responsibility to live the leader attributes while adopting and demonstrating Army Values at all times—both on and off campus. The qualities of an Army officer are not words professed for an exam or exercise. At the MSL III level, these qualities are the expression of a professional prepared to "support and defend the Constitution of the United States against all enemies, foreign or domestic." Your commitment to excellence in the Warrior Ethos, tactical proficiency, and adaptive team leadership is essential to the success of the Army of the future.

References

Field Manual 6-22, *Army Leadership: Competent, Confident, and Agile.* 12 August 2006.

Cadet Command Reg. 145-3, ROTC Precommissioning Training and Leadership Development.

INTRODUCTION TO TEAM DYNAMICS

Key Points

1 Effective Team Building Practices

2 The Three Stages of Team Development

3 The Role of Learning in Developing Team Excellence

All United States military doctrine is based upon reliance on the ingenuity of the individual working on his own initiative as a member of a team and using the most modern weapons and equipment which can be provided him.

GEN Manton S. Eddy, Commanding General, XII Corps, World War II

Introduction

You'll hear it again and again: The Army is a team. Every Soldier in every unit must have a sense of belonging to this team. On the battlefield, the sense of belonging to a team may be all that holds a unit together—the national cause, the mission's purpose, and all other concerns may not be at the forefront in the heat of combat.

The most important influence you have on your people is the example you set.

Building a team that will train and win under the toughest conditions takes hard work, patience, and an ability to deal with changing dynamics as people work together under stress. Your investment in learning how to apply team building practices will yield the ultimate reward: Good teams get the job done. Good teams finish their missions on time with the resources they have and with little wasted effort. In combat, good teams are the most effective and take the fewest casualties.

Good Teams—

- Work together to accomplish the mission

- Execute tasks thoroughly and quickly

- Meet or exceed the standard

- Thrive on demanding challenges

- Learn from their experiences and are proud of their accomplishments.

Soldiers Are Our Credentials

In September 1944 on the Cotentin Peninsula in France, the commander of a German stronghold under siege by an American force sent word that he wanted to discuss surrender terms. German MG Hermann Ramcke was in his bunker when his staff escorted the assistant division commander of the US 8th Infantry Division down the concrete stairway to the underground headquarters. MG Ramcke addressed BG Charles D. W. Canham through an interpreter: "I am to surrender to you. Let me see your credentials." Canham pointed to the dirty, tired, and disheveled but victorious American infantrymen who were crowding the dugout entrance and replied, "These are my credentials."

Critical Thinking

Think back to when you were part of a newly created team. Can you identify distinct stages or phases throughout the team's evolution? At what point did the team really begin to work well together to get things done?

Effective Team Building Practices

As an Army leader, you'll employ many practices to build effective teams. *Strong leadership* is key at all levels. *Individual coaching* reinforces positive behavior and strengthens the team as a whole. *Demanding training* builds team competence and cohesion. Finally, *mutual trust* and *respect* cement the bonds of loyalty that sustain the team through crisis and combat.

Small Team Leadership Is Fundamental

If the leaders of the Army's small teams are competent, and if team members trust one another, those teams and the larger team to which they belong will hold together and get the job done. When you belong to a successful team, you look at nearly everything in a positive light. You see problems as challenges rather than obstacles. Your winner's attitude is infectious, especially when you are part of a small team. A cohesive team gets the job done more efficiently than an uncoordinated group of individuals. Just as a football team practices to win on the gridiron, so must a team of Soldiers practice to be effective on the battlefield. They must also learn how to live in a dynamic environment where roles and attitudes often shift. You, as their leader and coach, must develop them into a team that will succeed in this environment.

Coaching Is Key to Small-Unit Success

Coaching involves you as a leader observing your subordinates, assessing their performance, and communicating with them to ensure they develop and execute individual plans of action to reinforce strengths and overcome weaknesses. Through effective coaching, you continually support your subordinates and the plan. When you are an effective coach, your Soldiers perform—for you, for other people in the squad or section, for others in the team or crew, or for the person on their right or left. This is the fundamental truth of human conduct in warfare: Soldiers perform because they will not let their buddies down. When your Soldiers trust you and the coaching you give them, the strengths of the team make the weaknesses of individuals insignificant.

Training Together Builds Trust

When Soldiers train together, they gain competence together. Trust is a product of that shared competence. As your team becomes more experienced and enjoys more successes, it becomes more cohesive. Subordinates will learn to trust you as a leader if you know how to do your job and act consistently—if you say what you mean and mean what you say.

What It Takes to Build Strong Teams

People will do the most extraordinary things for their friends. It's your job—your way of life—as an Army leader to draw each member into the team because someday, possibly tomorrow, you may ask that person for extraordinary effort. You must apply interpersonal leadership skills that transform individuals into reliable team members. If you've done your work, the team member won't let you down.

Remember that within a larger team, smaller teams may be at different stages of development. For instance, members of First Squad may be used to working together. They trust one another and get the job done—usually exceeding the standard—with no wasted motion. On the other hand, Second Squad in the same platoon may have just received three new Soldiers and a team leader from another company. As a *team*, Second Squad is less mature. It will take the members some time to get to the level of First Squad.

New team members have to learn how things work: The existing team must bring them on board and make them feel part of the team. They must learn the standards and the

Trust Earned

In a 1976 interview, Congressman Hamilton Fish of New York told of his experiences as a white officer with the 369th Infantry Regiment, an all-black unit in the segregated Army of 1917. Fish knew that his unit would function only if his Soldiers trusted him; his Soldiers, all of whom had volunteered for combat duty, deserved nothing less than a trustworthy leader. When a white regiment threatened to attack the black Soldiers in training camp, Fish, his pistol drawn, alerted the leaders of that regiment and headed off a disaster.

"There was one thing the African-American Soldiers wanted above all from a white officer," Fish recalled in an interview nearly 60 years later, "and that was fair treatment. Even in New York City [home of most of his Soldiers] they really did not get a square deal most of the time. But if they felt you were on the level with them, they would go all out for you. And they seemed to have a sixth sense in realizing just how you felt. I sincerely wanted to lead them as real Soldiers, and they knew it."

climate of their new unit. They'll have to demonstrate some competence before other members really accept them. Finally, they must practice working together. As a leader and coach who must build and oversee the team, you'll be better equipped if you know what to expect. Make use of the information on the next few pages. Learn what to look for—and stay flexible.

It's your job as an Army leader to pull each member into the team because you may someday ask that person for an extraordinary effort.

The Three Stages of Team Development

Use the following list as a guide to what you must do to pull a team together, move it in the right direction, and keep it moving until it reaches the goal. The foundation for success in the work ahead—as you get your team to pull together—is that your subordinates must strongly feel that they're a part of the team, that their contribution is essential to survival and success. They must know that you'll train them and listen to them. When they bond with you and their teammates, they will not let you down with shoddy work or half-baked efforts. To develop this bond of teamwork, you must constantly observe, counsel, develop, listen, and *lead*. You must be every bit the team player you want your subordinates to be—and more.

Stages of Team Development:

- Formation
- Enrichment
- Sustainment

Teams do not come together by accident. Leaders build and guide them through the stages of *formation, enrichment,* and *sustainment*. While our discussion in this chapter may make the process seem orderly, the dynamic reality is more complicated. Different teams develop differently, and the boundaries between stages are not hard and fast. Recognizing this, you must be sensitive to the characteristics of the team you're building and of its individual members—your Soldiers.

TABLE 1.1   Team Building Stages

FORMATION STAGE	Subordinate Actions	Leader & Organizational Actions
General Team Building	• Learn about team purpose, tasks, and standards. • Learn about leaders and other members. • Achieve belonging and acceptance.	• Design effective reception and orientation. • Create learning experiences. • Communicate expectations. • Listen to and care for subordinates. • Reward positive contributions. • Set example.
Team Building for Deployments	• Adjust to uncertainty across the spectrum of conflict. • Cope with fear of unknown injury and death. • Adjust to separation from home and family.	• Talk with each Soldier. • Reassure with calm presence. • Communicate vital safety tips. • Provide stable situation. • Establish buddy system. • Help Soldiers deal with immediate problems.
ENRICHMENT STAGE		
General Team Building	• Trust leaders and other members. • Cooperate with team members. • Share information. • Accept the way things are done. • Adjust to feelings about how things ought to be done.	• Trust and encourage trust. • Reinforce desired group norms. • Establish clear lines of authority. • Establish individual and unit goals. • Identify and grow leaders. • Train as a unit for mission. • Build pride through accomplishment.
Team Building for Deployments	• Demonstrate competence. • Become a team member. • Learn about the threat. • Learn about the area of operations. • Avoid life-threatening mistakes.	• Demonstrate competence. • Prepare as a unit for operations. • Know the Soldiers. • Provide stable unit climate. • Emphasize safety for improved readiness.
SUSTAINMENT STAGE		
General Team Building	• Trust others. • Share ideas and feelings freely. • Assist other team members. • Sustain trust and confidence. • Share missions and values.	• Demonstrate trust. • Focus on teamwork, training, and maintaining. • Respond to subordinate problems. • Devise more challenging training. • Build pride and spirit.
Team Building for Deployments	• Adjust to continuous operations. • Cope with casualties. • Adjust to enemy actions. • Overcome boredom. • Avoid rumors. • Control fear, anger, despair, and panic.	• Observe and enforce sleep discipline. • Sustain safety awareness. • Inform Soldiers. • Know and deal with Soldiers' perceptions. • Keep Soldiers productively busy. • Use in-process reviews (IPRs) and after action reviews (AARs). • Act decisively in face of panic.

Critical Thinking

Describe the key stages of team development and explain their significance for Army training.

Compare the characteristics of your team with the team building stage descriptions. Your comparison can help you determine what to expect of your team and what you must do to improve its capabilities. Teams, like individuals, have different personalities. The leader's job is not to make teams that are clones of one another: The job is to make best use of the team's peculiar talents, get it to work up to its full potential, and motivate it to aggressively fulfill its missions.

Formation Stage

Teams work best when new members quickly feel a part of the team. The two critical steps of the **formation stage**—reception and orientation—are dramatically different in peace and war. In combat, a good sponsorship process can make the difference between life and death for new arrivals and the entire team.

Reception is the leader's welcoming the new member to the organization. Time permitting, it should include a handshake and a personal introduction. In the **orientation** stage, the new member meets other team members, learns the workplace layout and schedule, and generally gets to know the environment. In combat, you may not have much time to spend with new members of your team. In that case, you assign new arrivals a sponsor. That person will orient them until they "know the ropes."

In combat, you have countless things to worry about, and the mental state of new arrivals might seem low on the list. But if your Soldiers cannot fight, your unit will suffer needless casualties and may fail to complete its mission.

formation stage

the first stage of team development, in which the team is forming and members are getting to know each other

reception

the step in the formation stage in which the leader welcomes the new member to the organization

orientation

the step in the formation stage in which the new member meets other team members, learns the workplace layout and schedule, and gets to know the environment

During combat, if you don't have time to spend with new arrivals, assign them a sponsor to help orient them.

Replacements in the European Theater of Operations

Most historians writing about World War II agree that the replacement system that fed new Soldiers into the line units was seriously flawed, especially in the European Theater of Operations. Troops fresh from stateside posts were shuffled about in tent cities where they were just numbers. 1LT George Wilson, an infantry company commander who received 100 replacements on December 29, 1944, in the midst of the Battle of the Bulge, remembers the results: "We discovered that these men had been on a rifle range only once; they had never thrown a grenade or fired a bazooka [antitank rocket], mortar, or machine gun." PVT Morris Dunn, another Soldier who ended up with the 84th Division after weeks in a replacement depot, recalls how the new Soldiers felt: "We were just numbers, we didn't know anybody, and I've never felt so alone and miserable and helpless in my entire life. We'd been herded around like cattle at roundup time. On the ride to the front it was cold and raining with the artillery fire louder every mile, and finally we were dumped out in the middle of a heavily damaged town."

Discipline and shared hardships pull people together in powerful ways. SGT Alvin C. York described cohesion clearly and simply:

The war brings out the worst in you. It turns you into a mad, fightin' animal, but it also brings out something else, something I jes' don't know how to describe, a sort of tenderness and love for the fellows fightin' with you.

Enrichment Stage

enrichment stage

the second stage of team development, in which team members learn to trust themselves, their peers, and their leaders

In the **enrichment stage**, the new team and the new team members gradually move from questioning everything to trusting themselves, their peers, and their leaders. As the leader, you learn to trust by listening, following up on what you hear, establishing clear lines of authority, and setting standards. Training takes a group of individuals and molds them into a team while preparing them to accomplish their missions. Although training occurs during all three stages of team building, it's especially important during the enrichment stage. It's at this point that the team is building *collective proficiency*—the ability to work together smoothly and competently.

Sustainment Stage

sustainment stage

the third stage of team development, in which members identify with the team and will do what needs doing without being told

During the **sustainment stages**, members identify with "their team." They own it, have pride in it, and want the team to succeed. At this stage, team members will do what needs doing without being told. Every new mission gives you, the leader, a chance to strengthen the team's bonds and challenge it to reach for new heights of accomplishment. You develop your subordinates because you know that they will be tomorrow's team leaders. The team should continuously train so that it stays proficient in the collective and individual tasks it must perform to accomplish its mission.

The Role of Learning in Developing Team Excellence

The Army is a learning organization: It harnesses the experience of its people and organizations to improve the way it does business. Based on their experiences, learning organizations adopt new techniques and procedures that get the job done more efficiently or effectively. Likewise, they discard techniques and procedures that have outlived their purpose.

You must remain flexible, however, when trying to make sense of your experiences. Leaders who work day after day and never stop to ask, "How can I do this better?" will not learn and will not improve themselves or their team. Leaders at all levels—from those in cadet leadership positions to major-command commanders—who daily look at their experience to find better ways of doing things will constantly and rapidly improve.

Based on their experiences, learning organizations adopt new techniques and procedures that get the job done more efficiently or effectively.

Challenge how you and your subordinates operate. Ask, "Why do we do it that way?" and never accept "Because we've always done it that way." Look closely at teams' habits. Just because a team has found a way that works doesn't mean that way is the best. Unless leaders are willing to question how things are, no one will ever know what might be.

For most men, the matter of learning is one of personal preference. But for Army leaders, the obligation to learn, to grow in their profession, is clearly a public duty.

GOA Omar N. Bradley

Critical Thinking

Apply the concept of a learning organization to the Army. Based on your current knowledge of the Army, in what ways does it foster organizational learning? In what ways might it inhibit organizational learning?

Don't be afraid to challenge how you and your subordinates operate.

"Zero Defects" and Learning

As a learning organization, the Army must guard against a "zero-defects" mentality. Leaders who are willing to learn will welcome new ways of looking at things, examine what's going well, and not be afraid to look at what's going poorly. When you stop receiving feedback from your subordinates, it's a good indication that something is wrong. If the message you hammer home is "There will be no mistakes," or if you lose your temper and "shoot the messenger" every time there's bad news, your Soldiers eventually will stop telling you when things go wrong or suggesting how to improve. That will guarantee you unpleasant surprises. Any time you have human beings in a complex organization doing difficult jobs, often under pressure, they will make mistakes. Effective leaders use those mistakes to figure out how to do things better and to share what they have learned with other leaders in the organization—including subordinate leaders, peers, and superiors.

Occupations That Require a Zero-Defect Standard

But the profession of arms also requires a zero-defects standard when training and combat do not allow for mistakes. Take a parachute rigger, for example. If a rigger makes a mistake, a parachutist will die. Helicopter mechanics live in a zero-defect environment as well. They can't allow risky aircraft to fly.

Of course, organizations and people make mistakes. Mistakes are part of training and may be the price of taking action. As a leader, you must make your intent clear and ensure your Soldiers understand the sorts of mistakes that are acceptable and those that are not.

Effective leaders use mistakes to figure out how to improve and to share what they have learned with other leaders in the organization.

Critical Thinking

Consider the following two statements: "There is no room for a zero-defects mentality in the organization," and "The profession of arms requires a zero-defects standard when training and combat allow for no mistakes." Are these statements contradictory? Explain your answer.

Strive for Organizational Excellence

Leaders can create a harmful zero-defects environment without realizing it. Good leaders want their organizations to excel. But if you're not careful, your organizational "standard" of excellence can quickly degenerate into a zero-defects mindset. For example, the published minimum standard for passing the Army Physical Fitness Test (APFT) is 180 points—60 points per event. If commanders routinely assign your unit to perform missions requiring highly strenuous physical activity, however, you must train your Soldiers to a higher-than-average fitness level. If you use APFT scores as the primary means of measuring physical fitness, your Soldiers will focus on the test rather than the need for physical fitness. A better course would be to train your Soldiers in mission-related skills that require the higher level of physical readiness, while at the same time motivating them to strive for their personal best on the APFT.

Barriers to Learning

Fear of mistakes isn't the only thing that can get in the way of learning. So can rigid, lockstep thinking and mental laziness. You can get so used to these learning barriers that you don't even notice them.

Fight this tendency. Challenge yourself. Use your imagination. Ask how other people do things. Listen to subordinates.

Helping People Learn

As an Army leader, you must create conditions that help people learn. First, you must motivate the Soldier to learn. Explain why the subject is important, or show how it will help the individual perform better. Second, involve the subordinate in the learning process—make it active. For instance, you would never try to teach someone how to drive a vehicle with classroom instruction alone; you have to put the person behind the wheel. That same approach applies to much more complex tasks. Keep lecture to a minimum and include as much hands-on time as possible.

Learning from experience isn't enough; you can't have every kind of experience. But if you take advantage of what others have learned, you get the benefit without having the experience. An obvious example is when combat veterans in a unit share their experiences with Soldiers who haven't been to war. Another is developing a professional reading program for your self-development. A less obvious, but no less important, example is when leaders share their experiences with subordinates during **developmental counseling**.

developmental counseling

subordinate-centered communication that produces a plan outlining actions necessary for subordinates to achieve individual or organizational goals

Critical Thinking

Describe the habits that create barriers to learning, along with practices that can help people learn.

Critical Thinking

Two lieutenants assemble their units after a training exercise in which the teams performed poorly. One gives his unit a "locker-room" lecture about what they did wrong. The other invites various team members to explain from their point of view what went wrong and how to fix it. Are both approaches valid? Which approach seems natural to you? How do you think each unit will respond and which will be more motivated to improve? Why?

After Action Reviews and Learning

Individuals benefit when the team learns together. The **after action review** (AAR) is a tool good leaders use to help their teams learn as a group. Properly conducted, an AAR is a professional discussion of an event, focused on how well units performed. It enables people to discover for themselves what happened, why it happened, and how to reinforce strengths and improve on weaknesses. Like warning orders and rehearsals, the AAR is a technique that all leaders can use whether on post or in the field. When your team sits down for an AAR, make sure that everyone participates and understands what the other participants are saying. The input from the whole team will teach your Soldiers more than if they just think about the experience by themselves.

after action review

a professional discussion of an event, focused on performance standards that enable people to discover for themselves what happened, why it happened, and how to reinforce strengths and improve on weaknesses; After Action Reviews are best conducted immediately after the event under review

CONCLUSION

Today's Army demands cohesive teams—teams that pull together. Leaders at all levels must know the stages teams go through—especially leaders who are closest to training or combat. Encourage your subordinates to strive for unit excellence. Challenge team members by involving them and seeking their input for building on team strengths and reducing team weaknesses.

Learning Assessment

1. Identify two effective team building practices.
2. List the three stages of team development.
3. Why is organizational learning important to building team excellence?
4. Identify two effective means for promoting organizational learning.

Key Words

formation stage
reception
orientation
enrichment stage
sustainment stage
developmental counseling
after action review

References

Department of the Army. (1972). *Quotes for the Military Writer*. Washington, DC.
Field Manual 6-22, *Army Leadership: Competent, Confident, and Agile*. 12 October 2006.

Section 2

LEADERSHIP DEVELOPMENT PROGRAM

Key Points

1 The Leadership Development Program (LDP)

2 Developing Leaders for the Future

3 LDP Reports and Forms

Schools and their training offer better ways to do things, but only through experience are we able to capitalize on this learning. The process of profiting from mistakes becomes a milestone in learning to become a more efficient Soldier.

Former Sergeant Major of the Army William G. Bainbridge

Introduction

Consider the challenge posed in Section 1, Team Dynamics. To build effective teams, you must first develop your own leadership capabilities. This chapter gives you a blueprint to do just that. Army leadership begins with what you as a leader must *be*—the values and attributes that shape your character. These values and attributes define who you are; they give you a solid footing. They are the same for all leaders, regardless of position, although your understanding of them grows as you gain experience and assume greater responsibility.

Your skills are those things you *know* how to do—your competence in everything from the technical side of your job to the people skills a leader requires. The skill categories of the Army leadership framework apply to all leaders. As you assume positions of greater responsibility, however, you must master additional skills in each category.

But character and knowledge are not enough. You cannot be effective, you cannot be a leader, until you apply what you know, until you act and *do* what you must. As with skills, you will learn more about how to act as a leader as you serve in different positions.

*You cannot **be** effective, you cannot be a leader, until you apply what you **know**, until you act and **do** what you must!*

Leadership Requirements Model

Attributes
What an Army Leader Is

A Leader of Character
- *Army Values*
- *Empathy*
- *Warrior Ethos*

A Leader with Presence
- *Military bearing*
- *Physically fit*
- *Composed, confident*
- *Resilient*

A Leader with Intellectual Capacity
- *Mental agility*
- *Sound judgment*
- *Innovation*
- *Interpersonal tact*
- *Domain knowledge*

Core Leader Competencies
What an Army Leader Does

Leads
- *Leads others*
- *Extends influence beyond the chain of command*
- *Leads by example*
- *Communicates*

Develops
- *Creates a positive environment*
- *Prepares self*
- *Develops others*

Achieves
- *Gets results*

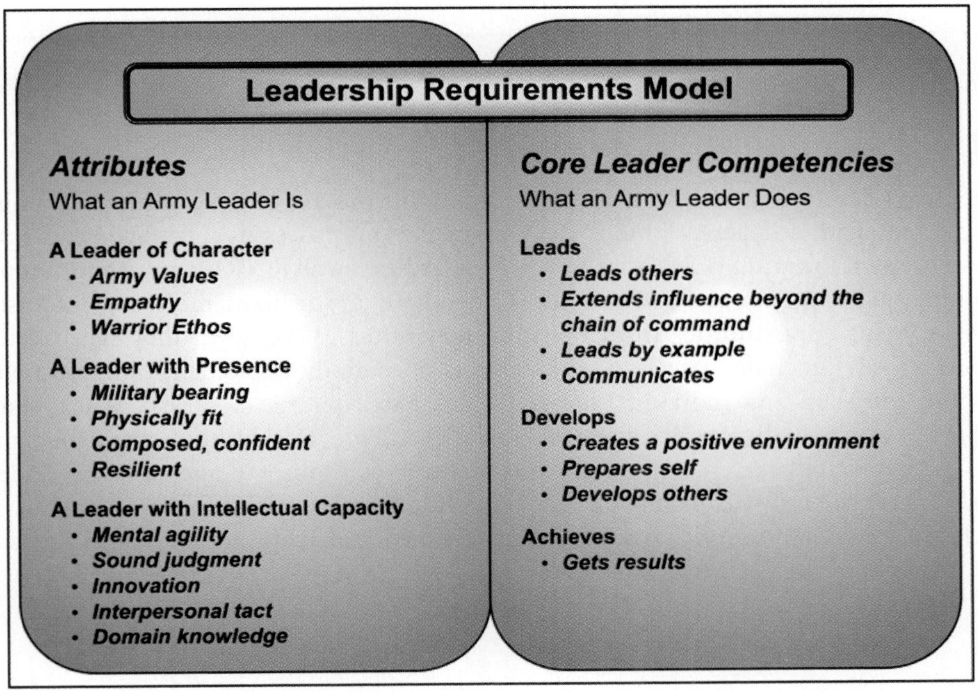

Figure 2.1 The Army Leadership Requirements Model

Leadership Builds Initiative: The 506th Parachute Infantry Regiment at Normandy

On 7 June 1944, the day after D-Day, nearly 600 paratroopers of the 506th Parachute Infantry Regiment were in position in the town of Ste. Mère Église in Normandy to block any German counterattack of the Allied invasion force. Although outnumbered by an enemy force of over 6,000 soldiers, the paratroopers attacked the German flank and prevented the enemy's assault. The paratroopers were motivated and well trained, and they all understood the absolute necessity of preventing the German counterattack. Even in the fog of war, they did what needed to be done to achieve victory. Their feat is especially noteworthy since many landed outside their planned drop zones and had to find their units on their own. They did so quickly and efficiently in the face of the enemy.

Because the leaders of the 506th built an environment with a shared purpose and a positive and ethical climate, cohesive, disciplined teams had the confidence and motivation necessary to fight and win in the face of uncertainty and adversity. Both leaders and Soldiers understood that no plan remains intact after a unit crosses the line of departure. Their leaders' initiative allowed the disciplined units to execute the mission by following the commander's intent, even when the conditions on the battlefield changed.

The Leadership Development Program (LDP)

Leadership Development Program

Cadet Command's process of developing individual Cadets' leadership abilities by providing a continuous cycle of leadership opportunities followed by assessment, feedback, counseling, and improvement

The Army develops its leaders through a continuous process of education and training, assessment, and feedback. Within Cadet Command, this process is called the **Leadership Development Program** (LDP). The LDP is standardized in all ROTC campus and summer training environments. The LDP provides Cadets with personalized, individual leadership development opportunities from the time they enter ROTC until they receive their commissions. It includes basic leadership instruction, periodic assessments, and counseling at both the team and individual levels. Cadets participate in a variety of leadership experiences to help them realize their full potential and predict their success as lieutenants. ROTC instructors serve as observers and mentors who observe and evaluate Cadets' performance, identify trends, and provide correction, retraining, and retesting in a constant cycle. The goal is for Cadets to constantly improve their leadership abilities, build on lessons learned, and realize their full potential.

Critical Thinking

What leadership attributes did the 506th Parachute Infantry Regiment display during their mission? What do you think the regiment's leaders did prior to this mission to prepare their Soldiers for success?

The LDP seeks to develop Cadets into officers who:

1. **BE:**
   a. Live by the Army *Values*
   b. Have specific mental, physical, and emotional *attributes*

2. **KNOW:**
   a. Demonstrate conceptual, technical, and tactical *skills*
   b. Exhibit interpersonal *skills*

3. **DO:** Act to
   a. *Influence* others through communication, decisiveness, and motivation
   b. *Operate* units by planning, executing, and assessing progress
   c. *Improve* the Army by developing people, teams, and self

Developing Leaders for the Future

ROTC develops Cadets to meet the Army's need for leaders of character who can take charge in any situation. The LDP provides Cadets with systematic problem-solving and self-analysis skills in a progressive cycle of training, periodic assessment, constructive counseling, retraining, and reassessment. Counseling and other feedback are based on those used throughout the US Army. Their purpose is to familiarize Cadets with what's expected of a leader and to build up their confidence and ability to lead Soldiers effectively. A Cadet's growth (or failure to grow) during the LDP process provides ROTC cadre with valuable insights into the Cadet's leadership potential. As robust as the LDP is, however, leadership development is a lifelong process. The limited time available in ROTC is simply the first phase in the process, during which Cadets develop basic leadership skills that will further their continued growth long after graduation and commissioning.

Leaders of character and competence act to achieve excellence by developing a force that can fight and win the nation's wars and serve the common defense of the United States.

LDP Reports and Forms

Cadet Command has adopted several standard administrative forms for instructors to record and report their observations. *The Leadership Development Program Handbook* gives instructions for using these forms.

Features of LDP

LDP uses an identical assessment process throughout the command, based on the following features:

Standardized Assessment Procedures

Each summer training and campus program assesses Cadets' behavior using a predetermined process as well as common performance standards and measures of leadership. ROTC cadre use standardized Cadet Command reports (e.g., **Cadet Evaluation**

Critical Thinking

Relate the Cadet Evaluation Report process to the Be-Know-Do approach to Army development.

Cadet Evaluation Report

an LDP developmental counseling tool that summarizes Cadet performance using a structure similar to the Army's Officer Evaluation Report

Job Performance Summary Card

an LDP developmental counseling tool used to track Cadet and assessor performance in all leadership environments

Report, Job Performance Summary Card—see Figures 2.2 and 2.3) to document Cadets' performance and potential. ROTC assessors ensure standardization not only through their own initial training, but also by compiling summary reports of all assessments made by each assessor. These reports are used to identify rating trends of individual assessors as well as help identify dimensional "blind spots," thus reducing any subjectivity and bias the assessor might show.

Individual Focus

The LDP identifies individual leader development needs, creates a development plan, trains Cadets, and assesses their performance. Following each assessment, Cadets receive timely individual counseling. Instructors thoroughly document a Cadet's performance in an individual file that contains the information used to measure performance and potential. The assessment of a Cadet's individual growth is based on how the Cadet performs over time.

Developmental Feedback

Timely and periodic feedback on their performance provides Cadets with tools for improvement. Each time they assess a Cadet's performance, instructors and Cadet leaders address the Cadet's notable strengths and weaknesses. They discuss with the Cadet in detail specific ways to improve. The feedback may be formal or informal, depending on the situation.

Common methods of feedback include performance test scores, counseling sessions, coaching, encouraging, and individual or team after action reviews (AARs).

Structuring Leadership Opportunities

Leadership opportunities are practical exercises in leading and caring for subordinates. Instructors use these opportunities as leader development tools to emphasize key teaching points.

The LDP uses structured leadership opportunities, in which instructors assign Cadets leadership duties with specific and implied tasks, give them time to plan and prepare, and allow them to carry out the assigned duties. Such structured opportunities allow instructors to give prompt and useful feedback and emphasize important points with examples from their own professional experiences. Without such exercises, your leadership development would be untested and likely to suffer from unidentified deficiencies. Using structured opportunities enables instructors to create scenarios that challenge Cadets and help them grow.

Assessor Qualifications

Your instructors are professionals in leadership development and assessment. The LDP is unique to Cadet Command, but its basic elements come from Army leadership principles. ROTC battalion instructors are familiar with those principles, and bring to their roles a variety of technical, tactical, and leadership experiences. But Cadet Command's greater emphasis on leader development requires more skill and standardization among assessors than most Army experiences require. To complement their previous experience, assessors

Critical Thinking

Evaluate how ROTC integrates an individual focus into its need for standardization in leader development.

Cadet Evaluation Report	Type of Report
For use of this form see CC Reg 145-3; staff proponent is USACC DOLD	CAMPUS

PART I - ADMINISTRATIVE DATA

a. NAME (LAST, FIRST, MIDDLE INITIAL)		b. SSN	c. SEX	d. REGION		e. REGT/CO/PLT
f. SCHOOL	g. SCHOOL CODE	h. APFT	i. DATE	j. ESTP (Y/N)	k. HEIGHT	l. WEIGHT

PART II - AUTHENTICATION

(Rated cadet's signature verifies cadet has seen completed part I-VI and the administrative data is correct)

(Rater & Sr. Rater's signatures verify that the cadet has been counseled)

a. NAME OF RATER (LAST, FIRST, MI)	b. SSN	c. RANK	d. POSITION	e. SIGNATURE	f. DATE
g. NAME OF SENIOR RATER (LAST, FIRST, MI)	h. SSN	i. RANK	j. POSITION	k. SIGNATURE	l. DATE
m. RATER'S TELEPHONE NUMBER		n. SENIOR RATER'S TELEPHONE NUMBER			
o. PERIOD COVERED FROM TO:		p. SIGNATURE OF RATED CADET			q. DATE

PART III - LEADERSHIP POSITIONS

List the evaluated leadership positions from the JPSC (Minimum of 5)

PART IV - PERFORMANCE DATA

NOT USED

PART V - PERFORMANCE EVALUATION - PROFESSIONALISM (Primary Assessor/PLT TAC)

CHARACTER Disposition of the leader: combination of values, attributes, and skills affecting leader actions

a. Values - Indicate "S" or "N" for each OBSERVED value   "N" Ratings must be justified by observation in Part VI below

	S	N		S	N
1. LOYALTY (LO): Bears true faith and allegiance to the Constitution, Army, Units and soldier			5. HONOR (HO): Adheres to ARMY'S CODE OF VALUES		
2. DUTY (DU): Fulfills professional, legal and moral obligations			6. INTEGRITY (IT): Exhibits high personal moral standards		
3. RESPECT (RE): Promotes dignity, consideration, fairness and EO			7. PERSONAL COURAGE (PC): Manifests physical and moral courage		
4. SELFLESS SERVICES (SS): Places Army priorities before self					

b. **LEADERSHIP ATTRIBUTES/SKILLS/ACTIONS:** Place an "X" in the appropriate rating block for dimension within Attributes, Skills, and Actions.

"E" and "N" must be justified by observations in Part VI.

ATTRIBUTES Fundamental qualities and characteristics	1. MENTAL (ME) Posses desire, will, initiative, and discipline	E	S	N	2. PHYSICAL (PH) Maintains appropriate level of physical fitness and military bearing	E	S	N	3. EMOTIONAL (EM) Display self control; calm under pressure	E	S	N
SKILLS Skill development is a part of self-development; prerequisite to action	4. CONCEPTUAL (CN) Demonstrates sound judgment, critical /creative thinking, moral reasoning	E	S	N	5. INTERPERSONAL (IP) Shows skill with people coaching, teaching, counseling, motivating, and empowering	E	S	N	6. TECHNICAL (TE) Possess the necessary expertise to accomplish all tasks and functions	E	S	N
	7. TACTICAL (TA) Demonstrates proficiency in inquired professional knowledge, judgment, and warfighting	E	S	N								
INFLUENCING Method of reaching goals while operating/improving	8. COMMUNICATING (CO) Display good oral, writing, and listening skills for individuals/ groups	E	S	N	9. DECISION MAKING (DM) Employs sound judgment, logical reasoning, and uses resources wisely	E	S	N	10. MOTIVATING (MO) Inspires, motivates, and guides other toward mission accomplishment	E	S	N
OPERATING Short-term mission accomplishment	11. PLANNING/ PREPARING (PL) Develops detailed executable plans that are feasible, acceptable, and executable	E	S	N	12. EXECUTING (EX) Shows tactical proficiency, meets mission standards, and takes care of people resources	E	S	N	13. ASSESSING (AS) Uses after action and evaluation tools to facilitate consistent improvement	E	S	N
IMPROVING Long-term improvement in the Army; its people and organizations	14. DEVELOPING (DE) Invests adequate time and effort to develop individual subordinates	E	S	N	15. BUILDING (BD) Spends time and resources improving individuals, teams, groups, and units; fosters ethical climate	E	S	N	16. LEARNING (LR) Seeks self-improvement and organizational growth; envisioning, adapting, and leading changes	E	S	N

ROTC CDT CMD FORM 67-9

Figure 2.2 Sample Cadet Evaluation Report

NAME	SSN	PERIOD COVERED FROM	TO

PART VI - PERFORMANCE AND POTENTIAL EVALUATION (PLT TAC/Primary Assessor)

a. EVALUATE THE RATED CADET'S PERFORMANCE DURING THE RATING PERIOD AND HIS/HER LEADERSHIP POTENTIAL FOR COMMISSIONING

☐ E-OUTSTANDING PERFORMANCE
MUST COMMISSION

☐ S-SATISFACTORY PERFORMANCE
COMMISSION

☐ N-NEEDS IMPROVEMENT
BEFORE COMMISSIONING

b. COMMENT ON SPECIFIC ASPECT OF THE PERFORMANCE AND POTENTIAL FOR COMMISSIONING

c. IDENTIFY ANY UNIQUE PROFESSIONAL SKILLS OR AREAS OF EXPERTISE OF VALUE TO THE ARMY THAT THIS CADET POSSESSES WHICH MAY ASSIST IN DETERMINING BRANCH AND COMPONENT SELECTION

PART VI - SENIOR RATER (PMS)

a. EVALUATE THE RATED CADET LEADER POTENTIAL FOR COMMISSIONING

☐ BEST QUALIFIED

☐ FULLY QUALIFIED

☐ QUALIFIED

b. PERFORMANCE COMPARE WITH CADETS IN THE SAME UNIT (Campus Only)

☐ BEST QUALIFIED

☐ FULLY QUALIFIED

☐ QUALIFIED

☐ OTHER

I RANK THIS CADET
_____ OF _____

c. COMMENT ON PERFORMANCE/POTENTIAL

ROTC CDT CMD FORM 67-9

Figure 2.2 *continued*

Date	Position	Assessor	As Obsvd	ME	PH	EM	CN	IP	TE	TA	CO	DM	MO	PL	EX	AS	DE	BD	LR	NET
			VALUES	ATTRIBUTES			SKILLS				INFLUENCING			OPERATING			IMPROVING			NET
7/11	SL	LT Anders	RE-DU-		S		S	E	S		E	S	S	N	S	S	S	N		S
7/16	FLRC	LT Colliins		S		E	S	S	S	E	S	S	S		S					S
7/17	PSG	MSG Wyse			S	S	S	S	S	E	S	S	S	S	S	S	S	S	S	S
7/19	SPOT	LTC Burrus						E			E	E					E	E		
7/24	SL	CPT Taylor			S	S		S	S	S	E	E		S	S	S	S	S		S
7/28	SSTX1	SFC Mayes		E	E	S	E	S	S	E	S	S	E		E		S	E		E
7/28	SPOT	SFC Mayes	PC+			E		E			E	E	E				E	E		
7/30	SSTX2	CPT Morris		S	S	S	S	S	S	E	S	S	S	S	S			E		S
8/2	SL	LT Anders			E	E	E	E	S		S	E		S	S	S	S		S	E
8/4	PSTX	SFC Smith		E	S	S	S	E	E	S	S	S		S	S	S				S
SUMMARY OF RATINGS BY DIMENSION				S	E	S	S	E	S	E	E	E	E	S	S	S	S	E	S	

APFT: PU   SU
RUN   TOTAL

LAND NAV: WR   DY
NT   TOTAL

BRM:

SQUAD PEER:
_____OF_____

RECONDO:
YES   NO

ROTC CDT CMD FORM 156-18A-R

Figure 2.3 Sample Job Performance Summary Card

receive leadership assessor training from the School of Cadet Command and subsequent on-the-job training directed by battalion commanders. Summer training evaluation staffs provide appropriate orientation and assessment training to cadre assigned as evaluators. These cadre members, known as *training committee evaluators*, are also qualified in the assessment process. They have specific responsibilities for their particular committees based on standardized LDP assessment policies and principles.

360-Degree Assessment

Assessments from other Cadets who are peers and subordinates provide Cadet leaders additional feedback on their own development. Battalion commanders and summer-training instructors use peer assessments to confirm instructors' assessments and to identify trends and issues within the Cadet team. Through peer assessments, the subordinates most affected can give their perspectives on the Cadet leader's performance. Because they are physically and socially closer to the Cadet leader, peers are often the first to identify issues affecting that performance. You will learn more about peer evaluations in a later chapter.

Link to Evaluation and Accessions

Cadet management decisions (e.g., contracting, Cadet promotions, overall summer training performance, commissioning) are based on Cadet performance on campus and during summer training. Instructors use the Cadet Evaluation Report to keep a complete record of a Cadet's performance and potential, both on campus and in summer training. This information is also placed in the Cadet's accessions packet.

The LDP Model

Leader development through the LDP model begins when the Cadet enters the ROTC program and continues until the Cadet is commissioned as a lieutenant. During this period, the focus shifts over time from basic life skills (interpersonal behavior, time management,

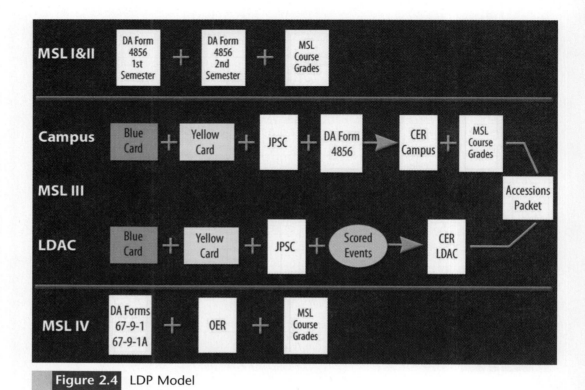

Figure 2.4 LDP Model

physical fitness, etc.) to the more complex, professional-level skills expected of a lieutenant. Figure 2.4 reflects the model for administering the LDP.

MSL I and MSL II Years

The Professor of Military Science (PMS) ensures that all MSL I and MSL II Cadets receive developmental counseling once a semester from their instructor, another cadre member, or an upper-class Cadet. The focus and intent of MSL I and II counseling should be more academic. Because of this, in most cases the counselor will be the MSL I and MSL II instructor. The counseling will be conducted using DA Form 4856, Developmental Counseling Form (Figure 2.5), focusing mainly on Cadet grades, class attendance, class participation, and time management. The counselor may also discuss available ROTC on-campus scholarship opportunities and how the MSL I or MSL II Cadet can become more competitive during the selection process.

MSL III Year

From the standpoint of training, assessment, and leadership development, the MSL III year is the most intensive of a Cadet's ROTC experience. You will serve in a series of leadership positions on campus, and you will also prepare for and attend the Leader Development and Assessment Course (LDAC). Data on your performance and potential both on campus and at LDAC will become part of your permanent evaluation and accessions record. Your PMS will record data on your performance during the MSL III year on your Cadet Evaluation Report (CER). (EXCEPTION: The CER reflects performance on campus for the year preceding LDAC attendance. Thus, for Cadets who attend LDAC after their MSL IV year, the CER reflects their performance during the MSL IV year.) Likewise, at LDAC, the platoon evaluator uses the Job Performance Summary Card (JPSC) and all scored events to develop a CER for each Cadet in his or her platoon. Following LDAC, battalion cadre use this feedback from summer training to determine the Cadet's developmental requirements for the MSL IV year.

MSL IV Year

As they prepare to enter the Army, MSL IV Cadets complete a DA Form 67-9-1A, Developmental Support Form, with help from battalion staff. The PMS counsels Cadets based on their performance, and completes a DA Form 67-9, Officer Evaluation Report, for each MSL IV Cadet during the last semester of the MSL IV year. These forms are available from *www.apd.army.mil*

DEVELOPMENTAL COUNSELING FORM
For use of this form, see FM 6-22; the proponent agency is TRADOC.

DATA REQUIRED BY THE PRIVACY ACT OF 1974

AUTHORITY: 5 USC 301, Departmental Regulations; 10 USC 3013, Secretary of the Army and E.O. 9397 (SSN)
PRINCIPAL PURPOSE: To assist leaders in conducting and recording counseling data pertaining to subordinates.
ROUTINE USES: For subordinate leader development IAW FM 6-22. Leaders should use this form as necessary.
DISCLOSURE: Disclosure is voluntary.

PART I - ADMINISTRATIVE DATA

Name (Last, First, MI)	Rank/Grade	Social Security No.	Date of Counseling
Organization		Name and Title of Counselor	

PART II - BACKGROUND INFORMATION

Purpose of Counseling: *(Leader states the reason for the counseling, e.g. Performance/Professional or Event-Oriented counseling, and includes the leader's facts and observations prior to the counseling.)*

See paragraph C-68, Open the Session

The leader should annotate pertinent, specific, and objective facts and observations made. If applicable, the leader and subordinate start the counseling session by reviewing the status of the previous plan of action.

PART III - SUMMARY OF COUNSELING
Complete this section during or immediately subsequent to counseling.

Key Points of Discussion:

See paragraphs C-69 and C-70, Discuss the Issues

The leader and subordinate should attempt to develop a mutual understanding of the issues. Both the leader and the subordinate should provide examples or cite specific observations to reduce the perception that either is unnecessarily biased or judgmental.

OTHER INSTRUCTIONS
This form will be destroyed upon: reassignment *(other than rehabilitative transfers)*, separation at ETS, or upon retirement. For separation requirements and notification of loss of benefits/consequences see local directives and AR 635-200.

DA FORM 4856, MAR 2006   EDITION OF JUN 99 IS OBSOLETE   APD PE v2.00

Figure 2.5 Guidelines for Completing a Developmental Counseling Form

Plan of Action: *(Outlines actions that the subordinate will do after the counseling session to reach the agreed upon goal(s). The actions must be specific enough to modify or maintain the subordinate's behavior and include a specified time line for implementation and assessment (Part IV below)*

See paragraph C-71, Develop a Plan of Action

The plan of action specifies what the subordinate must do to reach the goals set during the counseling session. The plan of action must be specific and should contain the outline, guideline(s), and time line that the subordinate follows. A specific and achievable plan of action sets the stage for successful subordinate development.

Remember, event-oriented counseling with corrective training as part of the plan of action can't be tied to a specified time frame. Corrective training is complete once the subordinate attains the standard.

Session Closing: *(The leader summarizes the key points of the session and checks if the subordinate understands the plan of action. The subordinate agrees/disagrees and provides remarks if appropriate.)*

Individual counseled:　　　　I agree　　　　disagree with the information above.
Individual counseled remarks:

See paragraphs C-72 through C-74, Close the Session

Signature of Individual Counseled:　　　　　　　　　　　　　　　　　　Date:

Leader Responsibilities: *(Leader's responsibilities in implementing the plan of action.)*

See paragraph C-76, Leader's Responsibilities

To accomplish the plan of action, the leader must list the resources necessary and commit to providing them to the Soldier.

Signature of Counselor:　　　　　　　　　　　　　　　　　　Date:

PART IV - ASSESSMENT OF THE PLAN OF ACTION

Assessment: *(Did the plan of action achieve the desired results? This section is completed by both the leader and the individual counseled and provides useful information for follow-up counseling.)*

Counselor:　　　　　　　　　Individual Counseled:　　　　　　　　　Date of Assessment:

Note: Both the counselor and the individual counseled should retain a record of the counseling.

REVERSE, DA FORM 4856, MAR 2006　　　　　　　　　　　　　　　　APD PE v2.00

Figure 2.5 *continued*

MSL Course Grades

Battalion cadre also examine the quality of a Cadet's in-class coursework throughout each academic year. On campus, Cadets must recognize and meet the challenge of balancing academics with the need to prepare and perform well in various leadership positions. MSL course grades are a critical element in determining a Cadet's future potential as an Army leader.

CONCLUSION

The LDP is a comprehensive leadership development and assessment process that focuses on Cadet performance in a variety of situations. The process is designed to mold Cadets into competent Army leaders who are capable of making significant contributions to their organizations, from first unit of assignment onward.

Learning Assessment

1. Discuss how the components of the LDP are uniquely suited to improve leadership performance at all levels.
2. Describe the forms and reports used in the LDP.

Key Words

Leadership Development Program
Cadet Evaluation Report
Job Performance Summary Card

References

Field Manual 6-22, *Army Leadership: Competent, Confident, and Agile.* 12 October 2006.

Leadership Development Program Handbook. 8 July 2008. *NOTE: The LDP handbook still makes reference to FM 22-100; this will be updated during the next rewrite.*

Section 3

LEADERSHIP STYLES

Key Points

1 Matching Leadership to the Situation

2 Five Leadership Styles

More than anything else, I had confidence in my Soldiers, junior leaders, and staff. They were trained, and I knew they would carry the fight to the enemy. I trusted them, and they knew I trusted them. I think in Just Cause, which was a company commander's war, being a decentralized commander paid big dividends because I wasn't in the knickers of my company commanders all the time. I gave them the mission and let them do it. I couldn't do it for them.

A Battalion Commander, Operation Just Cause Panama, 1989

Introduction

Some leaders can walk into a room full of strangers and within five minutes have everyone there thinking, "How have I lived so long without meeting this person?" Other competent leaders, however, are uncomfortable in social situations. Army leadership doctrine describes in detail how you should interact with subordinates and how you must strive to learn and improve your leadership skills. But the Army recognizes that you must always be yourself. Anything else comes across as fake and insincere.

Even so, effective leaders are flexible enough to adjust their leadership style and techniques to the people they lead and the demands they face. Some subordinates respond best to coaxing, suggestions, or gentle prodding; others need the verbal equivalent of a kick in the pants. Treating people fairly doesn't mean treating them as if they were clones of one another. In fact, if you treat everyone the same way, you're probably being unfair, because different people need different types of leadership from you.

Knowing Your People

"A General said, 'Each of our three regimental commanders must be handled differently. Colonel A does not want an order. He wants to do everything himself and always does well. Colonel B executes every order, but has no initiative. Colonel C opposes everything he is told to do and wants to do the contrary.' A few days later the troops confronted a well-entrenched enemy whose position would have to be attacked. The General issued the following orders: To Colonel A (who wants to do everything himself): 'My dear Colonel A, I think we will attack. Your regiment will have to carry the burden of the attack. I have, however, selected you for this reason. The boundaries of your regiment are so-and-so. Attack at X-hour. I don't have to tell you anything more.' To Colonel C (who opposes everything): 'We have met a very strong enemy. I am afraid we will not be able to attack with the forces at our disposal.' 'Oh, General, certainly we will attack. Just give my regiment the time of attack and you will see that we are successful,' replied Colonel C. 'Go then, we will try it,' said the General, giving him the order for the attack, which he had prepared some time previously. To Colonel B (who always must have detailed orders) the attack order was merely sent with additional details. All three regiments attacked splendidly."

Adolph von Schell, *German liaison to the Infantry School between the World Wars*

Matching Leadership to the Situation

As an Army leader, then, you must analyze the type of leadership to use in different situations based on the skills of those you are leading and the circumstances you face. You must fit your leadership style to your subordinates, just as you must fit training to the trainees' experience. For example, if you are leading a large group of Soldiers ranging in rank from private to senior NCO in a map reading exercise, you lead the NCOs differently than the privates. The senior NCOs know a great deal about the subject, while the privates know very little. To meet all their needs, you must teach the privates more than you teach the senior NCOs. If you train the privates only in the advanced skills the NCOs need, the privates will be lost. If you make the NCOs sit through training in the basic tasks the privates need, you'll waste the NCOs' time.

In the same way, you adjust your leadership style and techniques to your Soldiers' experience, your organization's characteristics, and the circumstances you face.

The easiest distinctions to make are those of rank and experience—as in the example above, you don't lead senior NCOs the same way you lead privates. But you must go deeper: You must also take into account your subordinates' different personalities, levels of self-confidence, and other elements. This complex mix of character traits and situational factors makes dealing with people so difficult, yet so rewarding. One of the many things that makes your job tough is that, in order to get their best performance, you must figure out what your subordinates need and what they're able to do—even when they don't know themselves.

When discussing leadership styles, many people focus on the extremes: autocratic and democratic. Autocratic leaders tell people what to do with no explanation. Their message is, "I'm the boss; you'll do it because I said so." Democratic leaders use interactive and collaborative approaches to persuade subordinates. But there are many leadership styles in between these extremes. The following paragraphs discuss five of them. Bear in mind, however, that competent leaders mix elements of all these styles to match to the place, task, and people involved. You must learn how to use different leadership styles in different situations and also how to apply elements of different styles to a single situation. Using only one leadership style generally leads to problems. When you are inflexible, you will have difficulty operating in situations where your preferred style does not fit—and there will be many.

The five different leadership styles we'll examine here are:

- the directing style
- the participating style
- the delegating style
- the transformational style; and
- the transactional style.

Competent leaders mix elements of all [leadership] styles to match the place, task, and people involved.

One of the many things that makes your job tough is that, in order to get their best performance, you must figure out what your subordinates need and what they're able to do even when they don't know themselves.

To get the best out of your men, they must feel that you are their real leader and must know that they can depend upon you.

General of the Armies John J. Pershing

Five Leadership Styles

Directing Leadership Style

The *directing style* centers on the leader. When you use this style, you don't solicit input from subordinates. Rather, you give detailed instructions on how, when, and where you want a task performed. You then supervise its execution very closely.

The directing style may be appropriate when time is short and you don't have a chance to explain things. You may simply give orders: Do this. Go there. Move. In fast-paced operations or in combat, you may revert to the directing style, even with experienced subordinates. If you have created a climate of trust, your subordinates will assume you have switched to the directing style because of the circumstances.

You may also find the directing style appropriate when leading inexperienced teams or individuals who aren't ready to operate on their own. In this kind of situation, you'll probably remain close to the action to make sure things go smoothly.

Adopting a directing style does not give you license to use abusive or demeaning language, or to threaten and intimidate subordinates. If you're ever tempted to be harsh, whether because of pressure, stress, or what seems like a subordinate's improper behavior, ask yourself: "Would I want to work for someone like me? Would I want my commander to see and hear me treat subordinates this way? Would I want to be treated this way?"

The directing leadership style may be appropriate when time is short and leaders don't have a chance to explain things.

Participating Leadership Style

In contrast to the directing style, the *participating style* centers on both the leader and the team. In this style, when you are given a mission, you ask your subordinates for input, information, and recommendations, but you make the final decision on what to do. This style is especially appropriate when you have time for such consultations or when you're dealing with experienced subordinates.

The participating leadership style rests on the team-building approach you studied earlier. When subordinates help create a plan, it becomes *their* plan—at least in part. This ownership gives subordinates a strong incentive to invest the effort necessary to make the plan work. When you ask for this kind of input, it's a sign of your strength and self-confidence as a leader. But asking for advice doesn't mean you're obligated to follow it. As the leader, you alone are always responsible for the quality of your decisions and plans.

The participating leadership style is especially appropriate when there is time to receive input, information, and recommendations from subordinates.

Delegating Leadership Style

The *delegating style* goes one step further: It gives subordinates the authority to solve problems and make decisions without clearing them through the leader. When you have mature and experienced subordinates—or you want to create a learning experience for subordinates—you often need only give them decision making authority, the necessary resources, and a clear understanding of the mission's purpose. As always, you are ultimately responsible for what happens, but in the delegating leadership style, you hold subordinate leaders accountable for their actions. Officers dealing with senior NCOs most often use this style, as do organizational and strategic leaders.

The delegating leadership style gives subordinates the authority to solve problems and make decisions without clearing them through the leader.

Critical Thinking

Contrast the directing, participating, and delegating leadership approaches, and identify in which situation to use each.

> **A man does not have himself killed for a few halfpence a day or for a petty distinction. You must speak to the soul in order to electrify the man.**
>
> Napoleon Bonaparte

Transformational and Transactional Leadership Styles

Napoleon's words capture the distinction between the *transformational* leadership style, which focuses on inspiration and change, and the *transactional* leadership style, which focuses on rewards and punishments. Napoleon obviously understood the importance of rewards and punishments, but he also understood that carrots and sticks alone don't inspire individuals to excellence.

Transformational Leadership Style

transformational leadership style

a developmental style of leadership that emphasizes individual growth and organizational enhancement

As the name suggests, the **transformational leadership style** aims to transform subordinates by challenging them to rise above their immediate needs and self-interests. The transformational style is developmental: It emphasizes individual growth (both professional and personal) and improving the organization. To successfully employ the transformational style, you must empower and motivate your subordinates—first as individuals, then as a group. You must have the courage to communicate your intent and then to step back and let your subordinates work. You must also be patient, because you often don't see the benefits until the mission is accomplished.

The transformational style allows you to take advantage of the skills and knowledge of experienced subordinates who may have better ideas on how to accomplish a mission. When you use this style, you communicate reasons for your decisions or actions. In the process, you build in subordinates a broader understanding and the ability to exercise initiative and operate effectively.

You can't use the transformational style in all situations, however. It's most effective during periods that call for change or present new opportunities. It also works well when organizations face a crisis, instability, mediocrity, or disenchantment. It may not be effective when subordinates are inexperienced, when the mission allows little deviation from accepted procedures, or when subordinates are not motivated. If you use only the transformational leadership style, you'll limit your ability to influence individuals in these and similar situations.

Transactional Leadership Style

transactional leadership style

a leadership style that motivates subordinates to work by offering rewards or threatening punishment

In contrast, some leaders employ only the **transactional leadership style**. This style includes such techniques as:

- Motivating subordinates to work by offering rewards or threatening punishment
- Prescribing task assignments in writing
- Outlining all the conditions of task completion, the applicable rules and regulations, the benefits of success, and the consequences—to include possible disciplinary actions—of failure
- "Management by exception," where leaders focus on their subordinates' failures, showing up only when something goes wrong.

Critical Thinking

Explain how both transformational and transactional leadership can complement a leader's overall approach within an organization. How could a leader apply transactional or transformational leadership through written orders, such as an operations order (OPORD)?

If you depend exclusively on the transactional style, rather than combining it with the transformational style, you'll evoke only short-term commitment from your subordinates and discourage risk-taking and innovation.

There are situations, however, where the transactional style is acceptable. For example, if you want to emphasize safety, you could reward your unit with a three-day pass if the members avoid any serious safety-related incidents over a two-month deployment. In this case, your Soldiers will clearly understand your intent: You won't tolerate unsafe acts and will reward safe habits.

If you use only the transactional style, however, your efforts can appear self-serving. In this example, your Soldiers might interpret your attempt to reward safe practices as an effort to look good by focusing on something that's unimportant, but that has the commander's attention. Such perceptions can destroy your subordinates' trust in you. If you use only the transactional style, you can also deprive subordinates of opportunities to grow, because you leave no room for honest mistakes.

The most effective leaders combine techniques from the transformational and transactional leadership styles to fit the situation. You'll elicit the most enthusiastic and genuine response from subordinates when you combine a strong base of transactional understanding with charisma, inspiration, and individualized concern for each person. Subordinates will be more committed, creative, and innovative. They will also be more likely to take calculated risks to accomplish their mission. They can explain why a course of action is important and what needs to be done, as well as take care of their fellow Soldiers.

Leaders can avoid misunderstanding of their intent by combining transformational techniques with transactional techniques.

CONCLUSION

Effective leaders are flexible enough to adjust their leadership style and techniques to the people they lead and the demands they face. You have read about five leadership styles: directing, participating, delegating, transformational, and transactional. You are not limited to any one style in a given situation. Use techniques from different styles to motivate your Soldiers to accomplish the mission.

Critical Thinking

Think about each of the scenarios below and discuss which leadership style would be most effective in the situation described, and why.

1. Your infantry unit is airlifted on 24-hours notice to a Pacific island to establish security and bring food and water to an area devastated by a typhoon (hurricane). No one in your unit knows the local language or customs, although one NCO practices the local religion.

2. You are traveling by convoy in a remote desert village in an area far from any known insurgency. Suddenly a rocket-propelled grenade hits and disables your lead vehicle and your unit comes under mortar and automatic-weapons fire.

3. Truck and humvee accidents have been a serious problem on post, and many Soldiers have been hurt or even killed. The division commander is offering a prize to the commander of the unit that compiles the best motor-vehicle safety record over the next six months. Your own unit has had two serious accidents in the last month.

4. You are given a mission in which several companies under your command must act independently in widely scattered villages at the same hour. It is extremely important that the companies act precisely at the designated times.

Learning Assessment

1. What type of situation is best suited for transformational leadership?

2. Describe a combat setting in which transactional leadership would be essential.

3. Describe what kind of leadership style you would use in leading MSL I cadets in a map-reading exercise and explain why you would use the style you chose.

Key Words

transformational leadership style
transactional leadership style

References

Leadership Development Program Handbook. 10 March 2005.

LEADERSHIP BEHAVIOR AND PEER EVALUATIONS

Key Points

1 Purpose and Use of Peer Evaluations

2 Effective Peer Feedback

3 Leadership Attributes and Core Leader Competencies

Good leadership promotes professionalism—a renaissance of standards, involving quality of life, service, discipline and total commitment to our Army and the United States of America.

— MG Albert Akers

Introduction

In Section 2, you read about ROTC's Leadership Development Program (LDP). A critical element of the LDP is timely and periodic feedback to provide Cadets with tools for improvement. An important element of this feedback is **peer evaluations**. Peer evaluations collect the observations of other Cadets to provide Cadet leaders additional feedback on their own development. Giving feedback to your peers and receiving feedback from them are both challenging tasks. This chapter will discuss briefly how to do both. It will also give you a basis on which to evaluate yourself and others using the Army's leadership attributes and core leadership competencies.

peer evaluations

an assessment and feedback process in which individuals other than supervisors and subordinates evaluate the observed behavior of fellow team members according to a set of established criteria

Purpose and Use of Peer Evaluations

By using peer evaluations, ROTC avoids a one-dimensional evaluation system. One dimensional, or "top-down," rating approaches tend to measure only whether an individual kept his or her boss happy. The key question becomes, "Was the mission accomplished?" Everyone agrees that military operations must accomplish their missions, but accomplishment should not be the sole factor in rating a leader's performance. Experience shows that such an evaluation system is seriously flawed. An evaluation system that uses mission accomplishment as its sole measure of success:

- Places individual interests (those of the boss and the subordinate) over those of the organization
- Provides an incomplete picture of leadership abilities and potential
- Discourages counseling and organizational skills
- Compromises integrity by circumventing honest, face-to-face assessments

Critical Thinking

At the conclusion of a recent leadership lab, Cadet Randall Brant confided in Cadet Armando Hernandez that he had a great deal of anxiety about an upcoming peer evaluation that he (Brant) had to write on fellow MSL III cadet, Cadet Bill Goodgion. Hernandez listened intently to Brant's concerns as they walked to the parking lot to leave the campus for the day. "Bill and I have worked a number of projects together. He's built a reputation among the officers as somebody who can 'get things done.' Sure, he's mission-focused and a good organizer, but often at the expense of his subordinates and colleagues. Bill is uncompromising and severe. He's very blunt and maybe unaware when he's stepping on people's toes and bruising their feelings. Sure, he can get things done, but there are few who want to work with him again." As the two cadets approached their cars, Brant called out to Hernandez: "Do you have any specific advice you can give me that will help me to write an effective peer evaluation?" You are Cadet Hernandez; what advice would you offer to Cadet Brant?

> One of my early learnings that has been crystallized into a strong bias in later years is that the led are the most accurate judges of the leader—in the leadership role . . . . The chairman of the board or the commander in chief or the plant manager might know best who is accomplishing the immediate results in the most impressive manner. But superiors rarely have access to the full picture. Their views are notably skewed toward highly visible outcomes, with "means" usually taking a back seat to "ends."
>
> LTG Walt Ulmer (ret.)

zero-defect mentality

a mindset that does not allow for acknowledgement of mistakes, the effect of which can be to prevent an organization from recognizing and improving upon its weaknesses

- Deters tough, long-term organizational development or team-building processes
- Fosters a **zero-defect mentality**
- May detract from an ethical climate that expresses and reinforces Army Values.

To avoid these flaws, the ROTC has expanded evaluations to include 360-degree feedback. An evaluation system using such **feedback** can take into account the perceptions of subordinates and peers as well as those of the boss. It also considers the state of the organization and its record of mission accomplishment. Such a system can address shortcomings in morale, organizational effectiveness, and leader development, which can eventually detract from the organization's ability to accomplish its mission.

Effective Peer Feedback

feedback

the return of information about the result of a process or activity, an evaluation

So how does **360-degree feedback** work? It's a process in which your performance is rated by people at all levels who know something about your work. It includes top-down feedback from superior officers, bottom-up feedback from subordinates, and lateral feedback from peers. In the civilian business world, this can include input not only from supervisors, subordinates, and peers, but also from customers and clients—anyone who knows something about the work of the person under review. Using 360-degree feedback can bring the following benefits to you, the individual, and to your organization:

360-degree feedback

a process in which an individual's performance is rated by people at all levels who know something about the individual's work; it includes top-down feedback from superior officers, bottom-up feedback from subordinates, and lateral feedback from peers

- It allows you to learn how different colleagues perceive you, leading to increased self-awareness
- It encourages self-development
- It increases your understanding of the behaviors required to make you and your organization more effective
- It promotes a more open culture where giving and receiving feedback is normal
- It increases communication within the organization
- It can be a powerful trigger for change.

Organizations must be careful to use 360-degree feedback appropriately, however. Cadets and others must understand how it will be used so they won't worry that jealous peers or disgruntled subordinates will unduly damage their performance ratings.

Beyond ROTC, the Army's current officer-evaluation process does not currently include formal peer or subordinate ratings. But effective officers who are committed to growing professionally will seek feedback from their peers and subordinates. As a leader, you can do this formally, through surveys and questionnaires, or informally, through counseling sessions and off-the-cuff conversations. When you receive feedback—regardless of whether it comes to you in written or spoken form and whether you ask for it or not—it is up to you how you will accept and use it. Thus, the next section deals with how to accept feedback and use it effectively.

Accepting Feedback

A key factor to remember about all feedback is that it is one person's opinion. It is up to you to consider it thoughtfully, compare it with other feedback you have received, and do something positive with it. Feedback is valuable because while we can't see ourselves as others see us, we must not let these blind spots hinder our ability to perform and lead. Here's a system for making the most of the feedback you get:

1. When receiving any feedback, listen or read without comment. Don't accept, don't deny, and don't rationalize, but do ask questions if you need clarification. Because people are rarely taught to give feedback well, you may receive feedback when the giver is angry about something. Recognizing this, you should always accept feedback enthusiastically; wait until later to evaluate the usefulness of that feedback.

2. Recognize the courage it takes to give honest feedback, and consider it a sincere gift intended to help you grow. If you have the opportunity, thank the giver for feedback—make it short, but something you can say sincerely, such as "You've really given me something to think about. Thanks!" It is hard to feel appreciation when someone is criticizing your behavior, so try to have simple words of gratitude prepared ahead of time.

3. If the feedback was spoken, immediately write down all you can remember, recording as many of the giver's words as possible. Allow yourself time to think about the information. (Experts recommend letting two days pass, but in an intense combat or training situation, you may need to react and adjust your behavior more quickly.) Before you change your perceived behavior, become aware of what you do and how others react to you. After a period of time, go back and look at the feedback or your notes. Take out any emotion-packed words, and look for the basic message.

4. Know that feedback can be tough to receive, even if we solicit it and are grateful for it. Although it is simply another person's view, it can shake up your feelings about yourself. Recognize that everyone has strengths and weaknesses. Strive to improve your weaknesses while emphasizing your strengths.

5. Discuss the feedback with friends or others whose opinions you respect, but only when you can honestly encourage them to be objective and blunt. It would be normal to want to invalidate criticism and get others to help you, but this can cause you to lose what may be a critical grain of truth.

6. Use feedback in a positive way as soon as practical. Like any effective leader, develop a plan to overcome an identified weakness. Once you have had time to adjust your behavior, you may want to ask for more feedback to ensure your plan is working. You may also want to ask a friend to help you monitor your improvement and to tactfully remind you if you slip back to old ways. A tactful reminder might be, "Jack, I don't want to sharp-shoot you, but you asked me to remind you if I noticed you acting indecisively."

Giving Feedback

Likewise, the ability to give good feedback—not only to peers but, more importantly, to subordinates—is a critical leader skill. Subordinate leadership development is one of the most important responsibilities of every Army leader. Developing the leaders who will come after you should be one of your highest priorities. As an Army leader, you should provide good counseling, taking dedicated, quality time to listen to and talk with your subordinates. You should help them develop goals, review performance, and plan for the future.

When you prepare an evaluation, make comments that apply specifically to the Cadet or Soldier you are evaluating. Be specific, precise, objective, and fair. Address behavior using concrete examples such as "You interrupted me when I was giving my SITREP" (situation report).

Timing is also a factor: Feedback is much more meaningful and accurate when it comes immediately after the behavior you're commenting on. You must provide those you evaluate with an objective assessment of their strengths and weaknesses. A good guide to use in evaluating leadership is the following list of Army leadership attributes and competencies. In MSL 401, you will learn more about giving feedback as part of the Army's counseling process.

PEER EVALUATION REPORT (ROTC Cdt Cmd Reg 145-3) ☐ I ☐ II (Check one)	REQUIREMENTS CONTROL SYMBOL ATCC-122	
CADET (RATER)	UNIT	DATE
CADET (RATED)	RANKING_____ OF_____	

WHAT ARE THIS INDIVIDUAL'S STRONGEST (ONE, TWO, OR THREE) LEADERSHIP DIMENSIONS AND WHY?

WHAT ARE THIS INDIVIDUAL'S WEAKEST (ONE, TWO, OR THREE) LEADERSHIP DIMENSIONS AND WHY?

CDT CMD Form 156-17-R Feb 96

Figure 4.1 Sample Peer Evaluation Report

Critical Thinking

How might you request and use peer feedback to identify and improve your areas of weakness?

Critical Thinking

Distinguish between evaluations as fault-finding and the evaluation process as leader development.

Leadership Attributes and Core Leader Competencies

The Army leadership **attributes** describe what an Army leader *is*. The **core leader competencies** describe what an Army leader *does*. The competencies stem directly from the Army definition of leadership:

> *Leadership is influencing people by providing purpose, motivation, and direction while operating to accomplish the mission and improve the organization.*

Note that the definition contains three basic goals:

1. to lead others
2. to develop the organization and its individual members
3. to achieve or accomplish the mission.

These goals extend from the Army's strategic goal of remaining relevant and ready through effective leadership. The Leadership Requirements Model, Figure 4.1, outlines the attributes and competences you as an Army leader must develop to accomplish these goals.

attributes

characteristics unique to an individual that moderate how well he or she learns and performs

core leader competencies

groups of related leader behaviors that lead to successful performance, common throughout the organization and consistent with the organization's mission and values—what leaders should do to influence individual and organizational success

---

Leadership Requirements Model

Attributes
What an Army Leader Is

A Leader of Character
- Army Values
- Empathy
- Warrior Ethos

A Leader with Presence
- Military bearing
- Physically fit
- Composed, confident
- Resilient

A Leader with Intellectual Capacity
- Mental agility
- Sound judgment
- Innovation
- Interpersonal tact
- Domain knowledge

Core Leader Competencies
What an Army Leader Does

Leads
- Leads others
- Extends influence beyond the chain of command
- Leads by example
- Communicates

Develops
- Creates a positive environment
- Prepares self
- Develops others

Achieves
- Gets results

Figure 4.2 The Army Leadership Requirements Model

Attributes

Complementing the core leader competencies, the attributes distinguish high-performing leaders of character. Attributes are characteristics unique to an individual that moderate how well he or she learns and performs. They shape how individuals behave in their environment. Attributes for Army leaders include:

- a leader of character (identity) (Figure 4.3)
- a leader with presence (Figure 4.4)
- a leader with intellectual capacity (Figure 4.5).

A Leader of Character (Identity) Factors internal and central to a leader, that which makes up an individual's core.	
Army Values	• Values are the principles, standards, or qualities considered essential for successful leaders. • Values are fundamental to help people discern right from wrong in any situation. • The Army has set seven values that must be developed in all Army individuals: loyalty, duty, respect, selfless service, honor, integrity, and personal courage.
Empathy	• The propensity to experience something from another person's point of view. • The ability to identify with and enter into another person's feelings and emotions. • The desire to care for and take care of Soldiers and others.
Warrior Ethos	• The shared sentiment internal to Soldiers that represents the spirit of the profession of arms.

Figure 4.3 Attributes Associated With a Leader of Character (Identity)

A Leader with Presence How a leader is perceived by others based on the leader's outward appearance, demeanor, actions, and words.	
Military bearing	• Possessing a commanding presence. • Projecting a professional image of authority.
Physically fit	• Having sound health, strength, and endurance that support one's emotional health and conceptual abilities under prolonged stress.
Confident	• Projecting self-confidence and certainty in the unit's ability to succeed in whatever it does. • Demonstrating composure and an outward calm through steady control over one's emotions.
Resilient	• Showing a tendency to recover quickly from setbacks, shock, injuries, adversity, and stress while maintaining a mission and organizational focus.

Figure 4.4 Attributes Associated With a Leader With Presence

Critical Thinking

Cadet Hastings interrupts as Cadet Stellar is giving a situation report and does not let her finish. In which leadership attribute might Cadet Hastings be weak?

A Leader with Intellectual Capacity The mental resources or tendencies that shape a leaders' conceptual abilities and impact of effectiveness.	
Agility	• Flexibility of mind. • The tendency to anticipate or adapt to uncertain or changing situations; to think through second- and third-order effects when current decisions or actions are not producing the desired effects. • The ability to break out of mental "sets" or habitual thought patterns; to improvise when faced with conceptual impasses. • The ability to quickly apply multiple perspectives and approaches to assessment, conceptualization, and evaluation.
Judgment	• The capacity to assess situations or circumstances shrewdly and to draw sound conclusions. • The tendency to form sound opinions and make sensible decisions and reliable guesses. • The ability to make sound decisions when all facts are not available.
Innovative	• The tendency to introduce new ideas when the opportunity exists or in the face of challenging circumstances. • Creativity in the production of ideas and objects that are both novel or original and worthwhile or appropriate.
Interpersonal tact	• The capacity to understand interactions with others. • Being aware of how others see you and sensing how to interact with them effectively. • Consciousness of character and motives of others and how that affects interacting with them.
Domain knowledge	• Possessing facts, beliefs, and logical assumptions in relevant areas. • Technical knowledge—specialized information associated with a particular function or system. • Tactical knowledge—understanding military tactics related to securing a designated objective through military means. • Joint knowledge—understanding joint organizations, their procedures, and their roles in national defense. • Cultural and geopolitical knowledge—understanding cultural, geographic, and political differences and sensitivities.

Figure 4.5 Attributes Associated With a Leader With Intellectual Capacity

Core Leader Competencies

The core leader competencies emphasize leaders' roles, functions, and activities. The following discussion and Figures 4.6 through 4.13 provide additional detail on what each competency involves.

Leads

Leading is about influencing others. Leaders set goals and establish a vision, then must motivate or influence others to pursue the goals.

As a leader, you influence others in one of two ways: Either you communicate directly with your followers, or you provide an example through your everyday actions. The key to effective communication is reaching a common or shared understanding. Leading by example is a powerful way to influence others and is the reason leadership must rest on a foundation of the Army Values and the Warrior Ethos. Serving as a role model requires you to display character, confidence, and competence to inspire others to succeed. Influencing others outside the chain of command is a new way to view your leadership responsibilities.

Leads Others

Leaders motivate, inspire, and influence others to take initiative, work toward a common purpose, accomplish critical tasks, and achieve organizational objectives. Influence is focused on compelling others to go beyond their individual interests and to work for the common good.

Establishes and imparts clear intent and purpose	• Determines goals or objectives. • Determines the course of action necessary to reach objectives and fulfill mission requirements. • Restates the higher headquarters' mission in terms appropriate to the organization. • Communicates instructions, orders, and directives to subordinates. • Ensures subordinates understand and accept direction. • Empowers and delegates authority to subordinates. • Focuses on the most important aspects of a situation.
Uses appropriate influence techniques to energize others	• Uses techniques ranging from compliance to commitment (pressure, legitimate requests, exchange, personal appeals, collaboration, rational persuasion, apprising, inspiration, participation, and relationship building).
Conveys the significance of the work	• Inspires, encourages, and guides others toward mission accomplishment. • When appropriate, explains how tasks support the mission and how missions support organizational objectives. • Emphasizes the importance of organizational goals.
Maintains and enforces high professional standards	• Reinforces the importance and role of standards. • Performs individual and collective tasks to standard. • Recognizes and takes responsibility for poor performance and addresses it appropriately.
Balances requirements of mission with welfare of followers	• Assesses and routinely monitors the impact of mission fulfillment on mental, physical, and emotional attributes of subordinates. • Monitors morale, physical condition, and safety of subordinates. • Provides appropriate relief when conditions jeopardize success of the mission or present overwhelming risk to personnel.
Creates and promulgates vision of the future	• Interprets data about the future environment, tasks, and missions. • Forecasts probable situations and outcomes and formulates strategies to prepare for them. • Communicates to others a need for greater understanding of the future environment, challenges, and objectives.

Figure 4.6 Competency of *Leads Others*

Extends Influence Beyond the Chain of Command	
Leaders need to influence beyond their direct lines of authority and beyond chains of command. This influence may extend to joint, interagency, intergovernmental, multinational, and other groups. In these situations, leaders use indirect means of influence: diplomacy, negotiation, mediation, arbitration, partnering, conflict resolution, consensus building, and coordination.	
Understands sphere of influence, means of influence, and limits of influence	• Assesses situations, missions, and assignments to determine the parties involved in decision making, decision support, and possible interference or resistance.
Builds trust	• Is firm, fair, and respectful to gain trust. • Identifies areas of commonality. • Engages other members in activities and objectives. • Follows through on actions related to expectations of others. • Keeps people informed of actions and results.
Negotiates for understanding, builds consensus, and resolves conflict	• Leverages trust to establish agreements and courses of action. • Clarifies the situation. • Identifies individual and group positions and needs. • Identifies roles and resources. • Facilitates understanding of conflicting positions. • Generates and facilitates generation of possible solutions. • Gains cooperation or support when working with others.
Builds and maintains alliances	• Establishes contact and interacts with others who share common interests, such as development, reaching goals, and giving advice. • Maintains friendships, business associations, interest groups, and support networks. • Influences perceptions about the organization. • Understands the value of and learns from partnerships, associations, and other cooperative alliances.

Figure 4.7 Competency of *Extends Influence Beyond the Chain of Command*

Leads By Example

Leaders constantly serve as role models for others. Leaders will always be viewed as the example, so they must maintain standards and provide examples of effectiveness through all their actions. All Army leaders should model the Army Values. Modeling provides tangible evidence of desired behaviors and reinforces verbal guidance through demonstration of commitment and action.

Displays character by modeling the Army Values consistently through actions, attitudes, and communications	• Sets the example by displaying high standards of duty performance, personal appearance, military and professional bearing, physical fitness and health, and ethics. • Fosters an ethical climate. • Shows good moral judgment and behavior. • Completes individual and unit tasks to standard, on time, and within the commander's intent. • Is punctual and meets deadlines. • Demonstrates determination, persistence, and patience.
Exemplifies the Warrior Ethos	• Removes or fights through obstacles, difficulties, and hardships to accomplish the mission. • Demonstrates the will to succeed. • Demonstrates physical and emotional courage. • Communicates how the Warrior Ethos is demonstrated.
Demonstrates commitment to the Nation, Army, unit, Soldiers, community, and multinational partners	• Demonstrates enthusiasm for task completion and, if necessary, methods of accomplishing assigned tasks. • Is available to assist peers and subordinates. • Shares hardships with subordinates. • Participates in team tasks and missions without being asked.
Leads with confidence in adverse situations	• Provides leader presence at the right time and place. • Displays self-control, composure, and positive attitude, especially under adverse conditions. • Is resilient. • Remains decisive after discovering a mistake. • Acts in the absence of guidance. • Does not show discouragement when facing setbacks. • Remains positive when the situation becomes confusing or changes. • Encourages subordinates when they show signs of weakness.
Demonstrates technical and tactical knowledge and skills	• Meets mission standards, protects resources, and accomplishes the mission with available resources using technical and tactical skills. • Displays appropriate knowledge of equipment, procedures, and methods.
Understands the importance of conceptual skills and models them to others	• Displays comfort working in open systems. • Makes logical assumptions in the absence of facts. • Identifies critical issues to use as a guide in making decisions and taking advantage of opportunities. • Recognizes and generates innovative solutions. • Relates and compares information from different sources to identify possible cause-and-effect relationships. • Uses sound judgment and logical reasoning.
Seeks and is open to diverse ideas and points of view	• Encourages respectful, honest communications among staff and decision makers. • Explores alternative explanations and approaches for accomplishing tasks. • Reinforces new ideas; demonstrates willingness to consider alternative perspectives to resolve difficult problems. • Uses knowledgeable sources and subject-matter experts. • Recognizes and discourages individuals seeking to gain favor from tacit agreement.

Figure 4.8 Competency of *Leads by Example*

Communicates	
Leaders communicate effectively by clearly expressing ideas and actively listening to others. By understanding the nature and importance of communication and practicing effective communication techniques, leaders will relate better to others and be able to translate goals into actions. Communication is essential to all other leadership competencies.	
Listens actively	• Listens and watches attentively. • Takes appropriate notes. • Tunes in to content, emotion, and urgency. • Uses verbal and nonverbal means to reinforce with the speaker that you are paying attention. • Reflects on new information before expressing views.
Determines information-sharing strategies	• Shares necessary information with others and subordinates. • Protects confidential information. • Coordinates plans with higher, lower, and adjacent individuals and affected organizations. • Keeps higher and lower headquarters, superiors, and subordinates informed.
Employs engaging communication techniques	• States goals to energize others to adopt and act on them. • Speaks enthusiastically and maintains listeners' interest and involvement. • Makes appropriate eye contact when speaking. • Uses gestures that are appropriate but not distracting. • Uses visual aids as needed. • Acts to determine, recognize, and resolve misunderstandings.
Conveys thoughts and ideas to ensure shared understanding	• Expresses thoughts and ideas clearly to individuals and groups. • Uses correct grammar and doctrinally correct phrases. • Recognizes potential miscommunication. • Uses appropriate means for communicating a message. • Communicates clearly and concisely up, down, across, and outside the organization. • Clarifies when there is some question about goals, tasks, plans, performance expectations, and role responsibilities.
Presents recommendations so others understand advantages	• Uses logic and relevant facts in dialogue. • Keeps conversations on track. • Expresses well-thought-out and well-organized ideas.
Is sensitive to cultural factors in communication	• Maintains awareness of communication customs, expressions, actions, or behaviors. • Demonstrates respect for others.

Figure 4.9 Competency of *Communicates*

Develops

Developing the organization involves three competencies: creating a positive environment in which the organization can flourish; preparing yourself; and developing other leaders. As a leader, you shape the environment by taking actions to foster:

- working together
- encouraging initiative
- personal acknowledgment of responsibility
- setting and maintaining realistic expectations
- demonstrating care for people—your No. 1 resource.

Preparing yourself involves:

- getting set for mission accomplishment
- expanding and maintaining your knowledge in such dynamic areas as cultural and geopolitical affairs
- being self-aware.

As a leader, you develop others through coaching, counseling, and mentoring. You also build teams and organizations through direct interaction, resource management, and providing for future abilities.

Creates a Positive Environment
Leaders have the responsibility to establish and maintain positive expectations and attitudes that produce the setting for healthy relationships and effective work behaviors. Leaders are charged with improving the organization while accomplishing missions. They should leave the organization better that it was when they arrived.

Fosters teamwork, cohesion, cooperation, and loyalty	• Encourages people to work together effectively. • Promotes teamwork and team achievement to build trust. • Draws attention to the consequences of poor coordination. • Acknowledges and rewards successful team coordination. • Integrates new members into the unit quickly.
Encourages subordinates to exercise initiative, accept responsibility, and take ownership	• Involves others in decisions and keeps them informed of consequences that affect them. • Allocates responsibility for performance. • Guides subordinate leaders in thinking through problems for themselves. • Allocates decision making to the lowest appropriate level. • Acts to expand and enhance subordinates' competence and self-confidence. • Rewards initiative.
Creates a learning environment	• Uses effective assessment and training methods. • Encourages leaders and their subordinates to reach their full potential. • Motivates others to develop themselves. • Expresses the value of interacting with others and seeking counsel. • Stimulates innovative and critical thinking in others. • Seeks new approaches to problems.
Encourages open and candid communications	• Shows others how to accomplish tasks while remaining respectful, resolute, and focused. • Communicates a positive attitude to encourage others and improve morale. • Reinforces the expression of contrary and minority viewpoints. • Displays appropriate reactions to new or conflicting information or opinions. • Guards against groupthink.
Encourages fairness and inclusiveness	• Provides accurate evaluations and assessments. • Supports equal opportunity. • Prevents all forms of harassment. • Encourages learning about and leveraging diversity.
Expresses and demonstrates care for people and their well-being	• Encourages subordinates and peers to express candid opinions. • Ensures that subordinates and their families are provided for, including their health, welfare, and development. • Stands up for subordinates. • Routinely monitors morale and encourages honest feedback.
Anticipates people's on-the-job needs	• Recognizes and monitors subordinates' needs and reactions. • Shows concern for the impact of tasks and missions on subordinate morale.
Sets and maintains high expectations for individuals and teams	• Clearly articulates expectations. • Creates a climate that expects good performance, recognizes superior performance, and does not accept poor performance. • Challenges others to match the leader's example.
Accepts reasonable setbacks and failures	• Communicates the difference between maintaining professional standards and a zero-defects mentality. • Expresses the importance of being competent and motivated but recognizes the occurrence of failure. • Emphasizes learning from one's mistakes.

Figure 4.10 Competency of *Creates a Positive Environment*

Prepares Self Leaders ensure they are prepared to execute their leadership responsibilities fully. They are aware of their limitations and strengths and seek to develop themselves. Leaders maintain physical fitness and mental well-being. They continue to improve the domain knowledge required of their leadership roles and their profession. Only through continuous preparation for missions and other challenges, being aware of self and situations and practicing lifelong learning and development can an individual fulfill the responsibilities of leadership.	
Maintains mental and physical health and well-being	• Recognizes imbalance or inappropriateness of one's own actions. • Removes emotions from decision making. • Applies logic and reason to make decisions or when interacting with emotionally charged individuals. • Recognizes the sources of stress and maintains appropriate levels of challenge to motivate self. • Takes part in regular exercise, leisure activities, and time away from routine work. • Stays focused on life priorities and values.
Maintains self awareness: employs self understanding, and recognizes impact on others	• Evaluates one's strengths and weaknesses. • Learns from mistakes and makes corrections, learns from experience. • Considers feedback on performance, outcomes associated with actions, and actions taken by others to achieve similar goals. • Seeks feedback on how others view one's own actions. • Routinely determines personal goals and makes progress toward them. • Develops capabilities where possible but accepts personal limitations. • Seeks opportunities where capabilities can be used appropriately. • Understands self-motivation under various task conditions.
Evaluates and incorporates feedback from others	• Determines areas in need of development. • Judges self with the help of feedback from others.
Expands knowledge of technical, technological, and tactical areas	• Keeps informed about developments and policy changes inside and outside the organization. • Seeks knowledge of systems, equipment, capabilities, and situations, particularly information technology systems.
Expands conceptual and interpersonal capabilities	• Understands the contribution of concentration, critical thinking (assimilation of information, discriminating relevant cues, question asking), imagination (decentering), and problem solving in different task conditions. • Learns new approaches to problem solving. • Applies lessons learned. • Filters unnecessary information efficiently. • Reserves time for self-development, reflection, and personal growth. • Considers possible motives behind conflicting information.
Analyzes and organizes information to create knowledge	• Reflects on what has been learned and organizes these insights for future application. • Considers source, quality or relevance, and criticality of information to improve understanding. • Identifies reliable sources of data and other resources related to acquiring knowledge. • Sets up systems or procedures to store knowledge for reuse.
Maintains relevant cultural awareness	• Learns about issues of language, values, customary behavior, ideas, beliefs, and patterns of thinking that influence others. • Learns about results of previous encounters when culture plays a role in mission success.
Maintains relevant geopolitical awareness	• Learns about relevant societies outside the United States experiencing unrest. • Recognizes Army influences on other countries, multinational partners, and enemies. • Understands the factors influencing conflict and peacekeeping, peace enforcing, and peacemaking missions.

Figure 4.11 Competency of *Prepares Self*

Develops Others	
Leaders encourage and support others to grow as individuals and teams. They facilitate the achievement of organizational goals through assisting others to develop. They prepare others to assume new positions elsewhere in the organization, making the organization more versatile and productive.	
Assesses current developmental needs of others	• Observes and monitors subordinates under different task conditions to establish strengths and weaknesses. • Notes changes in proficiency. • Evaluates subordinates in a fair and consistent manner.
Fosters job development, job challenge, and job enrichment	• Assesses tasks and subordinate motivation to consider methods of improving work assignments, when job enrichment would be useful, methods of cross-training on tasks, and methods of accomplishing missions. • Designs tasks to provide practice in areas of subordinates' weaknesses. • Designs ways to challenge subordinates and improve practice. • Encourages subordinates to improve processes.
Counsels, coaches, and mentors	• Improves subordinates' understanding and proficiency. • Uses experience and knowledge to improve future performance. • Counsels, coaches, and mentors subordinates, subordinate leaders, and others.
Facilitates ongoing development	• Maintains awareness of existing individual and organizational development programs and removes barriers to development. • Supports opportunities for self-development. • Arranges training opportunities as needed that help subordinates improve self-awareness, confidence, and competence.
Supports institutional-based development	• Encourages subordinates to pursue institutional learning opportunities. • Provides information about institutional training and career progression to subordinates. • Maintains resources related to development.
Builds team or group skills and processes	• Presents challenging assignments for team or group interaction. • Provides resources and support. • Sustains and improves the relationships among team or group members. • Provides realistic, mission-oriented training. • Provides feedback on team processes.

Figure 4.12 Competency of *Develops Others*

Achieves

Achieving is the third competency goal. Ultimately, leaders exist to accomplish those endeavors the Army gives them to do. Getting results, accomplishing the mission, and fulfilling goals and objectives are all ways of saying that leaders exist at the organization's discretion to achieve something of value. You get results through the influence you provide in direction and setting priorities. You develop and execute plans and must consistently accomplish goals to a high ethical standard.

The leader who chooses to ignore the Soldier's search for individual growth may reap a bitter fruit of disillusionment, discontent, and listlessness. If we, instead, reach out to touch each Soldier—to meet needs and assist in working toward the goal of becoming a "whole person"—we will have bridged the essential needs of the individual to find not only the means of coming together into an effective unit, but the means of holding together.

GEN Edward C. Meyer

Gets Results

A leader's ultimate purpose is to accomplish organizational results. A leader gets results by providing guidance and managing resources, as well as performing the other leader competencies. This competency is focused on consistent and ethical task accomplishment through supervising, managing, monitoring, and controlling of the work.

Prioritizes, organizes, and coordinates taskings for teams or other organizational structures/groups.	• Uses planning to ensure each course of action achieves the desired outcome. • Organizes groups and teams to accomplish work. • Plans to ensure that all tasks can be executed in the time available and that tasks depending on other tasks are executed in the correct sequence. • Limits overspecification and micromanagement.
Identifies and accounts for individual and group capabilities and commitment to task	• Considers duty positions, capabilities, and developmental needs when assigning tasks. • Conducts initial assessments when beginning a new task or assuming a new position.
Designates, clarifies, and deconflicts roles	• Establishes and employs procedures for monitoring, coordinating, and regulating subordinates' actions and activities. • Mediates peer conflicts and disagreements.
Identifies, contends for, allocates, and manages resources	• Allocates adequate time for task completion. • Keeps track of people and equipment. • Allocates time to prepare and conduct rehearsals. • Continually seeks improvement in operating efficiency, resource conservation, and fiscal responsibility. • Attracts, recognizes, and retains talent.
Removes work barriers	• Protects organization from unnecessary taskings and distractions. • Recognizes and resolves scheduling conflicts. • Overcomes other obstacles preventing full attention to accomplishing the mission.
Recognizes and rewards good performance	• Recognizes individual and team accomplishments; rewards them appropriately. • Credits subordinates for good performance. • Builds on successes. • Explores new reward systems and understands individual reward motivations.
Seeks, recognizes, and takes advantage of opportunities to improve performance	• Asks incisive questions. • Anticipates needs for action. • Analyzes activities to determine how desired end states are achieved or affected. • Acts to improve the organization's collective performance. • Envisions ways to improve. • Recommends best methods for accomplishing tasks. • Leverages information and communication technology to improve individual and group effectiveness. • Encourages staff to use creativity to solve problems
Makes feedback part of work processes	• Gives and seeks accurate and timely feedback. • Uses feedback to modify duties, tasks, procedures, requirements, and goals when appropriate. • Uses assessment techniques and evaluation tools (such as AARs) to identify lessons learned and facilitate consistent improvement. • Determines the appropriate setting and timing for feedback.
Executes plans to accomplish the mission	• Schedules activities to meet all commitments in critical performance areas. • Notifies peers and subordinates in advance when their support is required. • Keeps track of task assignments and suspenses. • Adjusts assignments, if necessary. • Attends to details.
Identifies and adjusts to external influences on the mission or taskings and organization	• Gathers and analyzes relevant information about changing situations. • Determines causes, effects, and contributing factors of problems. • Considers contingencies and their consequences. • Makes necessary, on-the-spot adjustments.

Figure 4.13 Competency of *Gets Results*

CONCLUSION

Peer evaluation is an essential part of the ROTC Leadership Development Program. Because they are physically and socially closer to the Cadet leader, peers are often the first to identify issues affecting the leader's performance. The Army needs leaders of competence and character who not only accomplish their mission but also improve themselves, their leaders, their units, and their peers to achieve excellence. The peer evaluation process uses formal and informal feedback to guide future Army leaders in attaining and maintaining Army leadership standards. The Army's leadership requirements model rests on the leadership attributes and core leadership competencies. Leadership assessment, including peer evaluations, is tied to performance indicators stemming from these attributes and competencies.

Learning Assessment

1. Why and how does ROTC use peer evaluations?
2. What should you do when you receive negative feedback about yourself?
3. List five guidelines to follow when giving feedback.
4. List and explain the Army leadership attributes.
5. List and explain the Army core leadership competencies.

Key Words

peer evaluations
zero-defect mentality
feedback
360-degree feedback
attributes
core leader competencies

References

City University London. (2005). Guidelines for Using 360-Degree Feedback in the Appraisal Process. Retrieved 2 March 2005 from http://www.city.ac.uk/hr/training/

Field Manual 6-22, *Army Leadership: Competent, Confident, and Agile.* 12 October 2006.

Leadership Development Program Handbook. 8 July 2008. *NOTE: The LDP handbook still refers to FM 22-100; this will be updated during the next rewrite.*

King, J. B. (2005). Gracefully Accepting Feedback a Key Employment Skill. Retrieved 2 March 2005 from http://ezinearticles.com/

Varljen, P. J. (2003). Leadership: More than Mission Accomplishment. *Military Review*, March–April 2003.

Warrior Forge, Western Development Region, Training Directives.

LEADERSHIP AND CULTURE

Key Points

1 Culture and Geopolitical Knowledge

2 Dimensions of Culture

3 Culture and Climate

If you can wear Arab kit when with the tribes you will acquire their trust and intimacy to a degree impossible in uniform.

T.E. Lawrence

Twenty-Seven-Articles (1917)

Introduction

Sociologists often describe the world we live in as a global village. Technologies from airplanes to computers allow us to interact as if we live next door to people halfway across the world. Soldiers experience the global village more than most Americans. The **Contemporary Operating Environment (COE)** in which Soldiers function brings them face to face with a host of different cultures. Experienced Soldiers constantly tell stories about Iraq, Afghanistan, Somalia, Greece, Germany, and countless other places they have served. The bottom line is that an understanding of culture is no longer a luxury for Soldiers. It is a necessity.

> **Contemporary Operating Environment**
>
> *the setting and surroundings in which Soldiers are currently stationed while waging the Global War on Terrorism*

What Is Taking So Long?

A group of Soldiers headed out to a local restaurant while on leave during a recent tour of duty in Qatar. A waiter came to greet them and take drink orders just as they sat down. But their drinks did not come to the table very quickly. Five minutes passed. Then ten. Finally the waiter came with their drinks, then promptly disappeared. Another ten minutes went by as the Soldiers finished their drinks and took bets on when they would see their waiter again. A young private began to grow increasingly impatient. He was clearly annoyed at how slow the service was. When the waiter returned, the private was furious.

"Where the hell have you been? Can't we get any service around here?" he practically shouted at the waiter.

The waiter returned the annoyed look and quietly took orders. But the service never changed much. By the end of the meal and several rounds of drinks, tensions and frustrations were mounting among most of the group. The young lieutenant who was the only officer in the group knew he needed to do something to calm everyone down, but wasn't quite sure what to do. He was rather frustrated himself. This whole experience had taken way too long.

Culture and Geopolitical Knowledge

Culture consists of people's shared beliefs, values, and assumptions about what is important. As an Army leader, you must be mindful of cultural factors in three contexts:

> **culture**
>
> *shared attitudes, values, goals, and practices that characterize a nation, institution, or organization*

- You must be sensitive to the different backgrounds of your team members to best leverage their talents
- You must be aware of the culture of the country in which your unit is operating
- You must consider and evaluate the possible implications of your partners' customs, traditions, doctrinal principles, and operational methods when you are working with the forces of another nation.

Understanding the culture of your adversaries and of the country in which your unit is operating is just as important as understanding the culture of your own country and unit. The Contemporary Operating Environment, which places smaller units into more culturally complex situations with continuous media coverage, requires even greater cultural and geopolitical awareness from every Army leader. Consequently, be aware of current events—particularly those in areas where America has national interests. Before deploying, ensure that your Soldiers and platoon are properly prepared to deal with the population of particular areas—either as partners, neutrals, or adversaries. The more that you and your Soldiers know about them, including their language, the better off your platoon will be.

Dimensions of Culture

Many factors contribute to differences in culture. Several major differences are related to the politics, economics, and geography of a culture. The overview offered here represents a very short summary of a great deal of research that has highlighted these differences.

Political Differences

A simple comparison of Afghanistan, Iraq, and the United States reveals some of the vast *political differences* in cultures. A person who has lived under the rule of tyranny develops a different set of beliefs and behaviors than someone who grew up with the freedom to vote, voice an opinion, or even travel freely from one place to another. Over time people develop mindsets toward leaders and authority figures that affect how they think and act. People who have lived many years under a dictator do not naturally trust anyone who represents political authority. In the COE of Iraq and Afghanistan, people will not quickly or easily trust any Soldiers, because they have learned not to trust political authority figures of any kind.

Economic Differences

The *economic status* of individuals and groups within a region or nation also affects their beliefs and behaviors. Matters like average income or the gross national product of a nation affect the culture. Men and women from an impoverished nation in East Africa, for instance, are much more concerned with what they need to do to survive than they are with the customer service at a local market. Concepts like investment, stock portfolio, profit margins, and discretionary spending have no meaning in many cultures.

Geographic Differences

Geography also affects cultural attitudes and actions. There are numerous words for snow in Alaska. By contrast, very few people in Miami own a winter coat. Meanwhile in Nebraska, no one earns a living by hiring out deep-sea fishing expeditions. Schools in Virginia will be canceled if it snows two inches. People who live along the Amazon River in Brazil are far more concerned with poisonous snakes than people who live in the mountains of Chile.

Orientation Differences

In addition, research has revealed cultural differences in *orientations* to time, relationships, authority, purpose, and community. These day-to-day differences often go unnoticed, yet have significant effects on how well we navigate in a different cultural setting. Many factors contribute to these differences. While those factors are interesting, it is critical that an officer develop some understanding of the general ways attitudes and actions differ across cultures. This knowledge will equip you to demonstrate adaptive leadership in cross-cultural settings. It is essential that you learn to **adapt** your behaviors and, on occasion, your beliefs when operating in a **cross-cultural context**.

adapt

to adjust perspectives and behaviors in order to be more effective in an unfamiliar environment

cross-cultural context

an environment in which people from two or more cultures or sub-cultures interact

Orientation to Time

Polychronic and *monochronic* are the terms scholars use to describe the ways people from different cultures approach space and time. Monochronic orientations to time emphasize schedules, promptness, and efficiency. The United States is generally a monochronic culture. Polychronic orientations to time give more attention to people and completing transactions than to sticking to schedules. The cultures of France and South and Central America are generally polychronic.

We experience these differences both when we plan events and participate in them. If a US Army Soldier sets a meeting for 1330 hours on Tuesday, he or she would expect the people attending that meeting to arrive by 1325 hours so the meeting can begin promptly as scheduled at 1330 hours. That works great if everyone attending is from a monochronic culture. But an individual from Venezuela, for instance, would complete whatever he or she was working on—especially if working with another person—before leaving for the meeting scheduled at 1330 hours. So he or she would consider it rude to leave their previous appointment in order to be "on time" for another meeting, and would think nothing of arriving at 1400 hours. Meanwhile, the Americans wait for half an hour, growing increasingly impatient.

Once the meeting finally begins, the Americans' orientation is to work until the next scheduled appointment. The work stops when it is "time" to leave. Those from monochronic cultures believe that being late to a meeting is exceptionally rude. Those from a polychronic culture, on the other hand, believe it's exceptionally rude to leave an existing meeting and the relationships with the people involved in order to arrive on time at another meeting. As an adaptive leader, you must learn to navigate between the two cultural orientations.

Orientation to Relationships

Scholars tend to describe people from polychronic cultures as "high context" in their orientation. That is another way of saying they are more concerned with building relationships with people than with producing measurable achievements. People from monochronic cultures tend to be "low context" in their orientation. High context and low context translate into the notions that people are relationship oriented (high context) or achievement oriented (low context). This does not mean that people who are relationship oriented don't care about achievements or that achievement-oriented people don't care about relationships. The cultural orientation to relationships does, however, affect the way people interpret events, and what they do in certain situations.

Context here refers to the information people have when they receive communication. People from high-context cultures either have or require a great deal of information when they communicate. People from low-context cultures, on the other hand, find the information they need in the message itself rather than in the context surrounding the message.

In practice this means low-context people will conduct business quickly and efficiently within minutes of meeting someone. People from high-context cultures, by contrast, require long periods of personal interactions before they are prepared to work on a project. A person from a low-context orientation can read a document, evaluate what needs to be done, and make a decision. A person from a high-context orientation, however, will want to meet the people who have written the document, find out who they know and what their concerns were, and establish a degree of trust before making any decisions.

The result is that low-context individuals make decisions and produce results much more quickly than high-context individuals. But the speed of their achievement orientation sometimes results in poor decisions that they must later change. High-context individuals are notoriously slow in making decisions. Once they make those decisions, however, they are frequently right on target. Their relationship orientation ensures that people will understand who is doing what. The drawback is that a lot of things can happen while people are waiting to build relationships of trust prior to making decisions.

Critical Thinking

How would you rate yourself and your fellow Cadets on this achievement-relationship scale? How many Cadets want to "get down to business immediately" and how many would prefer to "make friends first and then work on this project"? What consequences do you think these two conflicting perspectives might have?

Orientation to Authority

Scholars rate orientation to authority on a scale that is sometimes called "power distance." This refers to the degree of equality between the person in authority and a subordinate. An ROTC Cadet would never refer to his or her battalion commander by first name. This is because the Army has a high power-distance between those in authority and those in subordinate positions. Yet some students may refer to their professors on a first-name basis or use a shortened nickname like "Dr. K" or "Doc." This reflects a lower power-distance culture. The same is true when a young person calls an older person by his or her first name. The more equal subordinates are to authorities, the lower the power-distance in their cultural orientation.

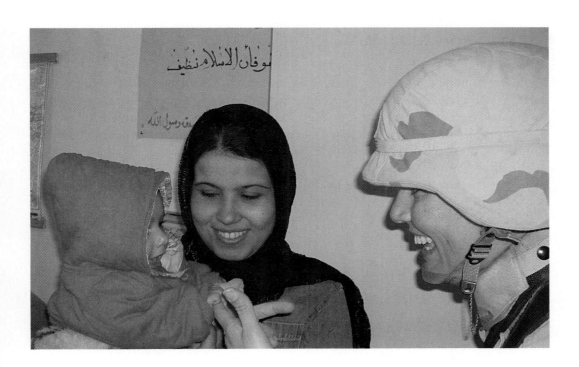

Here's an example of how differing orientations to authority can lead to misunderstanding. A professor from the United States was surprised and upset after teaching Japanese students. Not one student raised a question. No one interrupted her for a point of clarification during an entire day of teaching. She may have concluded that her teaching was ineffective or that her students weren't listening, but she would be wrong. Rather, what she experienced was a culture of extremely high power-distance, in which it is considered rude to interrupt someone in authority who is speaking.

Orientation to Purpose

Some cultures are more oriented to the goal of survival than others. This is clearly true in less economically privileged cultures. Cultures in which people are fairly prosperous tend to be more oriented to satisfaction or self-expression. It is rather obvious that the United States is a satisfaction-oriented culture. Language that refers to such concepts as "customer satisfaction" and "personal fulfillment" reflects this. As difficult as it may be to imagine, these concepts are foreign to some cultures in which people struggle merely to survive.

The movie *Saving Private Ryan* illustrates this well. As CPT Miller (Tom Hanks's character) and his squad move through various combat encounters, they are no longer worried about how satisfied they are or what kind of self-expression they can demonstrate. Their focus is clearly on completing their mission and on survival rather than personal satisfaction or expression.

Orientation to Community

American culture places a strong emphasis on individual rights. Yet many other cultures equally emphasize collective duties. For most societies, the interest of the group is more important than the interest of individuals. This is clearly true of the culture of the US Army. The Warrior Ethos places a clear focus on placing one's mission above individual interest. As Soldiers make the commitment to always place the mission first, never accept defeat, and never leave a fallen comrade, they intentionally enter a culture in which the good of the group is placed above the good of the individual. This does not mean that individual rights are not important. It simply reflects the Army culture, which values the collective good over individual rights.

Culture and Climate

climate

the specific environment of smaller organizations within the larger cultural framework; compared to culture, it relates to the short term

Climate is different from culture, but it is equally important. While culture describes the overall environment of the Army as an institution, the United States as a nation, or a cross-cultural COE, climate relates to the specific environment of units and smaller organizations within the larger cultural framework. For example, the Army expects leaders to take care of their people and to create a climate that encourages, pursues, and maintains excellence. Climate is short-term compared with culture and often depends on the individual personalities who make up a unit or smaller organization. As an Army leader, you must be aware of culture in order to adapt to the various expectations embedded in the cultural norms. Yet you have a more direct influence over the climate in which you operate.

Changing a Unit Climate—The New Squad Leader

SSG Withers was having a tough week. He had just been promoted to squad leader in a different company; he had new responsibilities, new leaders, and new Soldiers. Then, on his second day, his unit was alerted for a big inspection in two days. A quick check of the records let him know that the squad leader before him had let maintenance slip; the records were sloppy and a lot of the scheduled work had not been done. On top of that, SSG Withers was sure his new platoon sergeant didn't like him. SFC King was professional but gruff, a person of few words. The Soldiers in SSG Withers' squad seemed a little afraid of the platoon sergeant. After receiving the company commander's guidance about the inspection, the squad leaders briefed the platoon sergeant on their plans to get ready. SSG Withers had already determined that he and his Soldiers would have to work late. He could have complained about his predecessor, but he thought it would be best just to stick to the facts and talk about what he had found in the squad. For all he knew, the old squad leader might have been a favorite of SFC King. SFC King scowled as he asked, "You're going to work late?" SSG Withers had checked his plan twice: "Yes, sergeant. I think it's necessary." SFC King grunted, but the sound could have meant "Okay," or it could have meant "You're being foolish." SSG Withers wasn't sure. The next day SSG Withers told his Soldiers what they would have to accomplish. One of the Soldiers said that the old squad leader would have just fudged the paperwork. "No kidding," SSG Withers thought. He wondered if SFC King knew about it. Of course, there was a good chance he would fail the inspection if he didn't fudge the paperwork—and wouldn't that be a good introduction to the new company? But he told his squad that they would do it right: "We'll do the best we can. If we don't pass, we'll do better next time." SSG Withers then asked his squad for their thoughts on how to get ready. He listened to their ideas and offered some of his own. One Soldier suggested that they could beat the other squads by sneaking into the motor pool at night and lowering the oil levels in their vehicles. "SFC King gives a half day off to whatever squad does best," the Soldier explained. SSG Withers didn't want to badmouth the previous squad leader; on the other hand, the squad was his responsibility now. "It'd be nice to win," SSG Withers said, "but we're not going to cheat." The squad worked past 2200 hours the night before the inspection. At one point SSG Withers found one of the Soldiers sleeping under a vehicle. "Don't you want to finish and go home to sleep?" he asked the Soldier. "I . . . uh . . . I didn't think you'd still be here," the Soldier answered. "Where else would I be?" replied the squad leader. The next day, SFC King asked SSG Withers if he thought his squad's vehicle was going to pass the inspection. "Not a chance," SSG Withers said. SFC King gave another mysterious grunt. Later, when the inspector was going over his vehicle, SSG Withers asked if his Soldiers could follow along. "I want them to see how to do a thorough inspection," he told the inspector. As the Soldiers followed the inspector around and learned how to look closely at the vehicle, one of them commented that the squad had never been around for any inspection up to that point. "We were always told to stay away," he said. Later, when the company commander went over the results of the inspection, he looked up at SSG Withers as he read the failing grade. SSG Withers was about to say, "We'll try harder next time, sir," but he decided that sounded lame, so he said nothing. Then SFC King spoke up. "First time that squad has ever failed an inspection," the platoon sergeant said, "but they're already better off than they were the day before yesterday, failing grade and all."

Critical Thinking

Discuss how a leader's behavior can impact both the culture and the climate of an organization.

Critical Thinking

Explain how an organization like the US Army can create a unified culture despite the major cultural differences among individuals.

Critical Thinking

The commander in chief has dispatched your unit to a remote area on a humanitarian-relief mission. The province has long been engaged in a civil war against the central government, with ragtag ethnic militias set against the well-equipped, smartly uniformed national army. The rebels have long accused the national army of atrocities against civilians. How do you think those civilians might regard your Soldiers when you arrive bringing relief supplies?

CONCLUSION

What difference does all this make? As you lead in situations such as the Leader Development and Assessment Course (LDAC) and ultimately in the Contemporary Operating Environment, you will face the need to adapt your leadership to the cultural differences you experience. The Army will also expect you to establish a climate of high motivation and trust that leads to excellence. Men and women who have different cultural backgrounds will bring diverse beliefs and behaviors to the units you lead. It will be up to you as a leader to adapt. You'll need to be aware of the differences people have in their cultural perceptions and lead in a way that builds motivation and trust. As an adaptive leader, you'll be able to effectively navigate the cultural differences you experience and by doing so, build a climate in which your Soldiers excel.

Learning Assessment

1. Describe what is meant by orientation to each of the following:
   a. Time
   b. Relationships
   c. Authority
   d. Purpose
   e. Community
2. Differentiate between culture and climate.

Key Words

Contemporary Operating Environment (COE)
culture
adapt
cross-cultural context
climate

References

Adler, N. J. (1997). *International Dimensions of Organizational Behavior*. Third Edition. Cincinnati, OH: South-Western College Publishing.

Field Manual 6-22, *Army Leadership: Competent, Confident, and Agile*. 12 October 2006.

Hall, E. T. (1976). *Beyond Culture*. Garden City, NY: Anchor Press.

Hall, E. T., & Hall, M. R. (1990). *Understanding Cultural Differences*. Yarmouth, ME: Intercultural Press, Inc.

Harrison, L. E., & Huntington, S. P., eds. (2000). *Culture Matters: How Values Shape Human Progress*. New York: Basic Books.

Hofstede, G. (1991). *Cultures and Organizations: Software of the Mind*. New York: McGraw-Hill.

Section 1

ARMY BRIEFING TECHNIQUES

Key Points

1 The Four Types of Military Briefings

2 The Four Steps of Military Briefings

Be sincere; be brief; be seated.

Franklin Delano Roosevelt

Introduction

In the Army, you exercise command most frequently through the clear and concise spoken word. Commanders must explain the situation and their plan of action so that the troops understand it completely. You must pass along information in a coherent fashion. The fate of a battle often rests on a leader's ability to express concrete ideas in clear and unmistakable language.

You have a personal responsibility for improving yourself in the area of **effective communication**. Many officers try to put off this obligation with the common excuse: "I'm just a simple fighting man with no gift for speaking." Don't fall into that trap: Plan now to master this important skill by seizing every opportunity you have to practice it. This chapter will help you do so. It describes the types of military briefings, the formats for each type, and the four steps for delivering effective **briefings**.

The Gettysburg Address

This speech, regarded as one of Abraham Lincoln's finest works, was delivered at Gettysburg, Pennsylvania, on Nov. 19, 1863. Lincoln spoke at the dedication of a cemetery for those killed in the battle of July 1–3 between George Gordon Meade's Army of the Potomac and Robert E. Lee's Army of Northern Virginia. The main speaker was Edward Everett, a renowned orator.

When the board in charge of the event extended invitations to various national figures, it did not expect Lincoln to attend, but he made his attendance a priority. Contrary to legend, he did not write his speech on the back of an envelope as he traveled to the ceremonies by train. Like any good public speaker, he was well prepared ahead of time—having made two drafts of the remarks he planned to deliver. After Everett's two-hour oration, Lincoln spoke for only a few minutes. He began, "Four score and seven years ago, our fathers brought forth, upon this continent, a new nation, conceived in Liberty, and dedicated to the proposition that all men are created equal." He concluded that, "government of the people, by the people, for the people, shall not perish from the earth."

The ten sentences composing the speech received little attention at the time. Everett himself appreciated Lincoln's eloquence, however, writing him, "I should be glad if I could flatter myself that I came as near to the central idea of the occasion in two hours as you did in two minutes." Through the years, the address, considered a model of its kind, has been much studied, proving one of Lincoln's predictions wrong: "The world will little note, nor long remember, what we say here, but it can never forget what they did here" (Gettysburg Address, 1863).

---

effective communication

the successful exchange of information between individuals—an effective communicator succeeds in establishing an active two-way link with another individual or group

briefings

a means of presenting information to commanders, staffs, or other audiences—the purpose of the briefing, the desired response, and the role of the briefer determine the techniques you employ

The Four Types of Military Briefings

Briefings are a means of presenting information to commanders, staffs, or other audiences. The purpose of the briefing, the desired response, and the role of the briefer determine the techniques you employ. This section describes the types of military briefings and gives the format for each type.

There are four types of military briefings:

1. Information
2. Decision
3. Mission
4. Staff.

Information Briefing

An information briefing provides information in a form the audience can understand. It does not include conclusions or recommendations. No decisions result. Information briefings deal primarily with facts. Figure 1-1 shows the format for an information briefing.

You begin an information briefing by addressing the audience, identifying yourself and your organization, and giving the briefing's classification. You state that the purpose of the briefing is for information, and no decision is required. You then introduce and define the subject, orient the audience, and present the information. Examples of information appropriate for an information briefing are:

---

1. **Introduction**

   a. Greeting. Address the audience. Identify yourself and your organization.

   b. Type and Classification of Briefing. For example, "This is an information briefing. It is classified SECRET."

   c. Purpose and Scope. Describe complex subjects from general to specific.

   d. Outline or Procedure. Briefly summarize the key points and general approach. Explain any special procedures (such as, demonstrations, displays, or tours). For example, "During my briefing, I'll discuss the six phases of our plan. I'll refer to maps of our area of operations. Then my assistant will bring out a sand table to show you the expected flow of battle." The key points may be placed on a chart that remains visible throughout the briefing.

2. **Main Body**

   a. Arrange the main ideas in a logical sequence.

   b. Use visual aids to emphasize main ideas.

   c. Plan effective transitions from one main point to the next.

   d. Be prepared to answer questions at any time.

3. **Closing**

   a. Ask for questions.

   b. Briefly recap main ideas and make a concluding statement.

   c. Announce the next speaker.

Figure 1.1 Information Briefing Format

- High priority information requiring immediate attention
- Complex information—such as complicated plans, systems, statistics, or charts—that require detailed explanation
- Controversial information requiring elaboration and explanation.

Decision Briefing

A decision briefing obtains an answer to a question or a decision on a course of action. It presents the recommended solution resulting from analysis or study of a problem or problem area. Decision briefings vary in formality and detail depending on the level of command and the decision makers' knowledge of the subject.

In situations where the decision maker is familiar with the problem, the briefing format may resemble that of a decision paper: a problem statement, essential background information, impacts, and a recommended solution. However, you should be prepared to present assumptions, facts, alternative solutions, reasons for adopting the recommendation, and the coordination involved.

You begin by stating, "This is a decision briefing." At the conclusion, if the decision maker does not state a decision, ask for one. Be certain that you understand the decision. If uncertain, ask for clarification.

The recommendation that you ask the decision maker to approve should be precisely worded in a form that can be used as a decision statement. Presenting the recommendation

---

1. Introduction

    a. Greeting. Address the decision maker. Identify yourself and your organization.

    b. Type and Classification of Briefing. For example, "This is a decision briefing. It is UNCLASSIFIED."

    c. Problem Statement.

    d. Recommendation.

2. Body

    a. Facts. An objective presentation of both positive and negative facts bearing upon the problem.

    b. Assumptions. Necessary assumptions made to bridge any gaps in factual data.

    c. Solutions. A discussion of the various options that can solve the problem.

    d. Analysis. The criteria by which you will evaluate how to solve the problem (screening and evaluation). A discussion of each course of actions relative advantages and disadvantages.

    e. Comparison. Show how the courses of action rate against the evaluation criteria.

    f. Conclusion. Describe why the selected solution is best.

3. Closing

    a. Questions?

    b. Restatement of the recommendation.

    c. Request a decision.

Figure 1.2 Decision Briefing Format

this way helps eliminate ambiguities. If the decision requires an implementing document, you should prepare the document before the briefing and give it to the decision maker for signature if he or she approves the recommendation.

Mission Briefing

The mission briefing is an information briefing presented under tactical or operational conditions. The briefer may be the commander, an assistant, a staff officer, or a special representative. The mission briefing is used during operations and training. It is especially appropriate for critical missions or when it is necessary to give individuals or smaller units information not in the plan or order. The mission briefing serves to:

- Issue or reinforce an order
- Provide more detailed requirements or instructions
- Instill a general appreciation for the mission
- Review the key points of a forthcoming military operation
- Ensure participants know the mission's objective, their place in the operation, problems they may encounter, and ways to overcome them.

The type of mission or the nature of the information to be presented determines the mission-briefing format. The five-paragraph operation order is the most common format used. Others include the movement order, combat service support order, and reconnaissance order.

Staff Briefing

The purpose of a staff briefing is to coordinate unit efforts by informing the commander and staff of the current situation. The person who convenes the staff briefing sets the agenda. Staff representatives each present relevant information from their functional areas. Staff briefings may involve exchange of information, announcement of decisions, issuance of directives, or presentation of guidance. They may have characteristics of information briefings, decision briefings, and mission briefings.

Attendance at staff briefings varies with the size of the headquarters, type of operation, and commander's preferences. Generally, the commander, deputies or assistants, chief of staff (executive officer), and coordinating and special staff officers attend. Representatives from major subordinate commands may be present. The chief of staff (executive officer) usually presides. The commander usually concludes the briefing but may take an active part throughout it.

In garrison, staff briefings (sometimes called "staff calls") are often regularly scheduled. In combat, staff briefings are held as needed. The presentation of staff estimates culminating in a commander's decision to adopt a course of action is a form of staff briefing that incorporates aspects of a decision briefing. In this type of briefing, staff representatives use the staff estimate for their functional area as an outline.

Critical Thinking

Why is it important to give pros and cons in your briefings? How important is this to military problem solving and decision making?

The Four Steps of Military Briefings

A briefing assignment has four steps that correspond to the four activities of the operations process:

- Plan: Analyze the situation and prepare a briefing outline
- Prepare: Construct the briefing
- Execute: Deliver the briefing
- Assess: Follow up.

Plan: Analyze the Situation and Prepare a Briefing Outline

Upon receiving the task to conduct a briefing, you analyze the situation to determine the:

- Audience
- Purpose and type of briefing
- Subject of the briefing
- Physical facilities and support needed
- Preparation schedule.

Based on this information, prepare a briefing outline. The briefing outline is your plan for preparing, executing, and following up on the briefing. It is a tool to manage preparations for the briefing and refine it as new information is received.

Figure 1-3 lists factors you should consider when planning a briefing, as well as tasks to perform when preparing for it. In addition, you should determine the following:

- Audience preferences—if you are conducting a decision briefing, the audience preferences should be those of the decision maker
- The purpose of the briefing—the purpose determines the type of briefing
- The time allocated for the briefing—this dictates the style, physical facilities, and preparatory effort needed
- The availability of physical facilities, visual aids, and visual information specialists.

Estimate deadlines for each task and carefully schedule the preparatory effort. This includes scheduling facilities for rehearsals and requesting critiques. Alert support personnel and any assistants as early as possible.

Prepare: Construct the Briefing

The construction of your briefing will vary with its type and purpose. Your analysis provides the basis for this determination. The following are the major steps in preparing a briefing:

- Collect material
- Prepare first draft
- Revise first draft and edit
- Plan use of visual aids
- Practice.

1. Analyze Situation and Prepare a Briefing Outline.

  a. Audience.

- Number?

- Composition? Single service or joint? Civilians? Foreign nationals?

- Who are the ranking members?

- What are their official positions?

- Where are they assigned?

- How well do they know the subject?

- Are they generalists or specialists?

- What are their interests?

- What are their personal preferences?

- What is the anticipated reaction?

  b. Purpose and Type.

- Information briefing (to inform)?

- Decision briefing (to obtain decision)?

- Mission briefing (to review important details)?

- Staff briefing (to exchange information)?

  c. Subject of Briefing.

- What is the specific subject?

- What is the desired coverage?

- How much time will be allocated?

  d. Physical Facilities and Support Needed.

- Where will the briefing be presented?

- What arrangements will be required?

- What are the visual aid facilities?

- What are the deficiencies?

- What actions are needed to overcome deficiencies?

  e. Prepare Schedule.

- Finish analysis of the situation.

- Prepare preliminary outline.

- Determine requirements for training aids, assistants, and recorders.

- Edit or redraft.

- Schedule rehearsals, facilities, and critiques.

- Arrange for final review by responsible authority.

2. Construct Briefing.

  a. Collect Material.

- Research.

- Become familiar with the subject.

- Collect authoritative opinions and facts.

  b. Prepare First Draft.

- State problem (if necessary).

- Isolate key points (facts).

- Identify courses of action.

- Analyze and compare courses of action. (State advantages and disadvantages.)

- Determine conclusions and recommendations.

- Prepare draft outline.

- Include visual aids.

- Fill in appropriate material.

- Review with appropriate authority.

  c. Revise First Draft and Edit.

- Make sure that facts are important and necessary.

- Include all necessary facts.

- Include answers to anticipated questions.

- Polish material.

  d. Plan Use of Visual Aids.

- Check for simplicity and readability.

- Develop method for use.

  e. Practice.

- Rehearse (with assistants and visual aids).

- Polish.

- Isolate key points.

- Memorize outline.

- Develop transitions.

- Use definitive words.

3. Deliver Briefing.

4. Follow Up.

  a. Ensure understanding.

  b. Record decision.

  c. Inform proper authorities.

Figure 1.3 Briefing Checklist

Execute: Deliver the Briefing

The success of a briefing often depends on how well you present it. A confident, relaxed, and forceful delivery, clearly enunciated, helps convince the audience. You should always maintain a relaxed, but military, bearing. Use natural gestures and movement, but avoid distracting mannerisms. Conciseness, objectivity, and accuracy characterize good delivery. You should remain aware of the following:

- The basic purpose is to present the subject as directed and ensure that the audience understands it
- For brevity's sake, avoid a lengthy introduction or summary
- Conclusions and recommendations must flow logically from facts and assumptions.

Interruptions and questions may occur at any point. If and when they occur, answer each question before continuing, or indicate that you will answer the question later in the briefing. At the same time, do not permit questions to distract from the planned briefing. If answering the question later in the briefing, make specific reference to the earlier question when you introduce the material. Be prepared to support any part of the briefing. Anticipate possible questions and be prepared to answer them.

Assess: Follow Up

When the briefing is over, prepare a memorandum for record (MFR). This MFR records the subject, date, time, and place of the briefing, and the ranks, names, and positions of audience members. Concisely record the substance of your remarks. Also record recommendations and their approval, disapproval, or approval with modification, as well as any instruction or directed action. This includes who is to take action. When a decision is involved and doubt exists about the decision maker's intent, submit a draft of the MFR to him or her for correction before preparing it in final form. Distribute the MFR to staff sections and agencies required to act on the decisions or instructions, or whose operations or plans may be affected.

Critical Thinking

You've just learned that the chairman of the Joint Chiefs is stopping by your unit in Northern Kosovo the day after tomorrow on his way back to Washington from the Middle East. Your commander instructs you to prepare and present a briefing on the status of your mission. What kind of briefing will you prepare? How will you get ready? How will you ensure that you don't say something that may embarrass you, your commander, and your fellow Soldiers?

CONCLUSION

Mastering the spoken word is essential for all officers. Formal presentations and briefings are how the military communicates. The Army expects officers to master four types of briefings during their careers—information, decision, mission, and staff briefings. Each of these follows the same four-step process:

1. Analyze the situation.

2. Construct the briefing.

3. Deliver or present the briefing.

4. Follow up.

Remember: You've studied the subject, logically organized the information, and prepared yourself. You are the expert! Present with confidence. What you say, and how well you say it, will be major factors in how others assess your leadership.

Learning Assessment

1. What are the four types of military briefings and how do you distinguish among them?

2. What are the four steps you must take to present effectively?

Key Words

effective communication
briefings

References

Armed Forces Information Service Department of Defense. (1975). *The Armed Forces Officer* (DoD GEN-36). Washington, DC.

Field Manual 5-0, *Army Planning and Orders Production.* 20 January 2005.

The Reader's Companion to American History (n.d.). The Gettysburg Address. Retrieved 23 March 2005 from http://college.hmco.com/history/readerscomp/recah/html/ah_036300_gettysburgad.htm

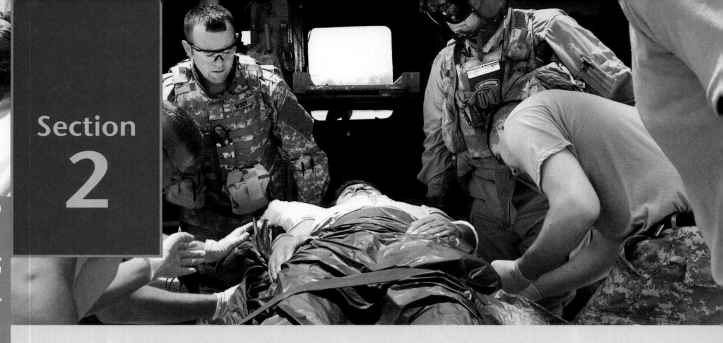
SUICIDE PREVENTION

Key Points

1 **Introduction to Suicide Prevention**

2 **Identifying Suicidal Behavior**

3 **The Army Suicide Prevention Program**

4 **Prevention**

All men are frightened. The more intelligent they are, the more they are frightened. The courageous man is the man who forces himself, in spite of his fear, to carry on.

GEN George S. Patton, Jr.

Introduction

The Army's strength rests with our Soldiers, civilians, retirees, and their families, each being a vital member of our institution. Suicide is detrimental to the readiness of the Army and is a personal tragedy for all those affected. Therefore, suicide has no place in our professional force! We all realize the inherent stress and burden placed upon us as Soldiers, civilians, and their family members. What defines us as an institution is our compassion and commitment to promoting a healthy lifestyle by emphasizing physical, spiritual, and mental fitness. This contributes to the overall well-being of the force and readiness of the Army. Therefore, we must remain cognizant of the potential suicidal triggers and warning signs so that we can raise awareness and increase vigilance for recognizing those who might be at risk for suicidal behaviors. Furthermore, we must create a command climate of acceptance and support that encourages help-seeking behavior as a sign of individual strength and maturity. Suicide prevention, like all leadership challenges, is a commander's program and every leader's responsibility at all levels. However, the success of the Army Suicide Prevention Program (ASPP) rests upon proactive, caring, and courageous Soldiers, family members, and Army civilians who recognize the imminent danger and then take immediate action to save a life. We need your help to minimize the risk of suicide within the Army to stop this tragic and unnecessary loss of human life. Suicide prevention is everybody's business and in the Army, EVERYONE MATTERS!

LTG John M. Le Moyne
Deputy Chief of Staff, G-1

The Cost of Suicide

During the 1990s, the Army lost an equivalent of an entire battalion task force to suicides (803 Soldiers). This ranked as the third leading cause of death for Soldiers, exceeded only by accidents and illnesses. Even more startling is that during this same period, five times as many Soldiers killed themselves as were killed by hostile fire.

To appreciate the magnitude and impact of suicide, consider that most suicides have a direct, lasting impact on between six to seven intimate family members (spouse, parents, children), and numerous others, including relatives, unit members, friends, neighbors, and others in the local community.

A leader is a dealer in hope.

– Napoleon

Introduction to Suicide Prevention

Army Suicide Prevention Program Goal

The goal of any Army Suicide Prevention Program (ASPP) is to minimize suicidal behavior among Soldiers, retirees, civilians, and family members. Suicidal behavior includes self-inflicted fatalities, non-fatal self-injury, and suicidal thoughts. Suicide prevention is an evolving science. It is the Army's responsibility to use the best-known available means to care for Soldiers, retirees, civilians, and family members. The success of the Army's efforts will be measured by the confidence and conscience of knowing that:

- the Army has created and fostered an environment where all Soldiers, civilians, and family members at risk for suicide will quickly be identified and receive successful intervention and appropriate care
- the Army encourages and accepts help-seeking behavior as a sign of individual strength, courage, and maturity
- all leaders teach and reinforce positive **life-coping skills**.

CSA Statement

In 2000, following a 27 percent increase in the number of reported suicides within the Army during 1997–1999, the Chief of Staff of the Army, GEN Eric K. Shinseki, stated that suicide is a "serious problem" and directed a complete review of the ASPP. He called for a campaign that would refine the ASPP by making use of the best-known available science, and would also invigorate suicide prevention awareness and vigilance. He further stated that for the program to be effective, the framework must:

- involve all commanders
- be proactive
- intensify preventive efforts against suicidal behavior
- invest in the Army's junior leaders
- improve current training and education.

Identifying Suicidal Behavior

We cannot possess what we do not understand.

Goethe

A Model for Explaining Dysfunctional Behavior

Human behavior is influenced by one's genetic composition and shaped by his or her developmental history. It is usually a reaction to a particular stimulus within one's environment. The model in Figure 2.1 graphically illustrates how one's genetics, background, current environment, as well as immediate events, can contribute to dysfunctional behavior.

Some individuals are born predisposed toward psychiatric illness and/or **substance abuse**. This makes them more susceptible or vulnerable to certain types of **dysfunctional behavior**, including suicide. Childhood experiences filled with abuse, trauma, or neglect will also hurt the development of positive life-coping skills. A "nonsupportive environment,"

life-coping skills

ability and strategies to deal successfully with the difficulties of life

substance abuse

the excessive use of addictive substances, especially alcohol and narcotic drugs

dysfunctional behavior

abnormal or impaired behavior

whether at work or home, filled with stress, resentment, ridicule, or ostracism from family or friends, might also lead to dysfunctional behavior.

Soldiers and civilians enter the Army with varying levels of life-coping skills. They also have various levels of resiliency, as determined by their genetic disposition, and developmental and environmental influences. Don't assume that all Soldiers and civilians entering the Army can adequately handle the stress of military service. They may not even be able to handle life in general, especially if they are already predisposed to psychiatric disorder. It is unrealistic to expect you to understand the genetic composition of the Soldier and civilian, or know their complete developmental history. However, you can make proper assessments of their life-coping skills by observation and personal dialogue. This section aims to explain the causes of suicide and inform you of common dangers and warning signs. Then you can anticipate suicidal or other dysfunctional behavior and refer individuals to mental health professionals before a crisis happens.

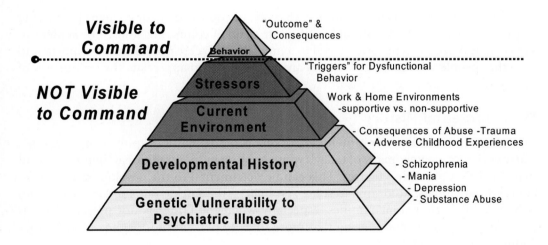

Figure 2.1 A Model for Understanding Dysfunctional Health-Risk Behaviors

Mental Disorders

Mental disorders are health conditions that include changes in thinking, mood, or behavior. They are associated with distress or impaired functioning and may lead to a host of problems, such as disability, pain, or death. Mental disorders occur throughout society and affect people regardless of age, gender, ethnic group, educational background, and socioeconomic level.

Mental illness is more common than cancer, diabetes, or heart disease, filling almost 21 percent of all hospital beds at any given time. Mental disorders affect youth, as well. At least 1 in 5 children and adolescents between the ages of 9 and 17 years has a diagnosable mental disorder in a given year, and about 5 percent of them are extremely impaired. Mental disorders vary in their severity and disabling effects. However, current treatments are highly effective. The treatment success rate for schizophrenia is 60 percent; for major depression, 65 percent; and for bipolar disorder, 80 percent. This compares with a success rate of between 41 percent and 52 percent for the treatment of heart disease.

In 1996, the assistant secretary of Defense for Health Affairs commissioned Dr. David Schaffer, a leading suicide prevention authority, to analyze the Department of Defense Suicide Prevention Programs. His study included an in-depth analysis of each service's suicide prevention program in 1997. Dr. Schaffer found that most suicides are associated with a diagnosable psychiatric disorder such as depression or substance abuse. These disorders generally appear as some form of clinical depression, a disorder that can increase suicidal risk as well as anxiety, impulsiveness, rage, **hopelessness**, and desperation.

Although it is the responsibility of mental health professionals to diagnose a mental disorder, certain behaviors indicate an underlying mental disorder. You should be aware of these warning behaviors that might place Soldiers at risk for suicide or other dysfunctional behavior. They are:

hopelessness

a feeling that there is no solution to a serious personal problem

- impulsiveness or aggressive-violent traits
- previous self-injurious acts
- excessive anger, agitation, or constricted preoccupations
- excessive alcohol use
- heavy smoking
- evidence of any sleep or eating disorder.

If you spot such behavior or suspect that one of your Soldiers or civilians is suffering from a mental disorder, you should notify your chain of command. Your commander can then decide whether to make a referral to a mental health care provider. It is important to note that people with mental disorders are often unable to appreciate the seriousness of their problem because of the disorder.

Developmental History

The home and family environment where one is reared has a deep influence on one's behavior. Unfortunately, many of today's youth grow up in "nontraditional" homes, without two consistent parenting figures. This can be detrimental to the development of well-adjusted individuals. According to some researchers, the suicide rate for America's youth is higher in single-parent families, especially when the father is not present. This is particularly alarming considering that more than 40 percent of today's youth are from "nontraditional" homes.

Childhood abuse or neglect might also lead to dysfunctional behavior and health-related problems, including smoking, obesity, depression, use of illegal drugs, promiscuity, and suicide.

A US Naval Behavioral Health Research Study released in 1995 reported that approximately 40 percent of all naval recruits reported having been raised in homes where they were physically or sexually abused or neglected. The same study said that 46 percent of all female recruits reported being sexually assaulted before entering the service.

The consequences of these adverse experiences could cause friction within the Army, because those recruits who have been abused can:

- have a significant distrust of authority figures
- have an over-reliance on self
- tend to form sexualized relationships prematurely
- have a increased risk for substance abuse
- do not easily transfer loyalty to institutions such as the Army
- have a "me-oriented" attitude, often seeking short-term payoffs.

Although today's youth tend to be more technologically astute than previous generations, generally they have less developed relationship skills. You will need to recognize this fact, attempt to assess those assigned to your charge, and determine who might require remedial assistance and mentoring.

Influence of the Current Environment

As an Army leader, you should strive to communicate constructive life-coping skills and create an environment of support, respect, and acceptance. Make your Soldiers feel they are an integral part of a team. The result of a supportive environment (represented in the top left "output" box in Figure 2.2) will be a better-adjusted individual. Conversely, if you create an environment that reinforces negative life-coping skills or ignores positive life-coping skills, it could lead to dysfunctional behavior (represented in the top right "output" box in Figure 2.2).

You play a crucial role in establishing and determining the conditions of the Soldier's work environment. Strive to have a positive influence on each by being a proper role model. For some Soldiers, their role and camaraderie within their unit and their relationship with you might be the only positive, life-sustaining resource available to them in times of adversity. Therefore, you should take this responsibility seriously.

You are responsible for the development of subordinate leaders to ensure that they are aware of the importance of being a proper role model. Constantly assess your subordinate leaders' ability to positively influence behavior. It could be a disastrous mistake to assume that all subordinate leaders are reinforcing positive life-coping skills in the presence of their Soldiers. More than half the Army suicides in 2001 were in the rank of sergeant or above—including commissioned officers.

Not all suicidal behavior is preventable, but the time invested in helping your Soldiers develop positive behavior can yield many benefits, especially for younger Soldiers.

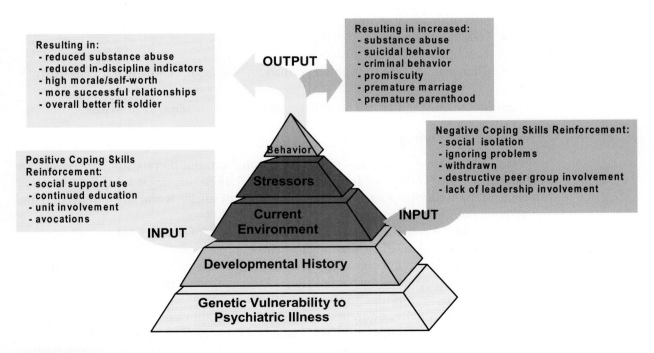

Figure 2.2 The Role of Environment in Behavior

Suicide Triggers

Although psychiatric illness or substance abuse contribute to a majority of all suicides, suicidal behavior is often linked with a significant emotional event, or **suicide trigger**. This can be a loss, separation, or any change in one's self-esteem and confidence. A review of Army psychological autopsies reveals that approximately 75 percent of all Soldiers who committed suicide were experiencing "significant problems" within a personal, intimate relationship. In addition, about half had just received or were pending some form of legal action, either civilian or military. About 42 percent were experiencing financial problems and 34 percent were known to be suffering from either drug or alcohol-abuse problems. Many of the Soldiers who completed suicides were experiencing more than one of these problems.

Each Soldier will handle a particular life stressor differently. Some will require assistance, which can range from talking with a friend to professional counseling. Ignored or untreated, the stressor can lead to suicidal thoughts or behavior. Therefore, you should anticipate potential "life crises" and ensure that your Soldier has the proper resources to handle the adversity. This might include appointing a "life-line" buddy to watch over him or her until the crisis has passed. Or you might refer the Soldier to the unit chaplain or other professional counselors.

Here is a list of potential triggers for suicide:

- Loss of a loved one to illness or death
- Loss of a significant, intimate relationship (divorce, separation, breakup)
- Loss of a child custody battle
- Loss of friendship or social status (social isolation or ostracism)
- Loss of a job or rank, or separation
- Military or civilian legal action
- Loss of freedom (incarceration)
- Loss of financial security (pay loss/reduction, gambling debts, bankruptcy)
- Loss of self-esteem (humiliation, passed over for promotion or schooling)
- Loss of hope or feeling helpless
- Change in lifestyle (unwanted permanent change of station, major deployment).

A common theme for all these potential suicide triggers is some form of loss.

Reasons for Dying

To the well-adjusted person, suicide is an irrational act. But don't assume that everyone shares this view. Some consider suicide a method of ending or escaping pain or other problems. An understanding of the psychodynamics of suicide is crucial for understanding and potentially predicting suicidal behavior.

According to researchers, suicide is driven by impulses of revenge, spite, or self-sacrifice, wishes to kill and be killed, or yearning for release into a better experience through death. Many suicides occur during or immediately following a problem with an intimate relationship. In these cases, by committing suicide, the victim believes he or she will have the final word by committing the final rejection.

Another potentially common reason for suicide within the Army is revenge against another person. An example could be a Soldier who returns from an extended deployment and discovers that his or her spouse is (or was) having an affair. The Soldier's feelings turn into a "murderous rage," which is then turned against himself or herself.

In some cases, perceived or actual failure causes self-hatred, which leads to suicide as a form of self-punishment. Researchers say that this reaction is more common in men who set extremely high standards for themselves. An example could be a Soldier who is pending court-martial action, or perhaps possible separation from the Army, and feels that he has failed and doesn't deserve to live.

The most frequent reasons for dying are listed here in descending order, beginning with the most frequent:

- General attitudes of giving up or needing a "rest"
- References to self such as "I feel awful" or "I'm not worth anything"
- References to other people such as "I want to stop hurting others"
- Statements referring to hopelessness, such as "Things may never get better" or "I may never reach my goals"
- Statements about lessening the pain, such as "I want to stop the pain"
- Statements that reflect loneliness, such as "I don't want to feel lonely anymore."

Suicide Danger Signs

Here is a list of immediate danger signs that suicidal behavior is imminent:

- Talking or hinting about suicide
- Formulating a plan to include acquiring the means to kill oneself
- Having a desire to die
- Obsession with death, including sad music or poetry or artwork
- Themes of death in letters and notes
- Finalizing personal affairs
- Giving away personal possessions.

If you recognize these warning signs in a Soldier, take immediate action. Talk to the Soldier; allow him or her to express his or her feelings. Ask the Soldier outright and bluntly, "Are you considering suicide?" or "Are you thinking about killing yourself?" If the Soldier's response is "yes," then take immediate life-saving steps. Ensure his or her safety. Notify the chain of command or chaplain, call for emergency services, or escort the individual to a mental health officer. Never ignore any of these suicide danger signs or leave the suicidal person alone. After all, you might be the last person with the opportunity to intervene.

Suicide Warning Signs

Although not as serious as the danger signs, these warning signs might precede suicidal behavior. Do not disregard them. Intervene personally, if needed:

- Obvious drop in duty performance
- Unkempt personal appearance
- Feelings of hopelessness or helplessness
- Family history of suicide
- Previous suicide attempts
- Drug or alcohol abuse
- Social withdrawal
- Loss of interest in hobbies
- Loss of interest in sexual activity
- Reckless behavior, self-mutilation
- Physical health complaints, changes/loss of appetite
- Complaints of significant sleep difficulties.

These signs signal that the person might be experiencing a life crisis and requires assistance. Watch for these danger and warning signs. Realize that the Soldier might not be capable of helping himself or herself and therefore may require immediate action.

In addition to the danger and warning signs, there are certain feelings or emotions that might precede suicide. The following is a list of possible feelings or attitudes that the individual at risk for suicide might be feeling. This does not suggest that everyone who has these feelings is at risk, but if these feelings persist, it could signal that the person is having difficulty coping. The most common feelings are:

- hopelessness or helplessness
- anger or vindictiveness
- guilt or shame
- desperation
- loneliness
- sadness or depression.

You must be confident that the life crisis has resolved itself before assuming the person is no longer suicidal. Some individuals might appear to be over their crisis, when in fact, they only appear "normal" because they have decided that they are definitely going to commit suicide.

Resources for Living

It is important to understand what causes suicidal behavior. However, it is also important to understand the resources that offer protection against dysfunctional, self-injurious behavior. The following are protective factors against suicide:

- Social supports, including marriage
- Active religious affiliation or faith
- Presence of dependent young children
- Ongoing supportive relationship with a caregiver
- Absence of depression or substance abuse
- Living close to medical and mental health resources
- Awareness that suicide is a product of illness, not weakness
- Proven problem-solving and coping skills.

Just as important as reasons for suicidal behaviors are reasons for living. Here is a list of the top reasons for living (in descending order beginning with the most prominent):

- Family: Any mention of a family member's love
- Future: Statements that express hope for the future
- Specific plans and goals: Future-oriented plans
- Enjoyable things: Activities or objects that the person enjoys
- Friends: Any mention of friends
- Self: Statements about qualities of self such as "I don't want to let myself down"
- Responsibilities to others: Any mention of obligations owed to others or the thought of protecting others
- Religion: Statements referring to religion

You should understand what serves as a source of strength or life-sustaining resource for the Soldier. Use it when counseling him or her through a particular crisis. Also, by understanding a Soldier's life resources you can alert your leadership to potential problems when one of those resources has been removed or is in danger.

The Army Suicide Prevention Model

The Army Suicide Prevention Model focuses on maintaining the Soldier's individual readiness. Occasionally, through normal life experiences, a person enters a path that, if followed, could lead to mental disorder or a life crisis. This, in turn, could lead to thoughts of suicide, suicidal behavior, and possible injury or death. Parallel to the suicidal path is a safety net that represents the Army's continuity of care. As the actual suicidal risk escalates, so does our response by becoming more directive and involving more health care professionals.

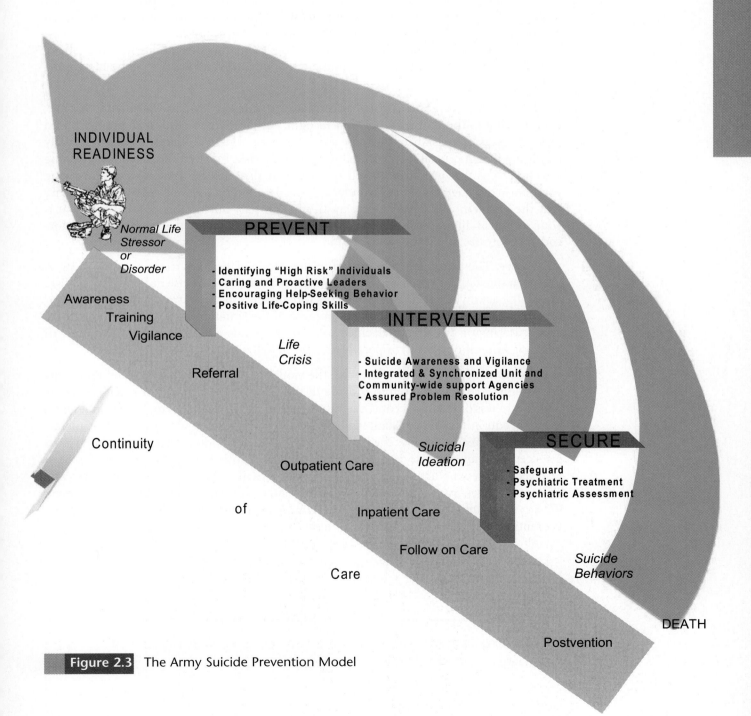

Figure 2.3 The Army Suicide Prevention Model

Three "barriers" represent actions that can prevent a person from progressing down the suicidal path. (See Figure 2.3) These actions are prevent, intervene, and secure. They represent specific programs and initiatives for varying degrees of risk.

Below is a quick outline of each of these barriers:

Prevent. Prevention is the Army's main effort to minimize suicidal behavior. It focuses on preventing normal life stressors from turning into a life crisis. "Prevention programming" focuses on equipping the Soldier with the coping skills to handle overwhelming life circumstances. This barrier allows the individual to operate "in the green" or at a high state of individual readiness. Prevention includes early screening to establish baseline mental health. It offers specific remedial programs before dysfunctional behavior occurs. Prevention is dependent on caring. It also depends on proactive small-unit leaders like you who make the effort to know their subordinates. This includes estimating their ability to handle stress, and offering a positive, cohesive environment that nurtures and develops good life-coping skills.

Intervene. Intervention is the barrier that prevents any life crisis or mental disorder from leading to thoughts of suicide. It recognizes that there are times when one should seek professional assistance to handle a crisis or treat a mental illness. In this area, early involvement is a crucial factor in reducing suicide risk. Intervention includes changing the conditions that produced the current crisis. It also includes treating any underlying psychiatric disorder(s) that contributed to suicidal thoughts. Always follow up to ensure that the problem is resolved. You play an integral part during this phase, because it is your responsibility to ensure that the problem has been resolved. This barrier is color-coded yellow because it warrants caution.

Secure. The third and final barrier in this model is perhaps the last opportunity to prevent a suicidal act. When a person becomes suicidal, someone else must take immediate life-saving action and secure him or her before the person can harm himself or herself or others. This barrier is color-coded red because of the situation's severity. This individual is considering or has already decided to commit suicide and is in imminent danger of harming himself or herself, or possibly others as well.

Continuity of Care. The safety net in the model labeled "Continuity of Care" represents the care the Army is required to provide to those individuals at risk for suicide. It starts with awareness of the impact and magnitude of suicide within the Army. It continues with training, education, and constant vigilance toward those who might be at risk for suicide. As the risk increases, so does the level of required care, including referrals to professional gatekeepers. If appropriate, in-patient care is provided until it's clear the problem has been resolved. Those who actually commit a suicidal act will require the most intensive care. This care ranges from medical care and psychiatric therapy to bereavement counseling for surviving family members and personal counseling for unit members. The Army Suicide Prevention Model is designed to assist those who have any ambivalence toward dying.

Knowing is not enough, we must apply. Willing is not enough, we must do.

Goethe

No suicide prevention plan will completely eliminate suicidal behavior. Some people travel the path to suicide without ever displaying recognizable danger signs. Some don't want any intervention. Suicide is an individual decision and therefore, ultimately, the responsibility of the individual. That doesn't diminish your obligation or the Army's. You and your fellow leaders must be vigilant so you can identify all who are at risk and apply the appropriate level of intervention.

Prevention

A commander should have a profound understanding of human nature.

Sir Basil Liddell Hart

When a recruit goes through pre-screening upon arrival for initial entry training (IET), the Army searches for signs that the individual is at high risk for suicidal behavior. Because the mental health of Army inductees may be less than perfect, the Army must be proactive in identifying potential problems, as well as providing education or intervention that can help solve them. This early action will help the first-term Soldier avoid some of the normal pitfalls that can lead to mental health dysfunction and subsequent early attrition. These pitfalls include:

- Premature marriage
- Premature parenthood
- Excessive debt
- Substance abuse
- Dysfunctional behaviors resulting in military legal action
- Difficulties with authority
- Inability to form positive supportive relationships
- Excessive time demands that overwhelm time-management skills
- Problems that are acute and unresolved from the past
- Disconnect between expectations and reality.

Caring and Proactive Leaders

You are the Army's most valuable player in suicide prevention. The most important resources entrusted to your care are your Soldiers. Suicide prevention requires active and concerned leadership, including a sincere interest in the overall welfare of your subordinates. This means taking the time to learn as much as you can about their personal dynamics. You must be able to recognize serious personal problems before they become dangerous dysfunctional behavior. You should know how to recognize the basic symptoms of serious mood disorders such as depression and substance abuse. The intent is not to train you to make a clinical diagnosis. That's not your job. Rather, you should alert the chain of command about a particular concern, so that your commander can make an informed decision about possible referral to a professional.

In addition, you should be familiar with stressors and potential suicide triggers. You want to be able to recognize when one of your Soldiers is experiencing a crisis and might be at risk. Strive to create an environment of acceptance for all members of your unit. No one should make any member of a unit feel unwelcome, regardless of his or her action.

Everyone should feel that he or she is a valuable part of the team and that others depend on him or her.

Encouraging Help-Seeking Behavior

You should encourage help-seeking behavior among your subordinates. Make sure they do not fear repercussions. Many Soldiers fail to seek professional assistance from a mental health organization (MHO) for fear of reprisals, embarrassment, guilt, or shame. According to a 1998 DoD Survey of Health Related Behaviors Among Military Personnel, only 24 percent of soldiers surveyed believed that receiving mental health counseling would not hurt their career. It's therefore easy to understand that although 17.8 percent of soldiers feel they have needed mental health counseling in the past, only 5.6 percent actually sought and received help.

Clearly, for the Army Suicide Prevention Program to be effective, it must reduce the perceived **stigma** of seeking mental health counseling. Ensure that there is no inadvertent discrimination toward your Soldiers who receive mental health counseling. Also, support confidentiality between the individual and MHO. Confidentiality in the face of suicide risk must strike a balance between safeguarding the individual and/or the public and protecting his or her privacy rights. Respect and honor patient-doctor privacy rights and never disclose confidential mental health care communications except as provided by DoD Regulations. Exceptions to this general rule include, but are not limited to:

stigma

a mark of disgrace

- when the patient has given consent
- when the mental health professional believes that a patient's mental or emotional condition makes the patient a danger to himself or herself, or to any other person
- when the mental disorder indicates a degree of impairment otherwise suggesting unsuitability for retention in military service
- when there has been an adjustment disorder of a military member during the member's initial 180 days of military service
- where there is a military necessity to ensure the safety and security of military personnel, family members, or government property.

Therefore, mental health professionals will inform the responsible unit commander when a Soldier is at an elevated risk for suicide, or at risk for other dangerous behavior. Otherwise, the individual's privacy takes priority and the Army will respect it.

Teach Positive Life-Coping Skills

Prevention also includes developing the Soldier's mental resiliency. Discuss with Soldiers how to avoid premature stress-inducing decisions, such as getting married too young, or starting a family too early. If possible, facilitate training in positive life-coping skills, such as alcohol-abuse avoidance, financial management, stress and anger reduction, conflict management, and parenting and family-life skills. The Building Strong and Ready Families (BSRF) seminar that originated within the 25th Infantry Division is one good example. BSRF offers married couples an opportunity to strengthen their relationship through instruction and exercises. The seminar is targeted at newly married couples who are interested in improving their communication skills and generally being better equipped to handle the stresses of married life, including child-rearing. Programs such as BSRF are a great example of how to develop life-coping skills that will have a positive impact on reducing suicidal behavior.

CONCLUSION

Some people are hesitant to seek help for depression or suicidal thoughts because of the stigma associated. The more Army leaders are willing to talk openly about suicide and all that is associated with it, the more the stigma will diminish.

Suicide can affect anyone, regardless of rank, age, sex, military occupational specialty, race, or ethnicity. Although there are no demographics that will predict suicidal behavior with certainty, it is important to examine the Army suicide population in an attempt to infer potential suicide risk indicators for use in prevention efforts. Vigilance and awareness must extend to everyone in the Army. It is also important not to use demographics to "profile" or "discriminate" at-risk populations.

You must always take serious suicide attempts or suicidal thoughts. If you are thinking or talking about hurting or killing yourself, or know someone who is, seek help immediately. You can turn to a physician, your commander, coach or adviser, a member of the clergy, a local suicide hotline or emergency hotline (one number is 1-800-SUICIDE), or 911.

Learning Assessment

1. List some potential triggers for suicide.
2. Discuss the consequences of adverse childhood experiences.
3. Discuss the leader's role in suicide prevention.

Key Words

life-coping skills
substance abuse
dysfunctional behavior
hopelessness
suicide triggers
stigma

References

T340, *Army Suicide Prevention – A Guide for Installations and Units.* October 2004.

WARRIOR ETHOS OVERVIEW

Key Points

1 **The Warrior Ethos**

2 **The Soldier's Creed**

3 **Black Hawk Down**

Yours is the profession of arms—the will to win, the sure knowledge that in war there is no substitute for victory; that if you lose, the nation will be destroyed; that the very obsession of your public service must be Duty, Honor, and Country . . . .

General of the Army Douglas MacArthur

Introduction

Americans hold their country's Armed Forces to a high standard and expect their military professionals to reflect American values. They expect you as an Army officer to uphold the Constitution and have a strong respect for the rule of law, human dignity, and individual rights. Soldiers, not machines, fight and win wars. Because of this, every Soldier must reflect the Army's seven core values and live the Warrior Ethos.

The effect of the Warrior Ethos is that all Soldiers understand they must be prepared and confident in their ability to accomplish their assigned tasks—even in the face of enemy resistance—anytime, anywhere on the battlefield. In a non-linear environment where the lines between enemy and friendly forces are blurred, the American Soldier must possess the will to close with the enemy force and destroy it. This is a crucial point: Many other Soldiers depend on what you do. You cannot allow any obstacle or enemy action to prevent you from accomplishing your assigned task.

This lesson covers the general concepts of the Warrior Ethos: its building blocks, its tenets, and how the Soldier's Creed ties its concepts together.

PFC Ernest E. West

PFC West was a Soldier assigned to L Company, 14th Infantry Regiment in the 25th Infantry Division, during the Korean War. On 12 October 1952, near Sataeri, Korea, PFC West voluntarily accompanied a contingent to locate and destroy a reported enemy outpost. Nearing the objective, the patrol was ambushed and suffered numerous casualties. Observing his wounded leader lying in an exposed position, PFC West ordered the troops to withdraw and then braved intense fire to reach and assist him.

While attempting evacuation, he was attacked by three hostile soldiers employing grenades and small-arms fire. Quickly shifting his body to shelter the officer, he killed the assailants with his rifle and then carried the helpless man to safety. He was critically wounded, losing an eye in this action, but courageously returned through withering fire and bursting shells to assist other wounded Soldiers. While evacuating two comrades, he closed with and killed three more enemy soldiers. PFC West's loyalty to his fellow Soldiers and intrepid actions inspired all who observed him. He received the Congressional Medal of Honor.

Soldier
- Adaptive
- Competent • Confident
- Physical & Mental toughness

Warrior Ethos Tenets
- Mission First
- Never Quit
- Never Accept Defeat
- Never Leave a Fallen Comrade

Army Values

Loyalty, Duty, Respect, Selfless Service, Honor, Integrity, Personal Courage

Commitment to Serve the Nation

Figure 1.1 The Building Blocks of Warrior Ethos

The Warrior Ethos

GEN Eric Shinseki, former Army chief of staff, described the need for a common warrior ethos with emphasis on the uniformed members of the Army team:

> *Every organization has an internal culture and **ethos**. A true warrior ethos must underpin the Army's enduring traditions and values.... Soldiers imbued with an ethically grounded warrior ethos clearly symbolize the Army's unwavering commitment to the nation we serve. The Army has always embraced this ethos but the demands of Transformation will require a renewed effort to ensure that all Soldiers truly understand and embody this warrior ethos.*

The **Warrior Ethos** refers to the professional attitudes and beliefs that characterize the American Soldier. It echoes through the precepts of the Code of Conduct and reflects a Soldier's selfless commitment to the nation, mission, unit, and fellow Soldiers. The Warrior Ethos was developed and sustained through discipline, commitment to the Army Values, and pride in the Army's heritage. Lived by Soldiers and supported by dedicated Army civilians, a strong Warrior Ethos is the foundation for the winning spirit that permeates the institution.

ethos

the disposition, character, or fundamental values peculiar to a specific person, people, culture, or movement

Warrior Ethos

the professional attitudes and beliefs that characterize the American Soldier; the Warrior Ethos is the foundation for the American Soldier's total commitment to victory in peace and war

Critical Thinking

Explain the basic values underlying the Warrior Ethos, using your own examples.

Commitment to Serve

You can view the Warrior Ethos as a pyramid of concepts, values, tenets, and individual attributes. It begins with your commitment to serve the nation. While your professional calling as a Soldier is to support and defend the Constitution, your challenge is to learn the profession well enough to accomplish any mission effectively while protecting the force. The Soldiers of the United States Army serve around the world in many different missions and roles. Like you, they are all volunteers. Although there are many reasons each Soldier joins the service, at some level each has the desire to serve our nation.

Army Values

Your individual effectiveness as part of the Army team comes from within, from your upbringing, your character, and your values. The Army is guided by values. Army Values are the basic building blocks that enable us to see what is right or wrong in any situation. Army Values and the Warrior Ethos are mutually dependent—you can't fully follow one while ignoring the other.

The Warrior Ethos concerns character, shaping who you are and what you do. In that sense, it's clearly linked to Army Values such as *personal courage, loyalty to comrades,* and *dedication to duty.* Both loyalty and duty involve putting your life on the line, even when there's little chance of survival, for the good of a cause larger than yourself. That's the clearest example of *selfless service.* American Soldiers never give up on their fellow Soldiers, and they never compromise on doing their duty. *Integrity* underlies the Army's character, as well. The Warrior Ethos requires unrelenting and consistent determination to do what is right and to do it with pride, both in war and in other military operations. Understanding what is right requires *respect* for both your comrades and other people involved in such complex missions as peacekeeping operations and nation assistance. In such situations, decisions whether to use lethal or nonlethal force will severely test your judgment and discipline. In whatever conditions you find yourself as an Army leader, you turn your personal Warrior Ethos into a collective commitment to win with *honor.*

Warrior Ethos Tenets

- Always place the mission first
- Never accept defeat
- Never quit
- Never leave a fallen comrade.

Everywhere you find Soldiers, you find them taking action to protect the nation. The Warrior Ethos spurs the lead tank driver across a line of departure into uncertainty. It drives the bone-tired medic to continually put others first. It pushes the sweat-soaked gunner whose muscles are near failure to keep up the fire. It drives the heavily loaded infantry Soldier into an icy wind, steadily uphill to the objective. It presses the Signal Corps Soldier through fatigue to provide communications. And the Warrior Ethos urges the sleep-deprived truck driver across mined roads because fellow Soldiers at an isolated outpost need supplies.

Such tireless motivation arises in part from the comradeship that the Warrior Ethos creates. Soldiers fight for each other; they would rather die than let their buddies down. That loyalty runs front to rear as well as left to right. Mutual support marks Army culture regardless of who you are, where you are, or what you are doing.

Competent, Confident, Flexible, and Adaptable Soldiers

The Warrior Ethos produces the will to win. You'll need a strong will and a winning spirit in situations beyond those just requiring physical courage. Sometimes you'll have to carry on for long periods in very difficult situations. The difficulties you face may not involve physical danger, but rather great physical, emotional, and mental stress—as can occur in support operations. Will empowers you to drive on during extended deployments, under appalling conditions, and without basic necessities.

Confidence enhances both physical courage and will. That confidence in the ability of leaders, fellow Soldiers, and the justness of the mission strengthens your resolve to fulfill your duty to the best of your ability. You know that if you are wounded, your buddies and the Army medical system will do everything in their power to save your life. You know that if you are captured or missing, the nation will spare no resource in returning you to US control. And you know that if you are killed in battle, you died fighting for your fellow Soldiers and protecting the American people in a just cause.

Self-confidence is the faith that you'll act correctly and ethically in any situation, even one in which you're under stress and don't have all the information you need. Self-confidence comes from competence. It's based on mastering skills, which takes hard work, realistic training, and dedication. Soldiers who know their own capabilities and believe in themselves are self-confident. Don't mistake loudmouthed bragging or self-promotion for self-confidence. Self-confident Soldiers don't need to advertise because their actions say it all. Self-confidence is important for leaders, Soldiers, and teams. Self-confident leaders instill confidence in their people. In combat, self-confidence helps Soldiers control doubt and reduce anxiety. Together with will and self-discipline, self-confidence helps leaders act—do what must be done in circumstances where it would be easier to do nothing—and to convince their people to act as well.

As part of gaining confidence, competence, flexibility, and adaptability, each Soldier must be completely proficient in fundamental tasks to ensure success. These critical warrior tasks and drills will be part of your ongoing Army training. You must train in these tasks and drills frequently to ensure you are prepared for combat—regardless of your specialty or rank.

Warrior Tasks and Drills

- React to contact (visual, improvised explosive device, direct fire)
- Avoid ambush
- React to ambush
- React to indirect fire
- React to chemical attack
- Dismount a vehicle
- Evacuate injured personnel from a vehicle
- Secure at a halt

The Warrior Ethos means you must be prepared at all times. You will demonstrate competence in these basic tasks and will consider them core to your role and responsibility.

The Soldier's Creed

The Warrior Ethos is embodied in the Soldier's Creed. The message of the Soldier's Creed is to shift your mindset from what you do as a Soldier—"I'm an artilleryman, I'm an infantryman, I'm a computer technician"—more toward seeing yourself as a warrior.

The Soldier's Creed helps Soldiers understand that, despite very diverse backgrounds, all Soldiers are warriors first and members of a team. The Creed also reinforces Army culture by encouraging examination of beliefs from a warrior's perspective.

Remember, the Army expects you to live by Army Values, the Warrior Ethos, and the Soldier's Creed.

I am an American Soldier. I am a warrior and a member of a team. I serve the people of the United States and live the Army Values. I will always place the mission first. I will never accept defeat. I will never quit. I will never leave a fallen comrade. I am disciplined, physically and mentally tough, trained and proficient in my warrior tasks and drills. I always maintain my arms, my equipment, and myself. I am an expert and I am a professional. I stand ready to deploy, engage, and destroy the enemies of the United States of America in close combat. I am a guardian of freedom and the American way of life. I am an American Soldier.

Critical Thinking

Describe how the Warrior Ethos serves to build a core of competent, confident, flexible, and adaptive Soldiers.

BLACK HAWK DOWN

Mark Bowden

In the late afternoon of Sunday, October 3, 1993 an elite group of commandos set out from their base at the Mogadishu, Somalia, airport on what they thought would be a routine mission. Their job was to extract a clan leader and his lieutenants from a safehouse in downtown Mogadishu. The mission was to take place in two stages. A convoy of Delta Force commandos would travel the streets of the city to the target house. Meanwhile, Black Hawk helicopters would insert Army Rangers around the block to secure the area. The entire mission was to take approximately one hour.

What happened has become a study of the problems of modern combat in "peacekeeping" situations. Although the vast majority of the force was composed of Army personnel, Navy SEALs and Air Force Parajumpers (CSAR) were also involved and performed heroically, some losing their lives in the fight. The night of October 3rd, 99 of America's most elite combat Soldiers were trapped in a hostile city. The next morning after the battle, 18 Americans and perhaps several thousand Somalis were dead.

As you read this excerpt from Black Hawk Down, *keep in mind some of the leadership principles you have studied. There is no greater test of leadership than combat and you should try to learn the lessons of this modern battle as they might apply to your leadership, whether in combat or not.*

In the convoy's second-to-last Humvee, where Ruiz was fighting for his life, Sergeant Burns couldn't get through to McKnight on the radio so he took off on foot. He feared if they didn't get Ruiz back to base immediately the young Texan was going to die. Burns noticed that the gunfire that had hurt his ears initially now sounded muffled, distant. His ears had adjusted to it. As he neared the front of the line he saw Joyce stretched out bloody and pale, with a medic working over him furiously on the back of a crowded Humvee. He was about to reach the front when a D-boy grabbed him.

"You've been hit," the Delta operator said.

"No I haven't."

Burns hadn't felt a thing. The D-boy slid his hand inside Burns's vest at his right shoulder and the sergeant felt a vicious stab of pain.

"Having trouble breathing?" the D-boy asked.

"No."

"Any tightness in your chest?"

"I feel all right," Burns said. "I didn't even know I was hit."

"You keep an eye on it," the D-boy said.

Burns made it up to McKnight, who was also bloody, and busy on the radio. So Burns told Sergeant Bob Gallagher about Ruiz. Burns thought they should allow a Humvee or two to speed right back to the base with Ruiz, as they had done earlier with Blackburn. But Gallagher knew the convoy could not afford to lose any more vehicles and firepower now. They still had roughly a hundred men waiting for them around the first crash site, then there was the second crash site. . . . Gallagher was already kicking himself for sending those three vehicles back with Blackburn. While he knew this might be a death sentence for Ruiz, he told Burns there was no way anybody was leaving.

"We have to move to the crash site and consolidate force," he said.

Disgusted, Burns began to make his way back down the column to his vehicle. He had only gone a few steps when the convoy started rolling again. He jumped on the back of a Humvee. It was already jammed. The rear of the vehicle was slick and sticky with blood. Moaning rose from the pile of Rangers. Beside him, Joyce looked dead, even though a medic was still working on him. Sergeant Galantine was screaming. "My thumb's shot off! My thumb's shot off!" Burns did not want to be on that Humvee.

From Bowden, Mark. (1999). *Black Hawk Down: A Story of Modern War.* New York: Grove/Atlantic, Inc. Reprinted by permission.

They were still pointed north. Some of the men were at the breaking point. In the same Humvee with Burns, Private Jason Moore saw some of his Ranger buddies just burying their heads behind the sandbags. Some of the unit's most boisterous chest-beaters were among them. A burly kid from Princeton, New Jersey, Moore had a dip of snuff stuffed under his lower lip and brown spittle on his unshaved chin. He was sweating and terrified. One RPG had passed over the vehicle and exploded with an ear-smarting crack against a wall alongside. Bullets were snapping around him. He fought the urge to lie down. *Either way I'm going to get shot.*

Moore figured if he stayed up and kept on shooting, at least he'd get shot trying to save himself and the guys. It was a defining moment for him, a point of clarity in the midst of chaos. He would go down fighting. He would not consider lying down again.

Not long after he saw Joyce shot, which really shook him up, Private Carlson felt a sudden blow and sharp pain in his right knee. It felt like someone had taken a knife and held it to his knee and then driven it in with a sledgehammer. He glanced down to see blood rapidly staining his pants. He said a prayer and kept shooting. He had been wildly scared for longer than he had ever felt that way in his life, and now he thought he might literally die of fright. His heart banged in his chest and he found it hard to breathe. His head was filled with the sounds of shooting and explosions and visions of his friends, one by one, going down, and blood splashed everywhere oily and sticky with its dank, coppery smell and he figured, *"This is it for me."* One second he was paralyzed with fear and pain and the next . . . he had stopped caring about himself.

He would think about this a lot later, and the best he could explain it was, his own life no longer mattered. All that did matter were his buddies, his brothers, that *they* not get hurt, and that *they* not get killed. These men around him, some of whom he had only known for months, were more important to him than life itself. It was like when Tescher ran out on the road to pull Joyce back in. Carlson understood that now, and it was heroic, but it also wasn't heroic. At a certain level Tescher had made no choice, just as he was not choosing to be unafraid. It had just happened to him, like he had passed through some barrier. He had to keep fighting, because the other guys needed him.

In the second of the three Humvees behind the truck, Private Ed Kallman sat behind the wheel amazed and alarmed by what he was seeing. He saw a line of trees on the sidewalk up ahead begin to explode, one after the other, as if someone had placed charges in each and was detonating them at about five-second intervals. Either that or somebody with a big gun was systematically taking out the trees, each about two stories high, thinking that they might be hiding snipers. He found it strange, anyway, the blasts walking their way toward him splintering the trees one by one.

Kallman, who had felt such a rush of excitement an hour earlier as he encountered battle for the first time, now felt nothing but nauseating dread; so far neither he nor anyone in his vehicle had been hit, but it seemed like just a matter of time. He watched with horror as the convoy disintegrated before him. He was a Soldier for the most powerful nation on earth. If they were having this much trouble, shouldn't somebody have stepped in? Where was a stronger show of force? Somehow it didn't seem right that they could be reduced to this, battling on these narrow dirt streets, bleeding, dying! This wasn't supposed to happen. He saw men he knew and liked and respected bellowing in pain on the street with gunshot wounds that exposed great crimson flaps of glistening muscle, men wandering in the smoke bleeding, dazed and seemingly unconscious, their clothing torn off. American Soldiers. Those who were not injured were covered with the blood of others. Kallman was young and new to the unit. If these more-veteran Soldiers were all getting hit, sooner or later he was going to get

hit. Oddly, the surprise he felt overshadowed the fear. He kept telling himself, *This is not supposed to happen!*

And Kallman's turn did come. As he slowed down before another intersection he looked out the open window to his left and saw a smoke trail coming straight at him. It all happened in a second. He knew it was an RPG and he knew it was going to hit him. Then it did. He awoke lying on his right side on the front seat with his ears ringing. He opened his eyes and was looking directly at the radio mounted under the dash. He sat up and floored the accelerator. Up ahead he saw the convoy making a left turn and raced to catch them.

Later, when he'd had a chance to inspect his Humvee, he saw that the RPG had hit his door, deeply denting it and poking a hole through the steel. He and the others inside had evidently been spared by the bulletproof glass panel behind the door—Kallman had the window rolled down. The brunt of the grenade's force had been absorbed by the Humvee's outer shell, and the glass barrier had been thick enough to stop it. Kallman's left arm began to swell and discolor, but otherwise he was fine.

▪ ▪ ▪

Dan Schilling felt better whenever they were moving. But the convoy seemed to inch along, stopping, starting, stopping, starting. Whenever they stopped the volume of fire would surge, so many rounds that at times it looked like the stone walls on both sides of the alley were being sandblasted. There were plenty of targets to shoot at. In the turret, Pringle unloosed the .50 cal on a group of armed Somalis. Schilling watched as one of them, a tall, skinny man wearing a bright yellow shirt and carrying an AK-47, came apart as the big rounds tore through him. Deep red blotches appeared on the yellow shirt. First an arm came off. Then the man's head and chest exploded. The rest of the Somalis scattered, moving around the next corner, where Schilling knew they'd again be waiting for them to cross.

As the Humvee came abreast of the alley Schilling didn't bother to use his sights, the men were that close. The first man he shot was just ten yards away. He was crouched down and had a painful grimace on his face. Maybe Pringle had hit him earlier. Schilling put two rounds in his chest. He shot the man next to him twice in the chest and as he did he felt a slam and a dull pain in his right foot. When they were through the intersection, Schilling inspected his boot. The door had taken two bullets. One had passed through the outer steel and been stopped by the bullet-proof glass window inside it. The second had hit lower, and had passed right through the door. The door, which was guaranteed to stop the AK-47's 7.62 mm round, had not stopped either bullet. The glass got the first, and the second had been slowed enough so that it hit with enough force to hurt, but not enough to penetrate the boot.

Pringle had just put doors on the vehicle earlier that day. They'd done the previous six missions without them, and these had just arrived in a shipment from the States. Schilling had mixed feelings about them. He liked the protection, but the doors made it a lot harder to move. When he had checked them out that morning, he couldn't get his window to roll down, so he'd started to remove the door. Pringle stopped him.

"Hey, I just put those on!" he shouted.

Schilling had showed him how the window stuck, and Pringle had fetched a hammer and simply-whacked the frame until the window dropped down. Now, Schilling was glad they'd kept the door, but some of the sense of invulnerability he'd felt was gone. Both bullets had gone completely through.

They continued north for about nine blocks, all the way up to Armed Forces Road, one of the main paved roads in Mogadishu. They'd gone past the crash site, only a block west of it, without stopping. The helicopters had directed them to turn right, but the alleyways looked too narrow to Schilling and the others in the lead Humvee. If the trucks got stuck they'd probably all be killed. So they continued on. Some of the men in the convoy saw the downed Black Hawk just a block over as they went past, but no one had told them that it was their objective. Many of the men in the vehicles still thought they were heading back to base. As they approached Armed Forces Street, they stopped again.

Schilling fought back feelings of futility. McKnight seemed dazed and overwhelmed. He was bleeding from the arm and the neck, and not his usual decisive self. Schilling muttered to himself, "We're going to keep driving around until we're all fucking dead."

He then decided to do something himself, since McKnight seemed stymied. Using a frequency he knew helicopter pilots used to talk among themselves, he bypassed the C2 Black Hawk and contacted the observation helicopters flying orbits higher up. Coordinating communications between the air and ground was Schilling's specialty. He asked them to vector him to the crash site. The choppers were eager to oblige. They told him to steer the convoy west on Armed Forces Road, and then hang another left. McKnight gave permission for Schilling to direct them, and the convoy was moving once again.

They made the left turn off Armed Forces and drove through the storm of gunfire for about seven blocks before Schilling saw up ahead the smoldering remains of the five-ton they had torched in front of the target building. They'd come full circle. Schilling hadn't told the observation bird pilots *which* crash site he wanted. The pilots could see how desperate things were around Durant's crash, where Somali mobs had begun to encircle the unprotected downed Black Hawk, and had taken it upon themselves to direct the convoy there. Schilling hadn't realized it until he saw the target house and the Olympic Hotel again.

"We're headed for the second crash site," he told McKnight.

The lieutenant colonel knew only what his orders were. He reiterated that they were to proceed to the *first* crash site.

On the command net, their wanderings had turned to black comedy. Matters were now complicated by the fact that a second vehicle convoy had been dispatched from the base to attempt a rescue at Durant's crash site.

—Danny, I think you've gone too far west trying to look at the second crash. You seem to have gone about four blocks west and five blocks south, over.

—Romeo Six Four [Harrell], this is Uniform Six Four [McKnight]. Give me a right turn, right turn! Right turn!

—Uniform Six Four, this is Romeo Six Four. . . . You need to go about four blocks south, turn east. There is green smoke marking the site south. Keep coming south.

A voice came over the busy command frequency pleading for order.

—Stop giving directions! . . . I think you're talking to the wrong convoy!

—This is Uniform Six Four, you've got me back in front of the Olympic Hotel.

—Uniform Six Four, this is Romeo Six Four. You need to turn east.

So the convoy now made a U-turn. They had just driven through a vicious ambush in front of the target house and were now turning around to drive right back through it. Men in the vehicles behind could not understand. It was insane! They seemed to be trying to get killed.

Things had deteriorated so badly that up in the C2 bird Harrell was considering just releasing the prisoners, their prize, the supposed point of this mission and of all this carnage. He instructed the Delta units on foot now closing in on the first crash site:

—As soon as we get you linked up with the Uniform element throw all the precious cargo. We're going to try and get force down to the second crash site.

The voices from various helicopters now trying to steer poor McKnight recorded the frustration of his fruitless twists and turns.

—Uniform Six Four, this is Romeo Six Four Next right. Next right! Alleyway! Alleyway!

—They just missed their turn.

—Take the next available right, Uniform.

—Be advised they are coming under heavy fire.

—Uniform Six Four, this is Romeo Six Four.

—God damn it, stop! God damn it, stop!

—Right turn. Right turn! You're taking fire. Hurry up!

In this terrible confusion the men on the convoy saw strange things. They passed an old woman carrying two plastic grocery bags, walking along calmly through the barrage. As the convoy approached, she set both bags down gently, stuck fingers in her ears, and kept on walking. Minutes later, heading in the opposite direction, they saw the same woman. She had the bags again. She set them down, stuck fingers in her ears, and walked away as she had before.

At every intersection now Somalis just lined up, on both sides of the street, and fired at every vehicle that came across. Since they had men on both sides of the street, any rounds that missed the vehicle as it flashed past would certainly have hit the men on the other side of the road. Sergeant Eversmann, who had found some better cover for himself in the back end of his Humvee, watched with amazement. What a strategy! He felt these people must have no regard for even their own lives! They just *did not care!*

The city was shredding them block by block. No place was safe. The air was alive with hurtling chunks of hot metal. They heard the awful slap of bullets into flesh and heard the screams and saw the insides of men's bodies spill out and watched the gray blank pallor rise in the faces of their friends, and the best of the men fought back despair. They were America's elite fighters and they were going to die here, outnumbered by this determined rabble. Their future was setting with this sun on this day and in this place.

Schilling felt disbelief, and now some guilt. He had steered the convoy the wrong way for at least part of the calamity. Stunned by the confusion, he struggled to convince himself this was all really happening. Over and over he muttered, "We're going to keep driving around until we're all fucking dead."

Specialist Spalding was still behind the passenger door in the first truck with his rifle out the window, turned in the seat so he could line up his shots, when he was startled by a flash of light down by his legs. It looked like a laser beam shot through the door and up into his right leg. A bullet had pierced the steel of the door and the window, which was rolled down, and had poked itself and fragments of glass and steel straight up his leg from just above his knee all the way up to his hip. He had been stabbed by the shaft of light that poked through the door. He squealed.

"What's wrong, you hit?" shouted Maddox.

"Yes!"

And then another laser poked through, this one into his left leg. Spalding felt a jolt this time but no pain. He reached down to grab his right thigh and blood spurted out between his fingers. He was both distressed and amazed. The way the light had shot through. He still felt no pain. He didn't want to look at it.

Then Maddox shouted, "I can't see! I can't see!"

The driver's helmet was askew and his glasses were knocked around sideways on his head.

"Put your glasses on, you dumb ass," Spalding said.

But Maddox had been hit in the back of the head. The round must have hit his helmet, which saved his life, but hit with such force that it had rendered him temporarily blind. The truck was rolling out of control and Spalding, with both legs shot, couldn't move over to grab the wheel.

They couldn't stop in the field of fire, so there was nothing to do but shout directions to Maddox, who still had his hands on the wheel.

"Turn left! Turn Left! Now! Now!"

"Speed up!"

"Slow down!"

The truck was weaving and banging into the sides of the buildings. It ran over a Somali man on crutches.

"What was that?" asked Maddox.

"Don't worry about it. We just ran over somebody."

And they laughed. They felt no pity and were beyond fear. They were both laughing as Maddox stopped the truck.

One of the D-boys, Sergeant Mike Foreman, jumped from the back of the truck, ran up, and opened the driver's side door to a cabin now splattered with blood.

"Holy shit!" he said.

Maddox slid over next to Spalding, who was now preoccupied with his wounds. There was a perfectly round hole in his left knee, but there was no exit wound. The bullet had evidently fragmented on impact with the door and glass and only the jacket had penetrated his knee. It had flattened on impact with his kneecap and just slid around under the skin to the side of the joint. The remainder of the bullet had peppered his lower leg, which was bleeding. Spalding propped both legs up on the dash and pressed a field dressing on one. He lay his rifle on the rim of the side window, changed the magazine, and, as Foreman got the truck moving again, resumed firing. He was shooting at everything that moved.

To make room for more wounded on the back of his Humvee, wounded Private Clay Othic, who had been shot in the arm at the beginning of the fight, jumped out the back and ran to the second truck. One of the men riding there proffered a hand to help him climb aboard, but with his broken arm Othic couldn't grab hold of anything. After several failed attempts he ran around to the cab, and Specialist Aaron Hand stepped out to let him squeeze in between himself and the driver, Private Richard Kowalewski, a skinny quiet kid from Texas whom they all called "Alphabet" because they didn't want to pronounce his name.

Kowalewski was new to the unit, and quiet. He had just met a girl he wanted to marry, and had been talking about leaving the regiment when his tour was up in a few months. His sergeant had been trying to convince him to stay. Minutes after Othic slid in next to him, Kowalewski was hit by a bullet in his shoulder, which knocked him back against the seat. He checked out the wound briefly and straightened back up behind the wheel.

"Alphabet, want me to drive?" asked Othic.

"No, I'm okay."

Othic was struggling in the confined space to apply a pressure dressing to the driver's bleeding shoulder when the RPG hit. It rocketed in from the left, severing Kowalewski's left arm and entering his chest. It didn't explode. The two-foot-long missile embedded itself in Kowalewski, the fins sticking out his left side under his missing arm, and point sticking out the right side. He was unconscious, but still alive.

Driverless, the truck crashed into the back end of the one before it, the one with the prisoners in back and with Foreman, Maddox, and Spalding in the cab. The impact threw Spalding against the side door and then his truck careened into a wall.

Othic had been knocked cold. He awakened to Specialist Hand shaking him, yelling that he had to get out.

"It's on fire!" Hand shouted.

The cab was black with smoke and Othic could see the rocket fuse glowing from what looked like inside Alphabet. The grenade lodged in his chest was unexploded, but something had caused a blast. It might have been a flashbang mounted on Kowalewski's vest or rocket propellant from the grenade. Hand jumped out his door. Othic reached over to grab Kowalewski and pull him out, but the driver's bloody clothes just lifted damply off of his pierced torso. Othic stumbled out to the street and noticed his and Hand's helmets had been blown off. Hand's rifle was shattered. They moved numbly and even a little giddily. Death had buzzed past close enough to kill Kowalewski and knock off their helmets but had left them virtually unscathed. Hand couldn't hear out of his left ear, but that was it. Both men found their helmets down the street—they had evidently blown right out the window.

Hand also found the lower portion of Kowalewski's arm. Just the left hand and a bit of wrist. He picked it up, ran back to the Humvee where the D-boys had placed Kowalewski, and put it in the mortally wounded man's pants pockets.

Still dazed, Othic crawled into a Humvee.

As they set off again he began groping on the floor with his good left hand collecting rounds that guys had ejected from their weapons when they jammed. Othic passed them back to those still shooting.

Many of the vehicles were running out of ammo. They had expended thousands of rounds. Three of the twenty-four Somali prisoners were dead and one was wounded. The back ends of the remaining

trucks and Humvees were slick with blood. There were chunks of viscera clinging to floors and inner walls. McKnight's lead Humvee had two flat tires, both on the right side. The vehicles were meant to run on flats, but at nowhere near normal speed. The second Humvee in line was almost totally disabled. It was dragging an axle and was being pushed by the five-ton behind it, the one that had been hit by the grenade that killed Kowalewski. The Humvee driven by the SEALs, the third in line, had three flat tires and was so pockmarked with bullet holes it looked like a sponge. SEAL Howard Wasdin, who had been shot in both legs, had them draped up over the dash and stretched out on the hood. Some of the Humvees were smoking. Carlson's had a gaping grenade hole in the side and four flat tires.

When the RPG hit Kowalewski in the cab of the first truck, it forced everything behind it to a halt. In the noise and confusion, no one in McKnight's lead Humvee noticed, so they proceeded alone up to Armed Forces Road, rolling now at about twenty miles per hour. The observation helicopters called for a right turn (the convoy had driven past the crash site a second time about seven blocks back, this time one block to the east of it, looking in vain for a street wide enough to make a left turn). When they reached Armed Forces Road, Schilling was surprised to find it deserted. They turned right and had gone only about forty yards, planning to turn right again and head back down toward the crash site, when Schilling saw out his right side window a Somali step out into an alley and level an RPG tube at them.

"RPG! RPG!" he shouted.

The Humvee's big turret gun was silent. Schilling turned to see why Pringle wasn't shooting, and saw the gunner down in back grabbing a fresh can of ammo. Pringle raised his hands to cover his head.

"GO!" Schilling screamed at the driver, Private Joe Harosky.

But instead of shooting out of the intersection, Harosky turned into it, and bore straight down on the man with the RPG tube. This happened in seconds. The grenade launched. Schilling saw a puff of smoke and heard the distinctive pop and the big ball of the grenade coming right for them. He froze.

He didn't even raise his weapon. The grenade shot straight past the Humvee at door level on his side. He felt it whoosh past.

"Back up! Back up!" he shouted.

Schilling got off a few rounds, and Pringle was back up working the .50 cal before they'd cleared the alley. When Schilling turned around, worried they'd ram the Humvee behind them, he discovered they were all alone. Harosky backed out into Armed Forces Road, where they turned around and headed west. They spotted the rest of the column where they'd left it, still facing north just shy of the main road.

McKnight, who had been silent ever since the U-turn back by the Olympic Hotel, seemed to recover himself at this point. He got out of the Humvee and conferred with Sergeant Gallagher outside by the hood of the vehicle. Gallagher was furious about the confusion. But as he confronted McKnight, he was hit with a round that knocked him to the street. He fell right at Schilling's feet. Bright red blood pumped in spurts from his arm. Schilling had never seen such scarlet blood. It was obviously arterial. It shot out in powerful squirts. He pressed his fingers to it and fished for a field dressing in his medical pouch. He patched up Gallagher as best he could, shoving in Curlex (a highly absorbent gauze that is used to help stop bleeding) and bandaging it tightly. In their weeks in Somalia, the PJs had given all the men additional training with field dressings. They'd practiced with live goats, shooting the animals and then having the men work on them, getting their hands in some real gore. The experience helped. Gallagher walked back to his own vehicle, but Schilling kept his weapon. He needed the ammo.

They had been wandering now for about forty-five minutes. McKnight was ready to pack it in. There were now far more dead and wounded in the convoy than there were at the first crash site. He called up to Harrell.

—*Romeo Six Four, this is Uniform Six Four. We've got a lot of vehicles that will be almost impossible to move. Quite a few casualties. Getting to the crash site will be awful tough. Are pinned down.*

Harrell was insistent.

—*Uniform Six Four, this is Romeo Six Four. Danny, I really need to get you back to that crash site. I know you turned left on Armed Forces [Road], what's your status?*

But McKnight and his men had had enough.

—*This is Uniform Six Four. I have numerous casualties, vehicles that are halfway running. Gotta get these casualties out of here ASAP.*

They weren't home yet.

They began moving, and everyone heartened as word passed back that they were finally pointed back to the base. Maybe some of them would make it out alive after all.

They found Via Lenin, a four-lane road with a median up the center that would lead them back down to the K-4 traffic circle and home. Spalding began to lose feeling in his fingertips. For the first time in the ordeal he felt panic. He thought he must be lapsing into shock. He saw a little Somali boy who looked no more than five years old with an AK-47, shooting wildly from the hip, bright flashes from the muzzle of the gun. Somebody shot the boy and his legs flew up into the air, as though he had slipped on marbles, and he landed flat on his back. It happened like a slow-motion sequence in a movie, or a dream. The D-boy driving, Foreman, was a helluva shot. He had his weapon in one hand and the steering wheel in the other. Spalding saw him gun down three Somalis without even slowing down. He was impressed.

He felt his hands curling up like someone with cerebral palsy.

"Hey, man, let's get the hell back," he said," I'm not doin' too good."

"You're doin' cool," said Foreman.

SEAL John Gay's Humvee was now in the lead. It was riddled with bullets and smoking and slowing down, running on three rims. There were eight wounded Rangers and Joyce's body in back, with Wasdin's bloody legs splayed out on the hood (he'd been shot once more in the left foot). Wasdin was yelling, "Just get me out of here!" The Sammies had stretched two big underground gasoline tanks across the roadway with junk and furniture and other debris and had set it all on fire. Afraid to stop the Humvee for fear it would not start back up, they crashed over and through the flaming debris, nearly flipping, but the wide, sturdy vehicle righted itself and kept on moving. The rest of the column followed.

It was 5:40 P.M. They had been battling through the streets now for more than an hour. Of the approximately seventy-five men in the convoy, Soldiers and prisoners, nearly half had been hit by bullets or shrapnel. Eight were dead, or near death. As they approached K-4 circle, they braced themselves for another vicious ambush.

A grenade came from somewhere. It was one of those Russian types that looked like a soup can on the end of a stick. It bounced off the car and then off Specialist Jason Coleman's helmet and radio and then it hit the ground.

Nelson, who was still deaf from Twombly's timely machine-gun blast, pulled his M-60 from the roof of the car and dove, as did the men on both sides of the intersection. They stayed down for almost a full minute, cushioning themselves from the blast. Nothing happened.

"I guess it's a dud," said Lieutenant DiTomasso.

Thirty seconds later another grenade rolled out into the open space between the car and the tree across the street. Nelson again grabbed the gun off the car and rolled with it away from the grenade. Everyone braced themselves once more, and this, too, failed to explode. Nelson thought they had spent all their luck. He and Barton were crawling back toward the car when a third grenade dropped between them. Nelson turned his helmet toward it and pushed his gun in front of him, shielding himself from the blast that this time was sure to come. He opened his mouth, closed his eyes, and breathed out hard in anticipation. The grenade sizzled. He stayed like that for a full twenty seconds before he looked up at Barton.

"Dud," Barton said.

Yurek grabbed it and threw it into the street.

Someone had bought themselves a batch of bad grenades. Wilkinson later found three or four more unexploded ones inside the body of the helicopter.

The American forces around Wolcott's downed Black Hawk were now scattered along an L-shaped perimeter stretching south. One group of about thirty men was massed around the wreck in the alleyway, at the northern base of the "L." When they learned that the ground convoy had gotten lost and delayed, they began moving the wounded through the hole made by the falling helicopter into the house of Abdiaziz Ali Aden (he was still hidden in a back room). Immediately west of the alley (at the bend of the "L") was Marehan Road, where Nelson, Yurek, Barton, and Twombly were dug in across the street at the northwest corner. On the east side of that intersection, nearest the chopper, were DiTomasso, Coleman, Belman, and Delta Captain Bill Coultrop and his radio operator. The rest of the ground force was stretched out south on Marehan Road, along the stem of the "L," which sloped uphill. Steele and a dozen or so Rangers, along with three Delta teams, about thirty men in all, were together in a courtyard on the east side of Marehan Road midway up the next block south, separated from the bulk of the force by half a block, a wide alley, and a long block. Sergeant Howe's Delta team, with a group of Rangers that included Specialist Stebbins, followed by the Delta command group led by Captain Miller, had crossed the wide alley and was moving down the west wall toward Nelson's position. Lieutenant Perino had also crossed the alley and was moving downhill along the east wall with Corporal Smith, Sergeant Chuck Elliot, and several other men.

As Howe approached Nelson's position, it looked to him as though the Rangers were just hiding. Two of his men ran across the alley to tell the Rangers to start shooting. Nelson and the others were still recovering from the shock of the unexploded grenades. Rounds were taking chips off the walls all around them, but it was hard to see where the shots were coming from. Howe's team members helped arrange Nelson and the others to set up effective fields of fire and placed Stebbins and machine-gunner Private Brian Heard at the southern corner of the same intersection, orienting them to fire west.

Captain Miller caught up with Howe, trailing his radioman and some other members of his element, along with Staff Sergeant Jeff Bray, an Air Force combat controller. With all the shooting at that intersection, Howe decided it was time to get off the street. There was a metal gate at the entrance to a courtyard between two buildings on his side of the block. He pushed against the gate, which had two doors that opened inward. Howe considered putting a charge on the door, but given the number of Soldiers nearby and the lack of cover, the explosion would probably hurt people. So the burly sergeant and Bray began hurling themselves against the gate. Bray's side gave way.

"Follow me in case I get shot," Howe said.

He plunged into the courtyard and rapidly moved through the house on either side, running from room to room. Howe was looking for people, focusing his eyes at midtorso first, checking hands. The hands told you the whole story. The only hands he found were empty. They belonged to a man and woman and some children, a family of about seven, clearly terrified. He stood in the doorway with his weapon in his right hand pointing at them, trying to coax them out of the room with his left hand. It took a while, but they came out slowly, clinging to each other. The family was flex-cuffed and herded into a small side room.

Howe then more carefully inspected the space. Each of the blocks in this neighborhood of Mogadishu consisted of mostly one-story stone houses grouped irregularly around open spaces, or courtyards. This block consisted of a short courtyard, about two car-lengths wide, where he now stood. There was a two-story house on the south side and a one-story house on the north. Howe figured this space was about the safest spot around. The taller building would shelter them from both bullets and lobbed RPGs. At the west end was some kind of storage shack. Howe began exploring systematically, making a more thorough sweep, moving from room to room, looking for windows that would give them a good vantage for shooting west down the alley. He found several but none that offered a particularly good angle. The alley to the north (the same one that the helicopter had crashed into one block west) was too narrow. He could only see about fifteen yards down in either direction, and all he saw was wall. When he returned to the courtyard, Captain Miller and the

others had begun herding casualties into the space. It would serve as their command post and casualty collection point for the rest of the night.

As he reentered the courtyard, one of the master sergeants with Miller told Howe to go back out to the street and help his team. Howe resented the order. He felt he was, at this point, the de facto leader on the ground, the one doing all the real thinking and moving and fighting. They had reached a temporary safe point, a time for commanders to catch their breath and think. They were in a bad spot, but not critical. The next step would be to look for ways to strong-point their position, expand their perimeter, and identify other buildings to take down to give them better lines of fire. The troop sergeant's command was the order of a man who didn't know what to do next.

Howe was built like a pro wrestler, but he was a thinker. This sometimes troubled his relationship with authority—especially the Army's maddeningly arbitrary manner of placing unseasoned, less-qualified men in charge. Howe was just a sergeant first class with supposedly narrower concerns, but he saw the big picture very clearly, better than most. After being selected for Delta he had met and married the daughter of Colonel Charlie A. Beckwith, the founder and original commander of Delta. They had met in a lounge by Fort Bragg and when he told her that he was a civilian, Connie Beckwith, a former Army officer then herself, nodded knowingly.

"Look," she said. "I know who you work for so let's stop pretending. My dad started that unit."

She had to pull out her driver's license to prove who she was.

Not that Howe had any ambition for formal Army leadership. His preferred relationship with officers was for them to heed his advice and leave him alone. He was frequently aghast at the failings of those in charge.

Take this setup in Mogadishu, for instance. It was asinine. At the base, the huge hangar front doors wouldn't close, so the Sammies had a clear view inside at all hours of the day or night. The city sloped gradually up from the waterfront, so any Somali with patience and binoculars could keep an eye on their state of readiness. Every time they scrambled to gear up and go, word was out in the city before they were even on the helicopters. If that weren't bad enough, you had the Italians, some of them openly sympathetic to their former colonial subjects, who appeared to be flashing signals with their headlights out into the city whenever the helicopters took off. Nobody had the balls to do anything about it.

Then there were the mortars. General Garrison seemed to regard mortars as little more than an annoyance. He had walked around casually during the early mortar attacks, his cigar clenched in his teeth, amused by the way everyone dove for cover. "Piddly-assed mortars," he'd said. Which was all well and good, except, as Howe saw it, if the Sammies ever got their act together and managed to drop a few on the hangar, there'd be hell to pay. He wondered if the tin roof was thick enough to detonate the round—which would merely send shrapnel and shards of the metal roof slashing down through the ranks—or whether the round would just poke on through and detonate on the concrete floor in the middle of everybody. It was a question that lingered in his mind most nights as he went to sleep. Then there were the flimsy perimeter defenses. At mealtimes, all the men would be lined up outside the mess hall, which was separated from a busy outside road by nothing more than a thin metal wall. A car bomb along that wall at the right time of day could kill dozens of Soldiers.

Howe did not hide his disgust over these things. Now, being ordered to do something pointless in the middle of the biggest fight of his life, he was furious. He began gathering up ammo, grenades, and LAWs off the wounded Rangers in the courtyard. It seemed to Howe that most of the men failed to grasp how desperate their situation had become. It was a form of denial. They could not stop thinking of themselves as the superior force, in command of the situation, yet the tables had clearly turned. They were surrounded and terribly outnumbered. The very idea of adhering to rules of engagement at this point was preposterous.

"You're throwing grenades?" the troop sergeant asked him, surprised when he saw Howe stuffing all of them he could find into his vest pockets.

"We're not getting paid to bring them back," Howe told him.

This was war. The game now was kill or be killed. He stomped angrily out to the street and began looking for Somalis to shoot.

He found one of the Rangers, Nelson, firing a handgun at the window of the building Howe had just painstakingly cleared and occupied. Nelson had seen someone moving in the window, and they had been taking fire from just about every direction, so he was pumping a few rounds that way.

"What are you doing?" Howe shouted across the alley.

Nelson couldn't hear Howe. He shouted back, "I saw someone in there."

"No shit! There are friendlies in there!"

Nelson didn't find out until later what Howe had been waving his arms about. When he did he was mortified. No one had told him that Delta had moved into that space, but, then again, it was a cardinal sin to shoot before identifying the target.

Already furious, Howe began venting at the Rangers. He felt that they were not fighting hard enough. When he saw Nelson, Yurek, and others trying to selectively target armed Somalis in a crowd at the other end of a building on their side of the street, Howe threw a grenade over its roof. It was an amazing toss, but the grenade failed to explode. So Howe threw another, which exploded right where the crowd was gathered. He then watched the Rangers try to hit a gunman who kept darting out from behind a shed about one block north, shooting, and then retreating back behind, it. The Delta sergeant flung one of his golf ball-sized minigrenades over the Rangers' position. It exploded behind the shed, and the gunman did not reappear. Howe then picked up a LAW and hurled it across the road. It landed on the arm of Specialist Lance Twombly, who was lying on his belly four or five feet from the corner wall. The LAW bruised his forearm. Twombly jumped to his knees, angry, and turned to hear Howe bellowing, "Shoot the motherfucker!"

Down on one knee, Howe swore bitterly as he fired. Everything about this situation was pissing him off, the goddamn Somalis, his leaders, the idiot Rangers . . . even his ammunition. He drew a bead on three Somalis who were running across the street two blocks to the north, taking a progressive lead on them the way he had learned through countless hours of training, squaring them in his sights and then aiming several feet in front of them. He would squeeze two or three rounds, rapidly increasing his lead with each shot. He was an expert marksman, and thought he had hit them, but he couldn't tell for sure because they kept running until they crossed the street and were out of view. It bugged him. His weapon was the most sophisticated infantry rifle in the world, a customized CAR-15, and he was shooting the Army's new 5.56 mm green-tip round. The green tip had a tungsten carbide penetrator at the tip, and would punch holes in metal, but that very penetrating power meant his rounds were passing right through his targets. When the Sammies were close enough he could see when he hit them. Their shirts would lift up at the point of impact, as if someone had pinched and plucked up the fabric. But with the green-tip round it was like sticking somebody with an ice pick. The bullet made a small, clean hole, and unless it happened to hit the heart or spine, it wasn't enough to stop a man in his tracks. Howe felt like he had to hit a guy five or six times just to get his attention. They used to kid Randy Shughart because he shunned the modern rifle and ammunition and carried a Vietnam-era M-14, which shot a 7.62 mm round without the penetrating qualities of the new green tip. It occurred to Howe as he saw those Sammies keep on running that Randy was the smartest Soldier in the unit. His rifle may have been heavier and comparatively awkward and delivered a mean recoil, but it damn sure knocked a man down with one bullet, and in combat, one shot was often all you got. You shoot a guy, you want to see him go down; you don't want to be guessing for the next five hours whether you hit him, or whether he's still waiting for you in the weeds.

Howe was in a good spot. There was nothing in front or behind him that would stop a bullet, but there was a tree about twenty feet south against the west wall of the street that blocked any view of him from that direction. The bigger tree across the alley where Nelson, Twombly, and the others were positioned blocked any view of him from the

north. So the broad-beamed Delta sergeant could kneel about five feet off the wall and pick off targets to the north with impunity. It was like that in battle. Some spots were safer than others. Up the hill, Hooten had watched Howe and his team move across the intersection while he was lying with his face pressed in the dirt, with rounds popping all around him. How can they be doing that? he'd thought. By an accident of visual angles, one person could stand and fight without difficulty, while just a few feet away fire could be so withering that there was nothing to do but dive for cover and stay hidden. Howe recognized he'd found such a safety zone. He shot methodically, saving his ammunition.

When he saw Perino, Smith, and Elliot creeping down to a similar position on the other side of the street, he figured they were trying to do what he was doing. Except, on that side of the street there were no trees to provide concealment.

He shouted across at them impatiently, but in the din he wasn't heard.

Perino and his men had moved down to a small tin shed, a porch really, that protruded from the irregular gray stone wall. They were only about ten yards from the alley where Super Six One lay. A West Point graduate, class of 1990, Perino at twenty-four wasn't much older than the Rangers he commanded. His group had gotten out ahead of Captain Steele and most of the Ranger force. They had pushed across the last intersection to the crash site after Goodale had been hit. They had cleared the first courtyard they passed on that block, and Perino had then led several of the men back out in the street to press on down Marehan Road. He knew they were close to linking up with Lieutenant DiTomasso and the CSAR team, which had been their destination when they started this move. The shed was just a few steps downhill from the courtyard doorway.

Sergeant Elliot was already on the other side of the shed. Corporal Smith was crouched behind it and Perino was just a few feet behind Smith. They were taking so much fire it was confusing. Rounds seemed to be coming from everywhere. Stone chips sprayed from the wall over Perino's head and rattled down on his helmet. He saw a Somali with a gun on the opposite side of the street, about twenty yards north of Nelson's position, blocked from those guys' view by the tree they were hiding behind. Perino saw the muzzle flash and could tell this was where some of the incoming rounds originated. It would be hard to hit the guy with a rifle shot, but Smith had a grenade launcher on his M-16 and might be able to drop a 203 round near enough to hurt the guy. He moved up to tap Smith on the shoulder—there was too much noise to communicate other than face-to-face—when bullets began popping loudly through the shed. The lieutenant was on one knee and a round spat up dirt between his legs.

Across the street, Nelson saw Smith get hit. The burly corporal had moved down the street fast and had taken a knee to begin shooting. Most of the men at that corner heard the round hit him, a hard, ugly slap. Smith seemed just startled at first. He rolled to his side and, like he was commenting about someone else, remarked with surprise, "I'm hit!"

From where Nelson was, it didn't look like Smith was hurt that badly. Perino helped move him against the wall. Now Smith was screaming, "I'm hit! I'm hit!"

The lieutenant could tell by the sound of Smith's voice that he was in pain. When Goodale had been hit he seemed to feel almost nothing, but the wound to Smith was different. He was writhing. He was in a very bad way. Perino pressed a field dressing into the wound but blood spurted out forcefully around it.

"I've got a bleeder here!" Perino shouted across the street.

Delta medic Sergeant Kurt Schmidt dashed toward them across Marehan Road. Together, they dragged Smith back into the courtyard.

Schmidt tore off Smith's pants leg. When he removed the battle dressing, bright red blood projected out of the wound in a long pulsing spurt. This was bad.

The young Soldier told Perino, "Man, this really hurts."

The lieutenant went back out to the street and crept back up to Elliot.

"Where's Smith?" Elliot asked.

"He's down."

"Shit," said Elliot.

They saw Sergeant Ken Boorn get hit in the foot. Then Private Rodriguez rolled away from his machine gun, bleeding, screaming, and holding his crotch. He felt no pain, but when he had placed his hand on the wound his genitals felt like mush and blood spurted thickly between his fingers. He screamed in alarm. Eight of the eleven Rangers in Perino's Chalk One had now been hit.

At the north end of the same block there was a huge explosion and in it Stebbins went down. Nelson saw it from up close. An RPG had streaked into the wall of the house across the alley from him, over near where Stebbins and Heard were positioned. The grenade went off with a brilliant red flash and tore out a chunk of the wall about four feet long. The concussion in the narrow alley was huge. It hurt his ears. There was a big cloud of dust. He saw—and Perino and Elliot saw from across the street—both Stebbins and Heard flat on their backs. *They're fucked up,* Nelson thought. But Stebbins stirred and then slowly stood up, covered from head to foot in white dust, coughing, rubbing his eyes.

"Get down, Stebbins!" shouted Heard. So he was okay, too.

Bullets were hitting around Perino and Elliot with increasing frequency. Rounds would come in long bursts, snapping between them, over their heads, nicking the tin shed with a high-pitched ring and popping right through the metal. Rounds were kicking up dirt all over their side of the street. It was a bad position, just as Howe had foreseen.

"Uh, sir, think that it would be a pretty good idea if we go into that courtyard," said Elliot.

"Do you really think so?" Perino asked.

Elliot grabbed his arm and they both dove for the courtyard where Schmidt was working frantically to save Smith.

Corporal Smith was alert and terrified and in sharp pain. The medic had first tried applying direct pressure on the wound, which had proved excruciatingly painful and obviously ineffective.

Bright red blood continued to gush from the hole in Smith's leg. The medic tried jamming Curlex into the hole. Then he checked Smith over.

"Are you hurt anywhere else?" he asked.

"I don't know."

Schmidt checked for an exit wound, and found none.

The medic was thirty-one. He'd grown up an Army brat, vowing never to join the military, and ended up enlisting a year after graduating from high school. He'd gone into Special Forces and elected to become a medic because he figured it would give him good employment opportunity when he left the Army. He was good at it, and his training kept progressing. By now he'd been schooled as thoroughly as any physician's assistant, and better than some. As part of his training he'd worked in the emergency room of a hospital in San Diego, and had even done some minor surgery under a physician's guidance. He certainly had enough training to know that Jamie Smith was in trouble if he couldn't stop the bleeding.

He could deduce that path the bullet had taken. It had entered Smith's thigh and traveled up into his pelvis. A gunshot wound to the pelvis is one of the worst. The aorta splits low in the abdomen, forming the left and right iliac arteries. As the iliac artery emerges from the pelvis it branches into the exterior and deep femoral arteries, the primary avenues for blood to the lower half of the body. The bullet had clearly pierced one of the femoral vessels. Schmidt applied direct pressure to Smith's abdomen, right above the pelvis where the artery splits. He explained what he was doing. He'd already run two IVs into Smith's arm, using 14-gauge, large bore needles, and was literally squeezing the plastic bag to push replacement fluid into him. Smith's blood formed an oily pool that shone dully on the dirt floor of the courtyard.

The medic took comfort in the assumption that help would arrive shortly. Another treatment tactic, a very risky one, would be to begin directly transfusing Smith. Blood transfusions were rarely done on the battlefield. It was a tricky business. The medics carried IV fluids with them but not blood. It he wanted to transfuse Smith, he'd have to find someone with the same blood type and attempt a direct transfusion. This was likely to create more problems. He could begin reacting badly to the transfusion. Schmidt decided not to attempt it. The rescue convoy was supposed to be arriving shortly. What this Ranger needed was a doctor, pronto.

Perino radioed Captain Steele.

"We can't go any further, sir. We have more wounded than I can carry."

"You've got to push on," Steele told him.

"We CANNOT go further," Perino said, "Request permission to occupy a building."

Steele told Perino to keep trying. Actually, inside the courtyard they were only about fifty feet from Lieutenant DiTomasso and the CSAR force, but Perino had no way of knowing that. He tried to reach DiTomasso on his radio.

"Tom, where are you?"

DiTomasso tried to explain their position, pointing out landmarks.

"I can't see," said Perino. "I'm in a courtyard."

DiTomasso popped a red smoke grenade, and Perino saw the red plume drifting up in the darkening sky. He guessed from the drift of the plume that they were about fifty yards apart, which in this killing zone was a great distance. On the radio, Steele kept pushing him to link up with DiTomasso.

"They need your help," he said.

"Look, sir, I've got three guys left, counting myself. How can I help him?"

Finally, Steele relented.

"Roger, strongpoint the building and defend it."

Schmidt was still working frantically on Smith's wound. He'd asked Perino to help him by applying pressure just over the wound so he could use his hands. Perino pushed two fingers directly into the wound up to his knuckles. Smith screamed and blood shot out at the lieutenant, who swallowed hard and applied more pressure. He felt dizzy. The spurts of blood continued.

"Oh, shit! Oh, shit! I'm gonna die! I'm gonna die!" Smith shouted. He knew he had an arterial bleed.

The medic talked to him, tried to calm him down. The only way to stop the bleeding was to find the severed femoral artery and clamp it. Otherwise it was like trying to stanch a fire hose by pushing down on it through a mattress. He told Smith to lean back.

"This is going to be very painful," Schmidt told the Ranger apologetically. "I'm going to have to cause you more pain, but I have to do this to help you."

"Give me some morphine for the pain!" Smith demanded. He was still very alert and engaged.

"I can't," Schmidt told him. In this state, morphine could kill him. After losing so much blood, his pressure was precariously low. Morphine would further lower his heart rate and slow his respiration, exactly what he did not need.

The young Ranger bellowed as the medic reached with both hands and tore open the entrance wound. Schmidt tried to shut out the fact that there were live nerve endings beneath his fingers. It was hard. He had formed an emotional bond with Smith. They were in this together. But to save the young Ranger, he had to treat him like an inanimate object, a machine that was broken and needed fixing. He continued to root for the artery. If he failed to find it, Smith would probably die. He picked through the open upper thigh, reaching up to his pelvis, parting layers of skin, fat, muscle, and vessel, probing through pools of bright red blood. He couldn't find it. Once severed, the upper end of the artery had evidently retracted up into Smith's abdomen. The medic stopped. Smith was lapsing into shock. The only recourse now would be to cut into the abdomen and hunt for the severed artery and clamp it. But that would mean still more pain and blood loss. Every time he reached into the wound Smith lost more blood. Schmidt and Perino were covered with it. Blood was everywhere. It was hard to believe Smith had any more to lose.

"It hurts really bad," he kept saying. "It really hurts."

In time his words and movements came slowly, labored. He was in shock.

Schmidt was beside himself. He had squeezed six liters of fluid into the young Ranger and was running out of bags. He had tried everything and was feeling desperate and frustrated and angry. He had to leave the room. He got one of the other men to continue applying pressure on the wound and walked out to confer with Perino. Both men were covered with Smith's blood.

"If I don't get him out of here right now, he's gonna die," Schmidt pleaded.

The lieutenant radioed Steele again.

"Sir, we need a medevac. A Little Bird or something. For Corporal Smith. We need to extract him now."

Steele relayed this on the command net. It was tough to get through. It was nearly five o'clock and growing dark. All of the vehicles had turned back to the air base. Steele learned that there would be no relief for some time. Putting another bird down in their neighborhood was out of the question.

The captain radioed Perino back and told him, for the time being, that Smith would just have to hang on.

Critical Thinking

Identify examples of the Warrior Ethos in the excerpt you have just read. Did you find any examples of failure to live by the Warrior Ethos? Do you think the Warrior Ethos minimized casualties and helped the trapped units to hang on until rescue came?

CONCLUSION

At its core, the Warrior Ethos is your refusal to accept failure and instead to overcome all obstacles with honor. It begins as your selfless commitment to the nation, mission, unit, and your fellow Soldiers. You develop and maintain this attitude through discipline, realistic training, commitment to Army Values, and pride in the Army's heritage.

The Warrior Ethos is both a goal and a direction for the Army. The Army is committed to it because it will develop, attract, and retain the flexible, adaptive, and competent Soldiers who live the Army's Warrior Culture. Such Soldiers are grounded in Army Values and live the Warrior Ethos in the field, in garrison, and in their contact with their fellow Americans.

Learning Assessment

1. Identify the four tenets of the Warrior Ethos.
2. Recite the Soldier's Creed from memory.
3. List the four building blocks of the Warrior Ethos.

Key Words

ethos
Warrior Ethos

References

Bowden, Mark. (1999). *Black Hawk Down: A Story of Modern War*. New York: Grove/Atlantic, Inc.

Field Manual 6-22, *Army Leadership: Competent, Confident, and Agile*. 12 October 2006.

COMPOSITE RISK MANAGEMENT

Key Points

1 The Composite Risk Management Process

Risk management is not an add-on feature to the decision making process but rather a fully integrated element of planning and executing operations. Risk management helps us preserve combat power and retain the flexibility for bold and decisive action. Proper risk management is a combat multiplier that we can ill afford to squander.

GEN Dennis J. Reimer, Army Chief of Staff

Introduction

By this point in the course, you should understand that you, as an Army leader, will be required to plan and execute difficult, complex, and dangerous operations. The best preparation for combat is tough, realistic training. From ROTC training exercises to FTX operations to intense combat scenarios, all involve risk-taking. To train and win with minimum losses, the Army applies the Composite Risk Management (CRM) process to give commanders and other leaders a framework to take only those risks necessary to accomplish the mission—to win. By following the composite risk management process combined with critical thinking, you can make informed, deliberate decisions about which risks will lead to the best outcome under the most difficult conditions. This chapter will cover the five steps of the risk management process.

During a deployment to a desert training area, a support platoon was driving many miles during both daylight and darkness in support of their tank battalion. During these movements, the dust from the vehicles could be seen for miles. The platoon sergeant, who had deployed to the desert numerous times throughout his career, informed his platoon leader of the problems associated with driving in the desert. The platoon leader did not think it was a major problem, so he did not take it into consideration while completing his daily risk assessment.

One day at the evening convoy briefing, the platoon leader instructed the drivers to maintain only 50 meters distance between vehicles during that night's movement to avoid separation among the vehicles. When several of the drivers expressed concern about this requirement, the platoon leader stated that it was unlikely that following so close would cause any problems, and that the drivers would just need to stay alert during the mission.

As you've probably already guessed, this platoon leader failed to properly gauge the impact of his decision. At one point during the night move, the platoon leader stopped his vehicle abruptly. The five-ton truck that was following him had to brake hard to avoid a collision. The next two vehicles were also able to avoid a collision. However, the last three vehicles in the convoy were not as fortunate. The collision resulted in two injured drivers and three heavily damaged vehicles. All because the platoon leader failed to properly assess the hazards his unit faced. Regrettably, he did not learn from the experience of the platoon sergeant; neither did he recognize that hair stood up on the back of his men's necks when he described the plan of operation; nor did he appreciate the courage it took for his platoon sergeant and his unit to raise concerns for their personal safety and the success of their mission.

No, the platoon leader didn't have the personal experience to adequately assess the hazard. But he had plenty of clues and opportunities to get to the truth about the risk and consider the consequences. One of the Army's great strengths is learning from the successes and failures of each other, and growing stronger on that foundation.

The next time you see something that just doesn't look right, take a moment, and ask yourself how this might impact you, or the Soldier next to you, or your unit, or the family of four who might be driving down the road as your convoy approaches. Safety is not a sometimes thing, and your actions don't just affect *you*. Exercise the courage to tell the truth about the hazards, and to face the *potential* consequences. That way, you and your unit can *avoid* those consequences.

Army Safety Center Website

Critical Thinking

Discuss how you would assess and manage the risks described in the vignette above.

The Composite Risk Management Process

risk management

the process of identifying, assessing, and controlling risks arising from operational factors and making decisions that balance risk costs with mission benefits

Composite **risk management** (CRM) is the Army's primary decision making process for identifying hazards and controlling risks across the full spectrum of Army missions, functions, operations, and activities. (See Figure 1.1.)

CRM is a decision making process used to mitigate risks associated with all hazards that have the potential to injure or kill personnel, damage or destroy equipment, or otherwise impact mission effectiveness. In the past, the Army separated **risk** into two categories, *tactical risk* and *accident risk*. While these two areas of concern remain, the primary premise of CRM is that it does not matter where or how the loss occurs, the result is the same—decreased combat power or mission effectiveness.

The Guiding Principles

risk

probability and severity of loss linked to hazards

Risk management formulates balanced controls to eliminate or mitigate mission hazards.

The guiding principles of CRM are as follows:

- Integrate CRM into all phases of missions and operations
- Make risk decisions at the appropriate level
- Accept no unnecessary risk
- Apply the process cyclically and continuously
- Do not be risk averse.

CRM is a five-step process:

Step 1 – Identify hazards

Step 2 – Assess hazards to determine risk

Step 3 – Develop controls and make risk decisions

Step 4 – Implement controls

Step 5 – Supervise and evaluate.

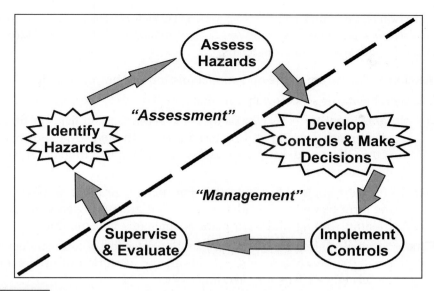

Figure 1.1 The Composite Risk Management Process

Step 1 – Identify Hazards

A **hazard** is a condition with the potential to cause injury, illness, or death of personnel; damage to or loss of equipment or property; or mission degradation. A hazard may also be a situation or event that can result in degradation of capabilities or mission failure. Hazards exist in all environments—combat operations, stability operations, base support operations, training, garrison activities, and off-duty activities.

The factors of mission, enemy, terrain and weather, troops and support available, time available, and civil considerations (METT-TC) serve as a standard format for identification of hazards, on-duty or off-duty. The factors of METT-TC are used because they are institutionalized in the Army. They are part of the common knowledge imparted through the Army's professional military education and initial entry training.

Sources of Hazards and Risks

Hazards may arise from any number of areas, including enemy activity, accident potential, weather or environmental conditions, health, sanitation, behavior, and/or material or equipment. CRM does not differentiate among the sources of the hazard. The loss of personnel, equipment, or material due to any hazard has the same disruptive impact on readiness or mission capabilities no matter what the source. You may have a greater influence to effect change in hazards arising from behavior, accident potential, equipment, or material than over hazards that arise from enemy action. The bottom line is the effect of the hazard, not its source.

The Role of METT-TC in Hazard Identification

The factors of METT-TC provide a standardized way to address both threat and hazard-based risk for tactical and nontactical operations and for off-duty activities. You can use METT-TC as part of the military decision making process (MDMP) for tactical missions. However, the same thought process works equally well for nontactical operations and the off-duty environment. The factors of METT-TC require no explanation for a tactical or operational environment. You can apply the same factors in nonmilitary activities. For the sake of clarity, however, the terms are different to reflect the nonmilitary application.

hazard

any actual or potential condition that can cause injury, illness, or death of personnel, damage to or loss of equipment, property or mission degradation; a condition or activity with potential to cause damage, loss, or mission degradation

For garrison and off-duty activities, the METT-TC factors become *activities, disrupters, terrain and weather, personnel, time,* and *legal considerations.* Both processes address similar considerations expressed in different terms.

Mission – The nature of the operational mission may imply specific hazards.

Enemy – Enemy presence/capabilities that pose hazards to the operation or mission.

Terrain and Weather – Use the factors of observation and fields of fire, avenues of approach, key and decisive terrain, obstacles, and cover and concealment (OAKOC) to identify and assess hazards impacting on mission-type operations.

Troops (or People) and Equipment – For mission-related **risk assessment**, use the term troops to consider hazards that are associated with the level of training, staffing, and equipment maintenance and condition.

Time – Insufficient time for mission preparation often forces commanders to accept greater risk in planning, preparation, and execution of orders and plans associated with mission planning.

Civil or Legal Considerations – This function expands the consideration of hazards to include those hazards that a tactical mission may pose to the civilian populace and noncombatants in the area of operations.

risk assessment

identification and assessment of hazards; an identified hazard is assessed to determine the risk (both the probability of occurrence and resulting severity) of a hazardous incident due to the presence of the hazard.

Risk assessment identifies and prioritizes hazards to mission safety and security.

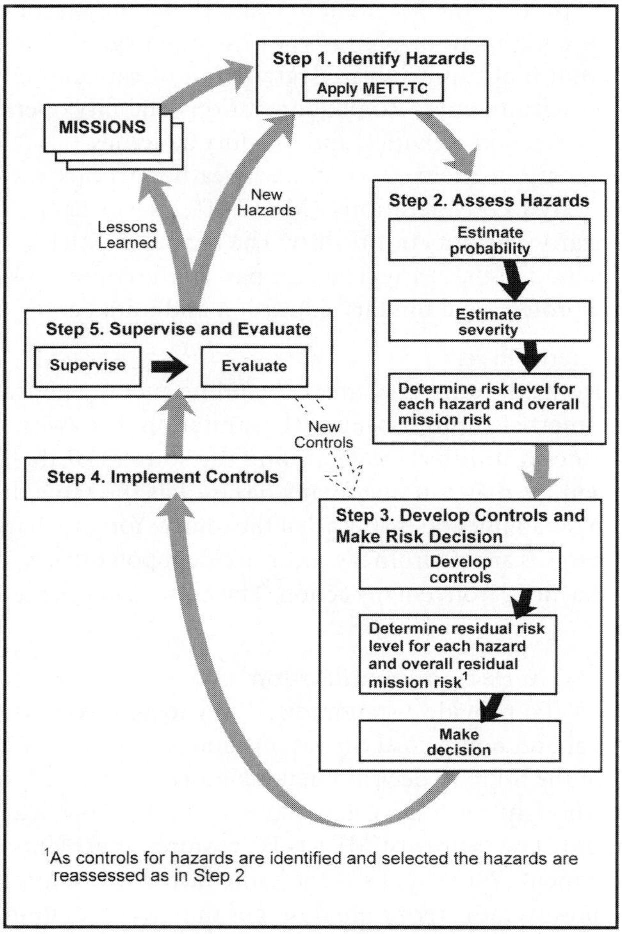

Figure 1.2 Continuous Application of Risk Management

TABLE 1.1	Hazard Probability
Frequent (A)	**Occurs very often, continuously experienced**
Single item	Occurs very often in service life. Expected to occur several times over duration of a specific mission or operation. Always occurs.
Fleet or inventory of items	Occurs continuously during a specific mission or operation, or over a service life.
Individual Soldier	Occurs very often in career. Expected to occur several times during mission or operation. Always occurs.
All Soldiers exposed	Occurs continuously during a specific mission or operation.
Likely (B)	**Occurs several times**
Single item	Occurs several times in service life. Expected to occur during a specific mission or operation.
Fleet or inventory of items	Occurs at a high rate, but experienced intermittently (regular intervals, generally often).
Individual Soldier	Occurs several times in career. Expected to occur during a specific mission or operation.
All Soldiers exposed	Occurs at a high rate, but experienced intermittently.
Occasional (C)	**Occurs sporadically**
Single item	Occurs several times in service life. May occur about as often as not during a specific mission or operation.
Fleet or inventory of items	Occurs several times in service life.
Individual Soldier	Occurs several times in career. May occur during a specific mission or operation, but not often.
All Soldiers exposed	Occurs sporadically (irregularly, sparsely, or sometimes).
Seldom (D)	**Remotely possible; could occur at some time**
Single item	Occurs in service life, but only remotely possible. Not expected to occur during a specific mission or operation.
Fleet or inventory of items	Occurs as isolated incidents. Possible to occur some time in service life, but rarely. Usually does not occur.
Individual Soldier	Occurs as isolated incident during a career. Remotely possible, but not expected to occur during a specific mission or operation.
All Soldiers exposed	Occurs rarely within exposed population as isolated incidents.

continued

TABLE 1.1	*continued*

Unlikely (E)	Can assume will not occur, but not impossible
Single item	Occurrence not impossible, but can assume will almost never occur in service life. Can assume will not occur during a specific mission or operation.
Fleet or inventory of items	Occurs very rarely (almost never or improbable). Incidents may occur over service life.
Individual Soldier	Occurrence not impossible, but may assume will not occur in career or during a specific mission or operation.
All Soldiers exposed	Occurs very rarely, but not impossible.

Step 2 – Assess the Hazards

Assess the hazards systematically using charts, codes, and numbers. These give you a way to assess probability and severity and thus obtain a standardized level of risk. The five-step CRM process is a method for expressing and depicting a normally intuitive and experience-based thought process. The risk management process is a disciplined application of five steps to obtain and express a risk level in terms that all levels of command readily understand. The methodology assesses and assigns risk in terms of how likely and how severe the adverse impact of an event or occurrence would be. This step considers the risk or likelihood of an event or incident adversely affecting the mission, capabilities, people, equipment, or property. In other words, what are the odds (probability) of something going wrong and what is the effect (severity) of the incident if it does occur?

You assess hazards and associated risks during the mission analysis, COA development, analysis, and rehearsal and execution steps of the MDMP. You also consider both mission- and non-mission-related aspects that may have an impact. The result of this assessment is an initial risk estimate for each identified hazard expressed as *extremely high, high, moderate,* or *low* as determined from your standardized application of the risk assessment matrix.

This step has three sub-steps:

1. Assess the probability of the event or occurrence
2. Estimate the expected result or severity of an event or occurrence
3. Determine the specified level of risk for a given probability and severity using the standard risk assessment matrix.

Assess Each Hazard on the Probability of the Event or Occurrence

Probability is the likelihood of an event. This is your estimate, given the information you know and what others have experienced. The probability levels that you estimate for each hazard are based on the mission, COA, or frequency of a similar event. For the purpose of CRM, there are five levels of probability—frequent, likely, occasional, seldom, and unlikely (see Table 1.1):

Frequent – Occurs very often, known to happen regularly
Likely – Occurs several times, a common occurrence
Occasional – Occurs sporadically, but is not uncommon
Seldom – Remotely possible, could occur at some time
Unlikely – Can assume will not occur, but not impossible.

Estimate the Expected Result or Severity of an Occurrence

Severity is the degree to which an incident will affect combat power, mission capability, or readiness. You use the following four levels on the risk assessment worksheet to express the degree of severity:

1. Catastrophic

2. Critical

3. Marginal

4. Negligible

Determine Specified Level of Risk

Using the standard risk assessment matrix in Figure 1.3, you convert probability and severity for each identified hazard into a specified level of risk. This matrix provides an assessment of probability and severity expressed as a standard level of risk.

This assessment is an estimate, not an absolute. It may or may not indicate the relative danger of a given operation, activity, or event. The levels of risk are listed in the lower left corner of the matrix. You must make sure the appropriate level of command approves all accepted residual risk.

Determining overall mission risk by averaging the risks of all hazards is not valid. If one hazard has high risk, the mission's overall residual risk is high, no matter how many moderate- or low-risk hazards are present.

Extremely High Risk – You won't be able to accomplish the mission if hazards occur.

High Risk – Significant degradation of mission capabilities: you won't be able to accomplish all parts of the mission, or you won't be able to complete the mission to standard if hazards occur during the mission.

Moderate Risk – Expected degraded mission capabilities: you won't be able to meet the required mission standard and will have more difficulty completing the mission capability if hazards occur.

Low Risk – Expected losses will have little or no impact on your ability to accomplish the mission.

RISK ASSESSMENT MATRIX						
		Probability				
Severity		Frequent A	Likely B	Occasional C	Seldom D	Unlikely E
Catastrophic	I	E	E	H	H	M
Critical	II	E	H	H	M	L
Marginal	III	H	M	M	L	L
Negligible	IV	M	L	L	L	L
E – Extremely High		H – High		M – Moderate		L – Low

Figure 1.3 Risk Assessment Matrix

Critical Thinking

Think of a situation in your ROTC training that involves risk of injury. Using the three-part process of assessing hazards, estimate the risk of this situation.

Step 3 – Develop Controls and Make Risk Decisions

controls

actions taken to eliminate hazards or to reduce their risk

In Step 2, you assessed hazards and determined an initial risk level. In this step, you develop and apply **controls,** then reassess the hazard to determine a residual risk. Continue the process of developing and applying controls and reassessing risk until you achieve an acceptable level of risk or until you can reduce all risks to a level where benefits outweigh the potential cost. You accomplish this step during the course of action (COA) development, COA analysis, COA comparison, and COA approval of the MDMP.

Develop Controls

After assessing each hazard, you develop one or more controls that either eliminate the hazard or reduce the risk (probability and/or severity) of a hazardous incident occurring. In developing controls, consider the reason for the hazard, not just the hazard itself.

Controls can take many forms, but normally fall into one of three basic categories:

1. Educational (awareness) controls
2. Physical controls
3. Avoidance/Elimination.

Find Control Measures

Other sources for selecting controls include:

- personal experience
- after action reports (AARs)
- accident data from automated risk management systems available through the United States Army Combat Readiness Center (USACRC)
- standing operating procedures (SOPs)
- regulations
- tactics, techniques, and procedures (TTPs)
- lessons learned from similar past operations.

CRM worksheets from previously executed missions provide another source for selecting controls. The key to effective control measures is that they reduce the effect of, or eliminate, the identified hazard.

Reassess Risk

With controls applied, you reassess risk to determine the residual risk associated with each hazard, as well as the overall residual risk for the mission. Continue the process of developing and applying controls and reassessing risk until you achieve an acceptable level of risk or until all risks are reduced to a level where benefits outweigh potential cost.

Residual risk is the risk remaining after you select controls for the specific hazard. Residual risk is valid only if you have implemented the identified controls. As you identify and select controls for hazards, reassess the hazards as in Step 2. Then revise the level of risk. Available controls may not be sufficient to warrant lowering the risk level of a given hazard.

Determine overall residual risk by considering the residual risks for all of the identified hazards. The residual risk for each hazard may be different, depending on the probability you assess and the severity of the hazardous incident. You determine overall residual risk based on the greatest residual risk of all the identified hazards. The overall residual risk of the mission will be equal to or higher than the highest identified residual risk.

Consider the number and type of hazards present. In some cases you may determine that the overall residual risk is higher than any one hazard. This is based on a number of lower-risk hazards if they present a greater hazard in combination. For example, a mission risk assessment may result in moderate residual risk for all identified hazards. However, based on the complexity of required controls and the potential interaction of all hazards, you may determine that the mission's residual risk is high.

Make Risk Decisions

The purpose of the CRM process is to provide you a basis for making sound decisions regarding individual and leadership risk. A key element of the risk decision is determining the acceptable level of risk. You do this by balancing risk or potential loss against expectations or expected gains. Risk decisions must always be made at the appropriate level of command or leadership based on the level of risk involved.

Step 4 – Implement Controls

You must ensure that controls are integrated into SOPs, written and verbal orders, mission briefings, and staff estimates. The critical check for this step is to ensure that controls are converted into clear and simple execution orders. Implementing controls includes coordinating and communicating with the following:

- Appropriate superior, adjacent, and subordinate units, organizations, and individuals
- Logistics Civil Augmentation Program (LOGCAP) organizations and civilian agencies that are part of the force or may be impacted by the activity, hazard, or its control
- The media and nongovernmental organizations (NGO) when their presence affects or is affected by the force.

The commander alone decides if controls are sufficient and acceptable and whether to accept the resulting residual risk. If the commander determines the risk level is too high, he or she directs the development of additional controls or alternate controls or modifies, changes, or rejects a given plan of action.

Be sure to explain how the controls will be implemented in areas such as the following:

- Overlays and graphics
- Drills for vehicle and aircraft silhouette identification
- Rehearsals and battle drills
- Refresher training on intensive threat and friendly vehicle identification for all anti-armor and air defense weapons crews
- Orientation for replacement personnel
- Installation and maintenance of communications links for key civilian organizations
- Operating convoys with a prescribed minimum number of vehicles
- Provisions to carry weapons and wear body armor and helmets when outside secure compounds
- Accident awareness, safety briefings, and warnings.

Step 5 – Supervise and Evaluate

In Step 5 of the CRM process you ensure that risk controls are implemented and enforced to standard. You also make sure the selected control measures are adequate and support the objectives and desired outcomes. Like other steps of the CRM process, you must supervise and evaluate throughout all phases of any operation or activity. In this way, you will be able to identify weaknesses and make changes or adjustments to controls based on performance, changing situations, conditions, or events.

Supervise

Supervision is a form of control measure. In Step 5 of CRM, supervision becomes an integral part of the process. During supervision, you ensure subordinates understand how, when, and where there are controls. You also ensure that controls are implemented, monitored, and remain in place.

Situational awareness is a critical component of the CRM process when identifying hazards. Situational awareness is equally important in supervision. It will enable you to make sure that complacency, deviation from standards, or violations of policies and risk controls do not threaten success. Monitor factors such as fatigue, equipment serviceability/availability, and the weather and environment. Then you can mitigate the hazards they present. Through supervision and oversight you can gain the situational awareness necessary to anticipate, identify, and assess any new hazards and to develop or modify controls as necessary.

You must have an extraordinary degree of discipline to avoid complacency from boredom or overconfidence when personnel are performing repetitive tasks. It can be easy, due to overconfidence or complacency, for people to ignore controls established and implemented for a prolonged period. During stability operations, for example, at the beginning of an operation, you may identify land-mine hazards and establish and enforce controls. However, over time and with success (no accidents or incidents), complacency may set in. Established controls may lose their effectiveness. A terrorist threat and personal security are examples. When personnel live or operate in an area that is not considered a high threat area or in cases where personnel have operated in a high threat area for an extended period without incident, they risk losing situational awareness and may fail to

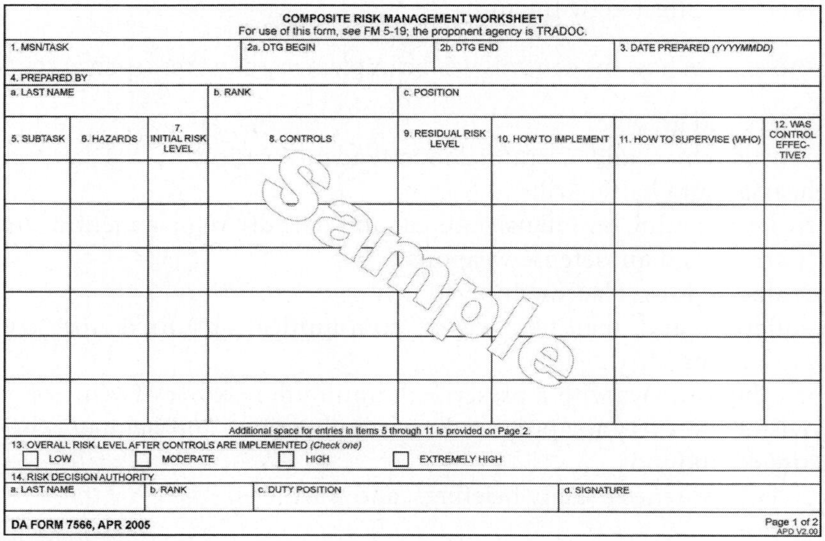
COMPOSITE RISK MANAGEMENT WORKSHEET
For use of this form, see FM 5-19; the proponent agency is TRADOC.

1. MSN/TASK	2a. DTG BEGIN	2b. DTG END	3. DATE PREPARED *(YYYYMMDD)*

4. PREPARED BY

a. LAST NAME	b. RANK	c. POSITION

5. SUBTASK	6. HAZARDS	7. INITIAL RISK LEVEL	8. CONTROLS	9. RESIDUAL RISK LEVEL	10. HOW TO IMPLEMENT	11. HOW TO SUPERVISE (WHO)	12. WAS CONTROL EFFEC-TIVE?

Additional space for entries in Items 5 through 11 is provided on Page 2.

13. OVERALL RISK LEVEL AFTER CONTROLS ARE IMPLEMENTED *(Check one)*
☐ LOW ☐ MODERATE ☐ HIGH ☐ EXTREMELY HIGH

14. RISK DECISION AUTHORITY

a. LAST NAME	b. RANK	c. DUTY POSITION	d. SIGNATURE

DA FORM 7566, APR 2005 Page 1 of 2 APD V2.00

Figure 1.4 Composite Risk Management Worksheet

TABLE 1.2   Worksheet Instructions

Item	Instruction
1 through 4	Self explanatory.
5	Subtask relating to the mission or task in block1.
6	Hazards – Identify hazards by reviewing METT-TC factors for the mission or task. Additional factors include historical lessons learned, experience, judgment, equipment characteristics and warnings, and environmental considerations.
7	Initial Risk Level – Includes historical lessons learned, intuitive analyses, experience, judgment, equipment characteristics and warnings, and environmental considerations. Determine initial risk for each hazard by applying risk assessment matrix (Figure 1.3). Enter the risk level for each hazard.
8	Controls – Develop one or more controls for each hazard that will either eliminate the hazard or reduce the risk (probability and/or severity) of a hazardous incident. Specify who, what, where, why, when, and how for each control. Enter controls.
9	Residual Risk Level – Determine the residual risk for each hazard by applying the risk assessment matrix (Figure 1.3). Enter the residual risk level for each hazard.
10	How to Implement – Decide how each control will be put into effect or communicated to the personnel who will make it happen (written or verbal instruction; tactical, safety, garrison SOPs, rehearsals). Enter controls.
11	How to Supervise (Who) – Plan how each control will be monitored for implementation (continuous supervision, spot-checks) and reassess hazards as the situation changes. Determine if the controls worked and if they can be improved. Pass on lessons learned.
12	Was Control Effective – Indicate "Yes" or "No." Review during AAR.
13	Overall Risk Level – Select the highest residual risk level and circle it. This becomes the overall mission or task risk level. The commander decides whether the controls are sufficient to accept the level of residual risk. If the risk is too great to continue the mission or task, the commander directs development of additional controls or modifies, changes, or rejects the COA.
14	Risk Decision Authority – Signed by the appropriate level of command.

remain vigilant. Other examples of long-term hazards include climatic extremes; nuclear, biological, and chemical (NBC) and hazardous-waste contamination; or diseases native to a particular area of operation or indigenous population.

Evaluate

Continue the evaluation process during all phases of the operation, and as part of the AAR and assessment following completion of the operation or activity.

- Identify any hazards that you did not identify as part of the initial assessment, or identify new hazards that evolved during the operation or activity—for example, any time that personnel, equipment, environment, or mission change the initial risk management analysis, re-evaluate the control measures
- Assess effectiveness in supporting operational goals and objectives. Did the controls positively or negatively impact training or mission accomplishment? Did the controls support existing doctrine, techniques, tactics, and procedures?
- Assess the implementation, execution, and communication of the controls
- Assess the accuracy of residual risk and effectiveness of controls in eliminating hazards and controlling risks
- Ensure compliance with the guiding principles of CRM. Was the process integrated throughout all phases of the operation? Were risk decisions accurate? Were they made at the appropriate level? Were there any unnecessary risks, and did the benefit outweigh the cost in terms of dollars, training benefit, and time? Was the process cyclic and continuous throughout the operation?

Tools and Techniques

Techniques may include spot-checks, inspections, situation reports (SITREPs), back briefs, buddy checks, and close oversight. AARs provide a forum in which you can assess the entire mission or operation. Include the effectiveness of the CRM process and an assessment of the criteria as a part of any AAR.

Based on your evaluation and assessment of the operation and the effectiveness of CRM, develop and disseminate to others lessons learned for incorporation into future plans, operations, and activities. The operations staff officer (S3) ensures that lessons learned from the CRM process, to include CRM worksheets, are captured and retained for use during future operations.

Poor Training Leads to High Risk

During an assembly area occupation, the overhead cover of a fighting position collapsed on a Soldier. The Soldier suffered a fractured spine, resulting in a permanent disability.

The fighting position collapsed because it was not built to standard. Specifically, the overhead stringers were improperly emplaced to support the weight of the overhead cover. One common construction error is the lack of support (beams) on which to stabilize the stringers. Another error is improper spacing (10" maximum) of overhead stringers. Eighteen inches of overhead cover provided by sandbags could weigh almost 4,000 pounds, so it is critical that fighting positions are built IAW the available appropriate references (FM 5-34).

The Soldiers built this position as they had been trained—but not to standard. The design was similar to many they had built in the past; clearly, this accident was just waiting for a time and place to happen. The preconditions were set—training and leader failure.

At least three training opportunities were missed that directly contributed to this accident. First, although every Soldier receives instruction on this task during Basic Training, hands-on performance is not a requirement. Most field commanders assume Soldiers are proficient in this skill-level-one task. These Soldiers were not proficient, and the first opportunity to prevent this accident was missed. Second, the task, Construct Individual Fighting Positions, was required in both the FY97 and FY98 Notice for Common Task Testing. Additionally, the skill-level-two task, Supervise Construction of a Fighting Position, was included in the FY97 Notice. Again, leaders missed an opportunity to prevent this accident by failing to train to standard. Finally, prior to the exercise, the unit identified the task as a weakness and programmed training to fix it. However, the train-up exercise was not properly planned, resourced, or executed. Another opportunity missed. The end result was that Soldiers didn't know what right looked like.

The Soldiers' supervisor checked on the position numerous times as it was being built. He failed to correct the deficiency because he too was not trained to standard. However, he did have at least two references readily available that explained the correct method for constructing overhead cover. This supervisor, and those leaders who did not certify his ability to supervise this task, failed to exercise their leadership responsibilities.

Training and leadership should have ensured that a Soldier didn't leave that fighting position on a stretcher. By failing to train to and enforce established standards, one Soldier paid an extremely high price. Soldier safety is a leader responsibility: they are our greatest asset, and we owe it to our Soldiers to do it right.

Army Safety Center Website

Critical Thinking

Consider the situation described above. Which of the controls is likely to be most effective? Would a combination be more effective than a single control?

Critical Thinking

Discuss how you would convert a control measure into an order.

CONCLUSION

When leaders become skilled in the process of risk management, they effectively identify, assess, and control risks inherent in training and combat operations. Through making calculated decisions that balance risk costs with the mission's goals, the vexing element of chance is reduced in dangerous training and combat situations. Leaders and Soldiers at all levels use risk management during all missions and in all environments in which Army operations take place. The ability to manage risk using the five-step risk management process is fundamental to your confidence and competence as an Army leader. It is critical to conserving combat power and resources.

Learning Assessment

1. What five steps comprise the risk management process?
2. What are the three basic types of controls?
3. What is residual risk?

Key Words

risk management
risk
hazard
risk assessment
controls

References

Field Manual 5-19, *Composite Risk Management.* 21 August 2006.

Truth or Consequences. Army Safety Center Website. *Risk Management Lessons Learned.* Retrieved 23 March 2005 from https://safety.army.mil

MAP READING I

Key Points

1 Marginal Information

2 Topographic Symbols

3 Elevation and Relief

4 Map Coordinate Systems

5 Measuring Distances on a Map

Introduction

War has three basic tenets: *move*, *shoot*, and *communicate*. It is no accident that *move* is the first. Every Soldier must be able to read and understand a map. A thorough knowledge of map reading is essential to your military career. Only through mastery of the skills this chapter presents can you hope to understand the more complex instruction that follows. Once you can get yourself from Point A to Point B, you can begin to incorporate the many other variables involved with moving troops and equipment (FM 3-25.26).

A map depicts three-dimensional natural and man-made objects on a two-dimensional surface. It indicates variations in terrain, heights of natural features, and the extent of vegetation cover. With military forces dispersed throughout the world, maps are necessary to provide information to our combat units and to carry out logistical operations far from our shores. Soldiers and materials must be transported, stored, and deployed at the proper time and place. You need maps to do much of this planning. Therefore, any operation requires a supply of maps. But the finest maps available are worthless unless the map user knows how to read them.

The 507th Maintenance Company

In the early morning hours of 20 March 2003, US Army, US Marine Corps, and coalition ground combat forces crossed from Kuwait into southern Iraq and attacked northward, beginning the ground phase of Operation Iraqi Freedom. By dawn on 23 March, major US ground combat units had advanced more than 200 miles into Iraq and were approximately 130 miles north of An Nasariyah. The rapid advance of coalition troops in thousands of vehicles and hundreds of aircraft was made possible by the determined, aggressive support of scores of logistics, medical, and maintenance units. Many moved constantly to maintain contact with the units they were supporting. One such unit was the 507th Maintenance Company.

CPT Troy King, commander of the 507th, was supposed to follow "Route Blue" on the map to a rendezvous point farther north called "Objective Ram." When he reached an intersection south of the southern Iraqi city of Nasariyah, which required a left turn to stay on "Route Blue," he directed the convoy straight north instead. This route took the Soldiers into the outskirts of the city and then straight into an ambush. As the convoy drove through Nasariyah it passed armed Iraqis manning checkpoints. But the Iraqis did not fire their weapons at this point. The US Soldiers held fire—the rules of engagement required the enemy to show hostile intent. When the convoy reached the northern edge of the city, CPT King realized for the first time that he had veered from the designated route. He had the company make a U-turn and head back into the city and ordered his troops to "lock and load" their weapons. The Soldiers again missed the required turn and had to make a second U-turn. Around this time, the 507th came under fire from grenade launchers and rifles. An intense 60- to 90-minute firefight marked by chaos and bravery ensued, with the convoy broken into three groups.

Once engaged in battle, the Soldiers of the 507th Maintenance Company fought hard. They fought the best they could until there was no longer a means to resist. They defeated ambushes, overcame hastily prepared enemy obstacles, defended one another, provided life-saving aid, and inflicted casualties on the enemy.

In the end, nine 507th Soldiers and two other Soldiers traveling with it were killed; six were taken prisoner, including PFC Jessica Lynch, who was rescued from a Nasariyah hospital eight days later by US special-operations forces. Sixteen Soldiers, including CPT King, managed to escape from the ambush when Marines came to the rescue.

Scarborough (2003); US Army Official Report on 507th Maintenance Co.

Marginal Information

The information contained in the margins (**marginal information**) explains how to read and use the map. All four margins can relay information, with the bottom margin usually containing the most. The following are just a few examples of what you might find:

marginal information

any information located in the margins of a map—the map's instructions

- *Information Date.* The first step with any map is to find the date it was made or last updated. This is called the Information Date, found immediately below the word "LEGEND" in the lower left margin of the map. The more current the date, the more accurate the information on the map (buildings, roads, power lines, etc.) should be.
- *Sheet Name.* You'll find the sheet name in bold print at the center of the top and in the lower left area of the map margin. A map is generally named for the largest or most populated settlement it covers, or for the largest natural feature located within the area when the map was drawn.
- *Sheet Number.* The sheet number is found in bold print in both the upper right and lower left areas of the margin, and in the center box of the adjoining sheets diagram, located in the lower right margin. It is used as a reference number to link specific maps to overlays, operation orders, and plans.
- *Series Name.* The map series name is found in the same bold print as the sheet number in the upper left corner of the margin. The series name is generally that of a major political subdivision, such as a state within the United States or a European nation. A map series usually includes a group of similar maps at the same scale and on the same sheet lines or format that cover a particular geographic area. It may also be a group of maps that serve a common purpose, such as the military city maps.
- *Series Number.* You can find the series number in both the upper right margin and the lower left margin. It is a sequence reference expressed either as a four-digit numeral (1125) or as a letter followed by a three- or four-digit numeral (M661; T7110).
- *Edition Number.* The edition number is found in bold print in the upper right area of the top margin and the lower left area of the bottom margin. Editions are numbered consecutively; if you have more than one edition, the highest numbered sheet is the most recent. The National Geospatial-Intelligence Agency (NGA) now publishes most military maps, but the US Army Map Service may have produced older editions of maps. Still others may have been drawn, at least in part, by the US Army Corps of Engineers, the US Geological Survey, or other agencies, some nongovernmental.

- *Scale.* The scale is located both in the upper left margin after the series name, and in the center of the lower margin. The scale note gives the ratio of a map distance to the corresponding distance on the earth's surface. For example, the scale note 1:50,000 indicates that one unit of measure on the map equals 50,000 units of the same measure on the ground.

- *Index to Boundaries.* The index to boundaries diagram appears in the lower or right margin of all sheets. This diagram, which is a miniature of the map, shows the boundaries within the map area, such as county lines and state borders.

- *Adjoining Sheets Diagram.* Maps at all standard scales contain a diagram that shows the adjoining sheets. On maps at 1:100,000 and larger scales and at 1:1,000,000 scale, the diagram is called the "index to adjoining sheets." It consists of as many rectangles representing adjoining sheets as needed to surround the rectangle that represents the sheet you are looking at. The diagram usually contains nine rectangles, but the number may vary depending on the locations of the adjoining sheets. Sheet numbers identify all represented sheets. Sheets of an adjoining series at the same scale, whether published or planned, are represented by dashed lines. The series number of the adjoining series appears along the appropriate side of the division line between the series.

- *Elevation Guide.* This is normally found in the lower right margin. It is a miniature characterization of the terrain on the map. The terrain is represented by bands of elevation, spot elevations, and major drainage features. The elevation guide provides the map reader with a way to rapidly recognize major landforms.

- *Declination Diagram.* This is located in the lower margin of large-scale maps and indicates the angular relationships of true north, grid north, and magnetic north. On maps at 1:250,000 scale, this information appears in a note in the lower margin. In recent edition maps, a note indicates the conversion of azimuths from grid to magnetic and from magnetic to grid next to the declination diagram. (An azimuth is the horizontal angle of the observer's bearing in surveying, measured clockwise from a referent direction, usually north.)

- *Bar Scales.* You'll find these in the center of the lower margin. They are rulers that convert map distance to ground distance. Maps have three or more bar scales, each in a different unit of measure. You should exercise care when using the scales, especially in selecting the unit of measure that you need.

- *Contour Interval Note.* This note appears in the center of the lower margin normally below the bar scales. It states the vertical distance between adjacent contour lines of the map. When supplementary contours are used, the note indicates the interval. Recent edition maps give the contour interval in meters instead of feet.

- *Spheroid Note.* This note is located in the center of the lower margin. Spheroids (ellipsoids) have specific parameters that define the X Y Z axis of the earth. The spheroid is an integral part of the datum (point of reference).

- *Grid Note.* You'll see this note in the center of the lower margin. It gives information about the grid system used and the interval between grid lines. It also identifies the Universal Transverse Mercator (UTM) grid zone number.

- *Projection Note.* The projection system is the map's framework. Military maps use a conformal framework: Small areas of the surface of the earth retain their true shapes on the projection; measured angles closely approximate true values; and the scale factor is the same in all directions from a single point. The projection note appears in the center of the lower margin.

- *Vertical Datum.* Located in the center of the lower margin, the vertical datum or vertical-control datum is any level surface (for example, mean sea level) used to determine elevations. In the United States, Canada, and Europe, the vertical datum refers to mean sea level. In parts of Asia and Africa, however, the vertical-control datum may vary locally and is based on an assumed elevation that has no connection to sea level.

- *Horizontal Datum Note.* This note appears in the center of the lower margin. The horizontal datum or horizontal-control datum is a geodetic reference point of which five quantities are known: latitude, longitude, azimuth of a line from this point, and two constants, which are the parameters of reference ellipsoid. These are the basis for horizontal-control surveys. The horizontal-control datum may extend over a continent or be limited to a small area.
- *Control Note.* You can find this note in the center of the lower margin. It shows the special agencies that control the technical aspects of all the information on the map.
- *Preparation Note.* This note is located in the center of the lower margin. It tells which agency prepared the map.
- *Printing Note.* This note is also found in the center of the lower margin. It indicates which agency printed the map and the printing date. Do not use the printing note to determine when the map information was obtained.
- *Grid Reference Box.* You can usually find this box in the center of the lower margin. It contains instructions for composing a grid reference.
- *Unit Imprint and Symbol.* The unit imprint and symbol is on the left side of the lower margin. It identifies the agency that prepared and printed the map. Use this information to evaluate the map's reliability.
- *Legend.* The legend is located in the lower left margin. It illustrates the topographic symbols that depict the more prominent features on the map. These symbols differ from map to map. Always refer to the legend to avoid errors when reading a map **(FM 3-25.26).**

> Do not use the printing note to determine when the map information was obtained. Use the information date, which shows how recently the map was charted.

Topographic Symbols

> **topographic symbols**
>
> *symbols used to represent natural and man-made features on the earth's surface*

Maps use **topographic symbols** to represent the natural and man-made features of the earth's surface. For example, you might find crossed pickaxes representing a mine; square black boxes for buildings; or a black box with a cross on top for a church. Along with symbols, maps use color as a tool to help identify certain things. Below are a few common ones:

- *Black*—Indicates cultural (man-made) features such as buildings and roads, surveyed spot elevations, and all labels
- *Red-Brown*—The colors red and brown are combined to identify cultural features, all relief features, non-surveyed spot elevations, and elevation—such as contour lines on red-light readable maps
- *Blue*—Identifies water features such as lakes, swamps, rivers, and drainage
- *Green*—Identifies vegetation with military significance, such as woods, orchards, and vineyards
- *Brown*—Identifies all relief features and elevations, such as contours on older maps and cultivated land on red-light readable maps
- *Red*—Classifies cultural features, such as populated areas, main roads, and boundaries, on older maps
- *Other*—Occasionally other colors may be used to show special information. As a rule, you'll find these in the marginal information.

Military Symbols

In addition to the topographic symbols and colors, military personnel require some way to show the identity, size, location, or movement of Soldiers, military activities, and installations. The symbols that represent these military features are known as military symbols. Maps do not usually contain these symbols because the features and units that they represent constantly move or change. Military security is also a consideration. These symbols and colors differ on different maps. Always refer to the legend to avoid errors when reading a map.

> *You will learn more about operational symbols later in the course. You can read FM 1-02, Operational Terms and Graphics, for further study.*

Elevation and Relief

Contour Lines

Contour lines make a map three dimensional by showing height and depth. They are the most common way to show relief and elevation on a standard topographic map. A contour line represents an imaginary line on the ground, above or below sea level. All points on the contour line are at the same elevation. Contour lines represent an elevation that is the vertical distance above or below sea level. A standard topographic map features three types of contour lines:

> **contour lines**
>
> *the most common method of showing relief and elevation on a standard topographic map*

- *Index*—Starting at zero elevation or mean sea level, every fifth contour line is a heavier line. These are index contour lines. Normally, each index contour line is numbered at some point to show the elevation of that line.
- *Intermediate*—The contour lines falling between the index contour lines are called intermediate contour lines. These lines are finer and do not give elevations. There are normally four intermediate contour lines between index contour lines.
- *Supplementary*—These contour lines resemble dashes. They show changes in elevation of at least one-half the contour interval. These lines are normally found where there is very little change in elevation, such as on fairly level terrain.

Contour lines show elevation and depressions. Before you can determine the elevation of any point on the map, you must know the contour interval for the map you are using. The contour interval measurement in the marginal information gives the vertical distance between adjacent contour lines.

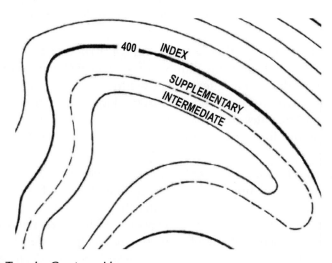

Figure 1.1 Terrain Contour Lines

Finding Elevation on a Map

1. Determine the contour interval and the unit of measure used, for example, feet, meters, or yards (Figure 1.2).

ELEVATION IN METERS
CONTOUR INTERVAL 20 METERS

Figure 1.2 Marginal Information Identifying Contour Units and Contour Intervals

2. Find the numbered index contour line nearest the point you are trying to determine the elevation of (Figure 1.3).

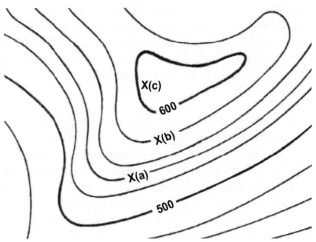

Figure 1.3 Map Terrain Contour Lines

3. Determine if you are going from lower elevation to higher, or vice versa. In Figure 1.3, Point A is between the index contour lines. The lower index contour line is numbered 500, which means any point on that line is at an elevation of 500 meters above mean sea level. The upper index contour line is numbered 600, or 600 meters. Going from the lower to the upper index contour line shows an increase in elevation.

4. To determine the exact elevation of Point A (Figure 1.3), start at the index contour line numbered 500 and count the number of intermediate contour lines to Point A. Locate Point A on the second intermediate contour line above the 500-meter index contour line. The contour interval is 20 meters (Figure 1.2), thus each one of the intermediate contour lines crossed to get to Point A adds 20 meters to the 500-meter index contour line. The elevation of Point A is 540 meters—the elevation has increased.

5. To determine the elevation of Point B (Figure 1.3), go to the nearest index contour line. In this case, it is the upper index contour line numbered 600. Locate Point B on the intermediate contour line immediately below the 600-meter index contour line. (Below means downhill or a lower elevation.) Therefore, Point B is located at an elevation of 580 meters. Remember, if you are increasing elevation, add the contour interval to the nearest index contour line. If you are decreasing elevation, subtract the contour interval from the nearest index contour line.

6. To determine the elevation to a hilltop Point C (Figure 1.3), add one-half the contour interval to the elevation of the last contour line. In this example, the last contour line before the hilltop is an index contour line numbered 600. Add one-half the contour interval, 10 meters, to the index contour line. The elevation of the hilltop would be 610 meters.

Finding Elevation with Greater Accuracy

There may be times when you need to determine the elevation of points to a greater degree of accuracy. To do this, you must determine how far between the two contour lines the point lies (Figure 1.4).

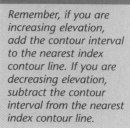

Remember, if you are increasing elevation, add the contour interval to the nearest index contour line. If you are decreasing elevation, subtract the contour interval from the nearest index contour line.

1. If the point is less than one-fourth the distance between contour lines, the elevation will be the same as the closest contour line. In Figure 1.4, the elevation of Point A will be 100 meters.

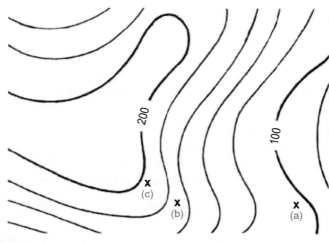

Figure 1.4 Map Terrain Contour Lines

2. To estimate the elevation of a point between one-fourth and three-fourths of the distance between contour lines, add one-half the contour interval to the last contour line. Point B is one-half the distance between contour lines. The contour line immediately below Point B is at an elevation of 160 meters. The contour interval is 20 meters; thus, one-half the contour interval is 10 meters. In this case, add 10 meters to the last contour line of 160 meters. The elevation of Point B would be about 170 meters.

3. A point located more than three-fourths of the distance between contour lines is considered to be at the same elevation as the next contour line. Point C is located three-fourths of the distance between contour lines. In Figure 1.4, Point C would be considered to be at an elevation of 200 meters.

Estimating the Depth of Depressions

To estimate the elevation to the bottom of a depression, subtract one-half the contour interval from the value of the lowest contour line before the depression. In Figure 1.5, the lowest contour line before the depression is 240 meters in elevation. Thus, the elevation at the edge of the depression is 240 meters. To determine the elevation at the bottom of the depression, subtract one-half the contour interval. The contour interval for this example is 20 meters. Subtract 10 meters from the lowest contour line immediately before the depression. The result is that the elevation at the bottom of the depression is 230 meters. The tick marks on the contour line forming a depression always point to lower elevations.

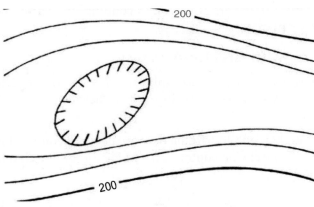

The tick marks on the contour line forming a depression always point to lower elevations.

Figure 1.5 Depressions

Bench Marks and Spot Elevations

In addition to the contour lines, bench marks and spot elevations are used to indicate points of known elevations on the map.

Bench Marks. The more accurate of the two, bench marks are symbolized by a black X, such as X BM 214. The 214 indicates that the center of the X is at an elevation of 214 units of measure (feet, meters, or yards) above mean sea level. To determine the units of measure, refer to the contour interval in the marginal information.

Spot Elevations. Spot elevations are shown by a brown X and are usually located at road junctions and on hilltops and other prominent terrain features. If the elevation is shown in black numerals, it has been checked for accuracy; if it is in brown, it has not been checked.

New maps are being printed using a dot instead of brown Xs.

Types of Slopes

The rate of rise or fall of a terrain feature is known as its slope. Depending on the military mission, Soldiers may need to determine not only the height of a hill, but the degree of the hill's slope as well. The slope of the ground or terrain feature affects the speed at which equipment or personnel can move. You can determine this slope from the map by studying the contour lines—the closer the contour lines, the steeper the slope; the farther apart the contour lines, the gentler the slope. Four types of slopes that concern the military are *gentle*, *steep*, *concave*, and *convex*.

- *Gentle.* Contour lines showing a uniform, gentle slope will be evenly spaced and wide apart (Figure 1.6). Considering relief only, a uniform, gentle slope allows the defender to use grazing fire. The attacking force has to climb a slight incline.
- *Steep.* Contour lines showing a uniform, steep slope on a map will be evenly spaced, but close together. Remember, the closer the contour lines, the steeper the slope (Figure 1.7). Considering relief only, a uniform, steep slope allows the defender to use grazing fire, and the attacking force has to negotiate a steep incline.
- *Concave.* Contour lines showing a concave slope on a map will be closely spaced at the top of the terrain feature and widely spaced at the bottom (Figure 1.8). Considering relief only, the defender at the top of the slope can observe the entire slope and the terrain at the bottom, but cannot use grazing fire. The attacker would have no cover from the defender's observation of fire, and the climb would become more difficult farther up the slope.

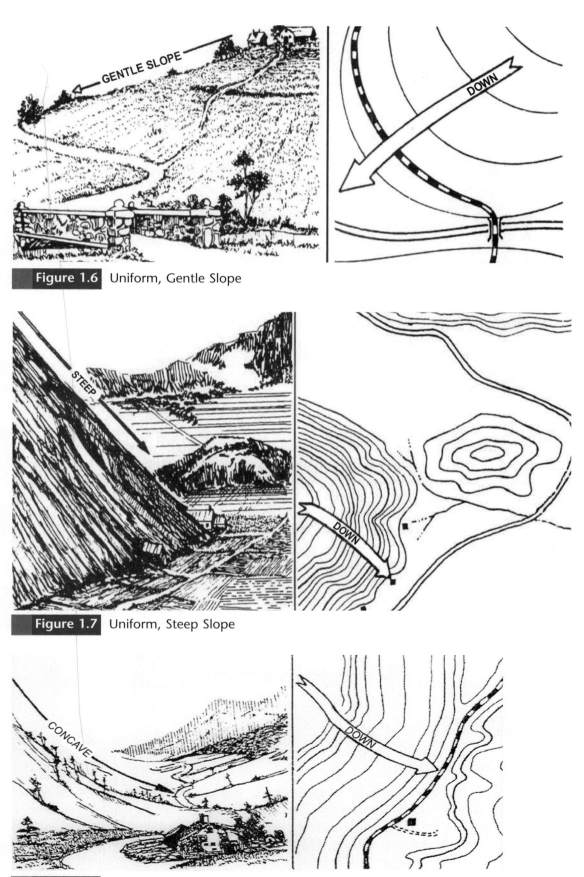

Figure 1.6 Uniform, Gentle Slope

Figure 1.7 Uniform, Steep Slope

Figure 1.8 Concave Slope

- *Convex.* Contour lines showing a convex slope on a map will be widely spaced at the top and closely spaced at the bottom (Figure 1.9). Considering relief only, the defender at the top of the convex slope can obtain a small distance of grazing fire, but cannot observe most of the slope or the terrain at the bottom. The attacker will have concealment on most of the slope and an easier climb near the top.

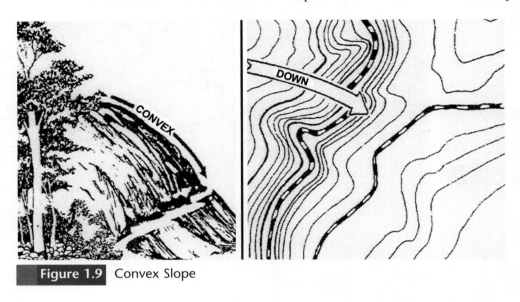

Figure 1.9 Convex Slope

Slope

As noted above, the slope of the ground and the limitations of the equipment affect the speed at which personnel and equipment can move up or down a hill. Because of this, you need a more exact way of describing a slope.

You can express slope in several ways, but all depend upon the comparison of vertical distance (VD) to horizontal distance (HD) (Figure 1.10). Before you can determine the percentage of a slope, you must know the VD of the slope. You determine the VD by subtracting the lowest point of the slope from the highest point. Use the contour lines to determine the highest and lowest point of the slope (Figure 1.11).

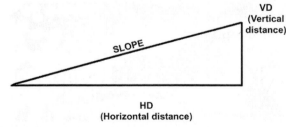

Figure 1.10 Slope Diagram

Percentage of Slope

To determine the percentage of the slope between Points A and B in Figure 1.11, determine the elevation of Point B (590 meters). Then determine the elevation of Point A (380 meters). Determine the vertical distance between the two points by subtracting the elevation of Point A from the elevation of Point B. The difference (210 meters) is the VD between Points A and B. Then measure the HD between the two points on the map in Figure 1.12. After

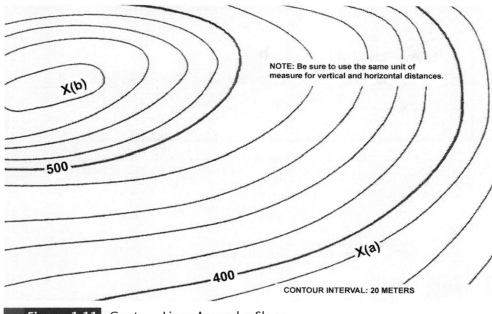

NOTE: Be sure to use the same unit of measure for vertical and horizontal distances.

CONTOUR INTERVAL: 20 METERS

Figure 1.11 Contour Lines Around a Slope

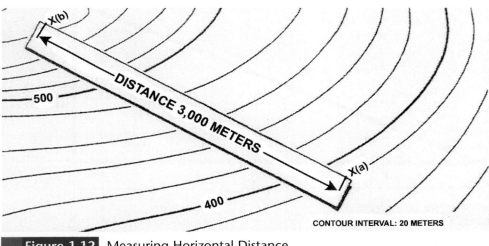

DISTANCE 3,000 METERS

CONTOUR INTERVAL: 20 METERS

Figure 1.12 Measuring Horizontal Distance

you have determined the horizontal distance, compute the percentage of the slope by using the formula shown in Figure 1.13.

You can also express the slope angle in degrees. To do this, determine the VD and HD of the slope. Multiply the VD by 57.3 and then divide the total by the HD (Figure 1.14). This method determines the approximate degree of slope and is reasonably accurate for slope angles less than 20 degrees.

You can also express the slope angle as a gradient. The relationship of horizontal and vertical distance is expressed as a fraction with a numerator of one (Figure 1.15).

Terrain Features

These three styles of contour lines allow you to see the five major, three minor, and two supplemental **terrain features** on a military map.

terrain features

characteristics of the land, such as hills, ridges, valleys, saddles, depressions, and so forth

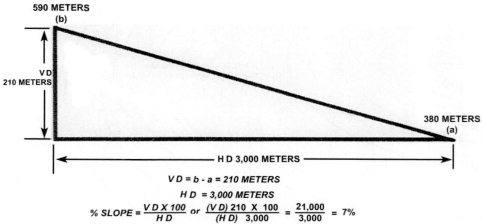

$$VD = b - a = 210 \text{ METERS}$$
$$HD = 3,000 \text{ METERS}$$
$$\% \text{ SLOPE} = \frac{VD \times 100}{HD} \text{ or } \frac{(VD)\ 210 \times 100}{(HD)\ 3,000} = \frac{21,000}{3,000} = 7\%$$

Multiply the vertical distance by 100. Divide the total by the horizontal distance. The result is the percentage of slope.

Figure 1.13 Percentage of Slope in Meters

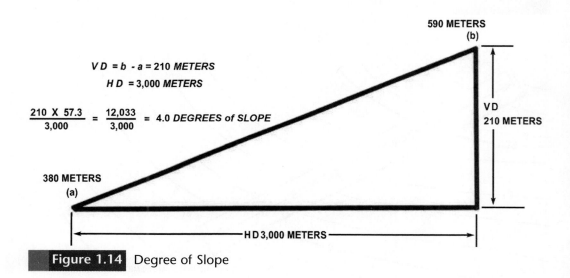

$$VD = b - a = 210 \text{ METERS}$$
$$HD = 3,000 \text{ METERS}$$

$$\frac{210 \times 57.3}{3,000} = \frac{12,033}{3,000} = 4.0 \text{ DEGREES of SLOPE}$$

Figure 1.14 Degree of Slope

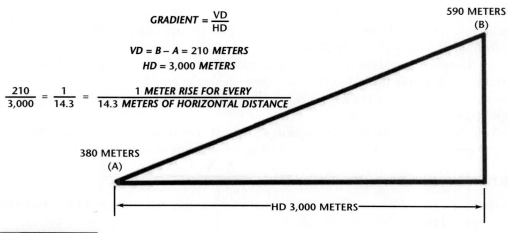

$$GRADIENT = \frac{VD}{HD}$$

$$VD = B - A = 210 \text{ METERS}$$
$$HD = 3,000 \text{ METERS}$$

$$\frac{210}{3,000} = \frac{1}{14.3} = \frac{1 \text{ METER RISE FOR EVERY}}{14.3 \text{ METERS OF HORIZONTAL DISTANCE}}$$

Figure 1.15 Gradient

Major Terrain Features

- *Hill*—A hill is an area of high ground. From a hilltop, the ground slopes down in all directions. A map shows a hill by contour lines forming concentric circles. The inside of the smallest closed circle is the hilltop (Figure 1.16).

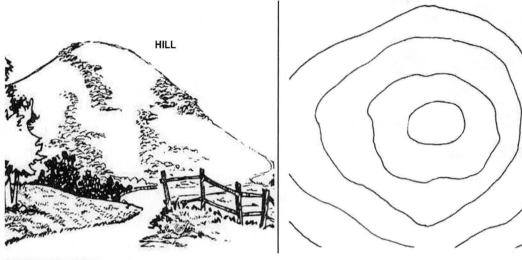

HILL

Figure 1.16 Major Terrain Feature—Hill

- *Saddle*—A saddle is a dip or low point between two areas of higher ground. A saddle is not necessarily the lower ground between two hilltops—it may be simply a dip or break along a level ridge crest. If you are in a saddle, you see high ground in two opposite directions and lower ground in the other two directions. Contour lines for a saddle normally resemble an hourglass.

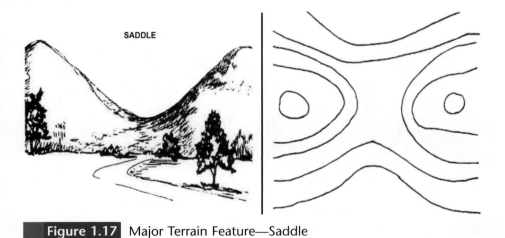

SADDLE

Figure 1.17 Major Terrain Feature—Saddle

- *Valley*—A valley is a stretched-out groove in the land, usually formed by streams or rivers. A valley begins with high ground on three sides, and usually has a course of running water through it. If you are standing in a valley, three directions offer high ground, while the fourth direction offers low ground. Depending on the valley size and where you are standing, you may not see high ground in the third direction,

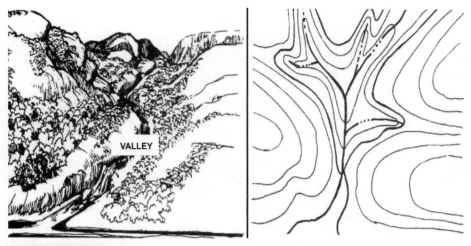

Figure 1.18 Major Terrain Feature—Valley

but water flows from higher to lower ground. Contour lines forming a valley are either U-shaped or V-shaped. To determine the direction the water is flowing, look at the contour lines. The closed end of the contour line (U or V) always points upstream or toward high ground (Figure 1.18).

- *Ridge*—A ridge is a sloping line of high ground. If you are standing on the centerline of a ridge, you will normally have low ground in three directions and high ground in one direction with varying degrees of slope. If you cross a ridge at right angles, you will climb steeply to the crest and then descend steeply to the base. When you move along the path of the ridge, depending on the location, you may find either an almost unnoticeable slope or a very obvious incline. Contour lines forming a ridge tend to be U-shaped or V-shaped. The closed end of the contour line points away from high ground (Figure 1.19).

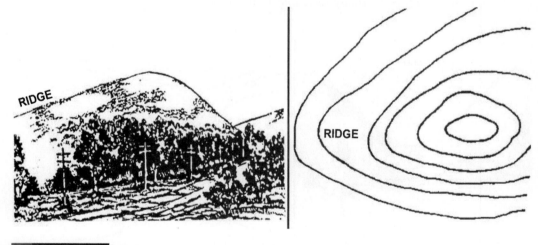

Figure 1.19 Major Terrain Feature—Ridge

- *Depression*—A depression is a low point in the ground or a sinkhole. It could be an area of low ground surrounded by higher ground in all directions, or simply a hole in the ground. A map usually shows only depressions that are equal to or greater than the contour interval. Depressions are represented by closed contour lines that have tick marks pointing toward the low ground (Figure 1.20).

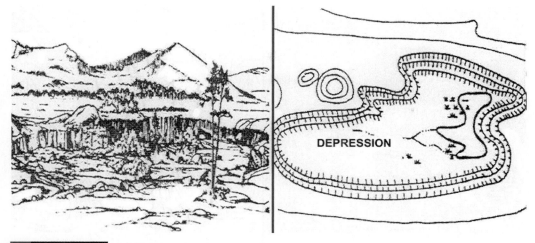

Figure 1.20 Major Terrain Feature—Depression

Minor Terrain Features

- *Draw*—A draw is a less developed stream course than a valley. A draw offers no level ground and, therefore little or no maneuvering room within its confines. If you are standing in a draw, the ground slopes upward in three directions and downward in the other direction. The contour lines depicting a draw are U-shaped or V-shaped, pointing toward high ground (Figure 1.21).

Figure 1.21 Minor Terrain Feature—Draw

- *Spur*—A spur is a short, continuous sloping line of higher ground, normally jutting out from the side of a ridge. A spur is often formed by two rough parallel streams, which cut draws down the side of a ridge. The ground slopes down in three directions and up in one direction. Contour lines on a map depict a spur with the U or V pointing away from high ground (Figure 1.22).
- *Cliff*—A cliff is a vertical or near-vertical feature. It is an abrupt change of the land's elevation. When a slope is so steep that the contour lines converge into one "carrying" contour of contours, this last contour line has tick marks pointing toward low ground (Figure 1.23). Contour lines very close together or touching each other also indicate cliffs (Figure 1.24).

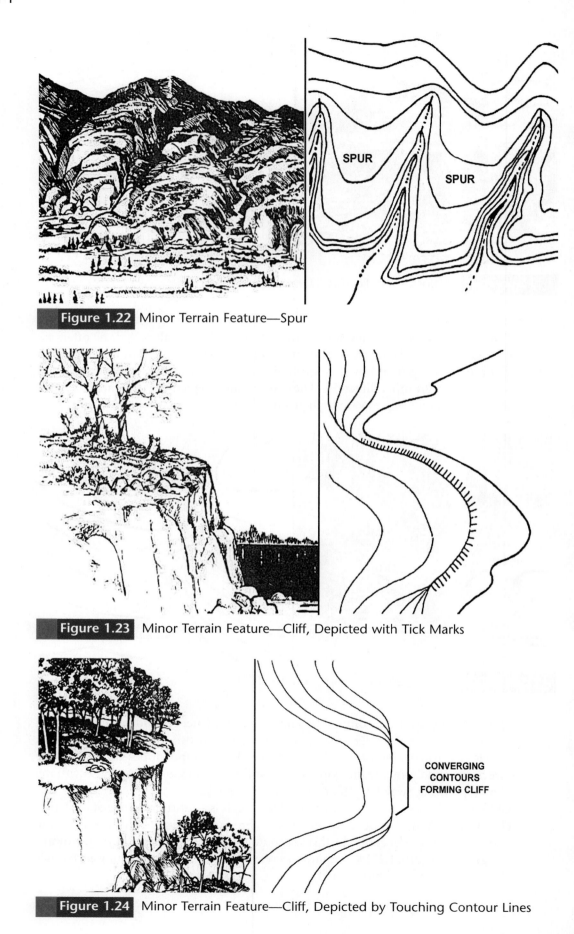

Figure 1.22 Minor Terrain Feature—Spur

Figure 1.23 Minor Terrain Feature—Cliff, Depicted with Tick Marks

Figure 1.24 Minor Terrain Feature—Cliff, Depicted by Touching Contour Lines

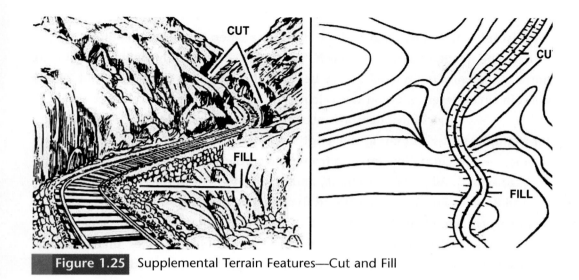

Figure 1.25 Supplemental Terrain Features—Cut and Fill

Supplemental Terrain Features

- *Cut*—A cut is a man-made feature that results from cutting through raised ground, usually to form a level bed for a road or railroad track. Cuts are shown on a map when they are at least 10 feet high. They are drawn with a contour line along the cut line. This contour line extends the length of the cut and has tick marks from the cut line to the roadbed, if the map scale permits this level of detail (Figure 1.25).
- *Fill*—A fill is a man-made feature that results from filling a low area, usually to form a level bed for a road or railroad track. Fills are shown on a map when they are at least 10 feet high. They are drawn with a contour line along the fill line. This contour line extends the length of the filled area and has tick marks that point toward lower ground. If the map scale permits, the length of the fill's tick marks are drawn to scale and extend from the base line of the fill symbol (Figure 1.25) **(FM 3-25.26)**.

Map Coordinate Systems

When it was first created, the Global Positioning Systems (GPS) was used mainly by rescuers to locate ships missing at sea. GPS units were large and cumbersome. Today, that same technology is now in our homes, cars, and even cell phones. The military cannot operate effectively without it, from smart bombs to the individual Soldier in the field. A Soldier with a GPS can navigate to within three meters, if not closer, of a specific location. This technology has revolutionized navigation. But what do you do if your GPS unit doesn't work? The batteries could be dead; the face plate might break; or sand and dirt might get into the works. That's why you need to know how to read grid coordinates and convey them to others.

What do you do if the GPS unit doesn't work?

Geographic Coordinates

One of the oldest methods of determining location is the geographic coordinate system. By drawing a set of east–west rings around the globe parallel to the equator, and a set of north–south rings crossing the equator at right angles and converging at the poles, a network of reference lines is formed from which you can locate any point on the earth's surface.

If Christopher Columbus had had the right data when he was calculating the distance he needed to travel to reach "the Indies" he probably would have stayed home. Academics in Columbus's day believed the earth was a sphere about 24,000 miles in circumference. Columbus calculated the earth's circumference at about 18,000 miles. Others have demonstrated that Columbus made additional mistakes; for example, underestimating the length of a degree (45 versus 57.3 miles). His reliance on inaccurate information from Marco Polo's **Description of the World** and Cardinal D. Ailly's **Imago Mundi**, and on a statement in the Apocryphal Second Book of Esdras—which stated that the Earth consisted of six parts land and one part sea, instead of the real 3:1 ratio—led to numerous miscalculations. To make matters worse, he made all his calculations in Italian miles, unaware they were shorter than the Arabic miles many contemporary maps used (DeMar).

Latitude

The distance of a point north or south from the equator is its *latitude*. The rings around the earth parallel to the equator are called parallels of latitude, or simply *parallels*. Lines of latitude (parallels) run east–west, but you measure north–south distances between them (Figure 1.26).

Longitude

A second set of rings around the globe at right angles to lines of latitude and passing through the poles is known as meridians of *longitude*, or simply *meridians*. One meridian is designated as the prime meridian. The prime meridian runs through Greenwich, England and is known as the Greenwich Meridian. The distance east or west from the prime meridian to a point is its longitude. Lines of longitude (meridians) run north–south but you measure east–west distances between them (Figure 1.27).

Angular Measure

Latitude and longitude are represented by units of angular measure expressed in degrees, minutes, and seconds (Figure 1.28). A circle is divided into 360 degrees; each degree into 60 minutes; and each minute into 60 seconds. The symbol for degree is °, for minute ', and for second ". Starting with 0° at the equator, the parallels of latitude are numbered to 90° north and south. The extremities are the North Pole at 90° north latitude and the South Pole at 90° south latitude. Latitude can have the same numerical value north or south of the equator, so you must always give the direction N or S. Starting with 0° at the prime meridian, longitude is measured both east and west around the world. Lines east of the prime meridian are numbered to 180° and identified as east longitude; lines west of the prime meridian are numbered to 180° and identified as west longitude. You must always give the direction E or W. You may refer to the line directly opposite the prime meridian, 180°, as either east or west longitude.

Coordinate Pair

You can express the location of any point on earth by a coordinate pair in latitude and longitude. The point is located at the intersection of the corresponding parallel and meridian. To navigate with some maps, you must understand coordinate locations expressed in latitude and longitude.

Geographic coordinates appear on all standard military maps. On some, they may be the only method of locating and referencing a specific point. The four lines that enclose

latitude

the distance of a point north or south of the equator

longitude

the distance of a point east or west of the Prime Meridian, which runs through Greenwich, England

Latitude and longitude are represented by units of angular measure expressed in degrees, minutes, and seconds. A circle is divided into 360 degrees; each degree into 60 minutes; and each minute into 60 seconds.

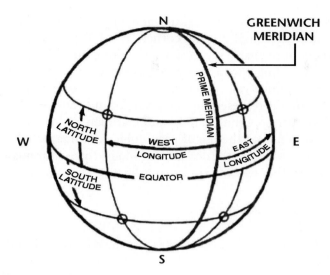

Figure 1.26 Lines of Latitude

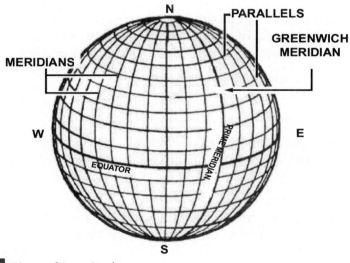

Figure 1.27 Lines of Longitude

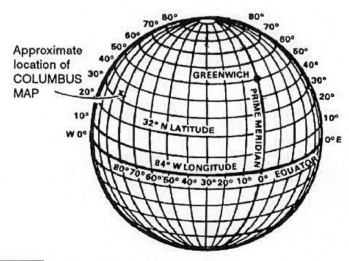

Figure 1.28 Angular Measures on the Earth

the body of the map (neat lines) are latitude and longitude lines. Their values are given in degrees and minutes at each of the four corners. In addition to the latitude and longitude at the four corners, at regularly spaced intervals along the sides of the map, you will see small tick marks extending into the body of the map. Each of these tick marks is identified by its latitude or longitude value. To locate any position on the map using a coordinate pair, find the tick marks representing the given latitude and longitude, then follow the intersection of the corresponding parallel and meridian.

It can be hard to master the use of geographic coordinates to find positions, and at times this may not provide you the detail needed to perform your mission. Because of this, military grids are another way to express coordinates—one that is more exact and easier to use.

Military Grids

The problem with geographic coordinates is that most lines of latitude and longitude are curved lines. The quadrangles formed by the intersection of these curved parallels and meridians have different sizes and shapes, which complicates locating the points and measuring the directions. The military grid system overcomes these shortfalls by superimposing a rectangular grid over the map. This grid (a series of straight lines intersecting at right angles) furnishes the map reader with a system of squares similar to the block system of most city streets. The dimensions and orientation of different types of grids vary, but three properties are common to all military grid systems:

1. They use true rectangles.
2. They are superimposed on the geographic projection.
3. They permit linear and angular measurements.

There are three common forms of grid reference systems: the Universal Transverse Mercator, the Universal Polar Stereographic Grid, and the United States Army Military Grid Reference System.

Universal Transverse Mercator Grid
The UTM grid was designed to cover the world between latitude 84°N and latitude 80°S. As its name implies, it is imposed on the transverse Mercator projection of the world. UTM subdivides this area into 60 *grid zones* 6 degrees wide. Each grid zone has its own origin at the intersection of its central meridian and the equator. The grid is identical in all 60 grid zones. Base values (in meters) are assigned to the central meridian and the equator, and the grid lines are drawn at regular intervals parallel to these two base lines. Since each grid line has a value that indicates its distance from the origin, the problem of locating any point becomes progressively easier. You always measure distances RIGHT and UP (east and north as you face the map). The assigned values are called "false easting" and "false northing."

Universal Polar Stereographic Grid
The UPS grid is used to represent the polar regions. A separate grid zone is applied to each of the two polar areas:

All flat maps are two-dimensional projections of a three-dimensional sphere. All projection processes introduce some level of distortion to the final representation, making it difficult to take accurate measurements. Different methods of projection distort different areas of the map to facilitate accurate measurement within confined areas of interest. In the UTM system, distortion becomes more pronounced closer to the poles.

Critical Thinking

Describe how the use of traditional features on military maps serves as an important tool in combat communications.

- *North Polar Area.* The North Pole serves as origin of the UPS grid applied to the north polar area. The "north–south" base line is the line formed by the 0° and 180° meridians; the "east–west" base line is formed by the two 90° meridians.
- *South Polar Area.* The South Pole is the origin of the UPS grid in the south polar area. The base lines are similar to those of the north polar area.

United States Army Military Grid Reference System

This grid reference system is meant for use with both the UTM and UPS grids. The coordinate value of points in these grids could contain as many as 15 digits if numerals alone were used. So the US Army military grid reference system shortens written coordinates by substituting single letters for several numbers. Using the UTM and the UPS grids, a point's location (identified by numbers alone) can be in many different places on the earth's surface. When you use the US Army military grid reference system, that cannot happen.

Grid Zone Designation. The US Army military grid reference system applies an alphanumeric map-labeling scheme to UTM and UPS grid zones to generate unique coordinate positions, eliminating any chance of ambiguity. The US Army military grid reference system begins by subdividing the UTM and UPS grid zones into smaller areas. It then assigns a unique alphanumeric *grid zone designation* to each (Figure 1.29).

- *Grid Zone Designation for UTM Grid.* The first major breakdown is the division of each zone into areas 6° wide by 8° high and 6° wide by 12° high. Remember, for the transverse Mercator projection, the earth's surface between 80°S and 84°N is divided into 60 N–S zones, each 6° wide. These zones are numbered from west to east, 1 through 60, starting at the 180° meridian. This surface is divided into 20 east–west rows: 19 are 8° high, and one row at the extreme north is 12° high. These rows are then lettered, from south to north, C through X (I and O were omitted). You identify any 6° by 8° zone or 6° by 12° zone by giving the number and letter of the grid zone and row in which it lies. You read these RIGHT and UP, so the number is always written before the letter. This combination of zone number and row letter constitutes the grid zone designation.
- *Grid Zone Designation for UPS Grid.* The remaining letters of the alphabet, A, B, Y, and Z, are used for the UPS grids. Each polar area is divided into two zones separated by the 0-180° meridian. In the south polar area, the letter A designates the grid zone for the area west of the 0–180° meridian, while B designates the area to the east. In the north polar area, Y designates the grid zone designation for the western area and Z the eastern area.

100,000-Meter Grid Square. Each grid zone designation area is further subdivided into 100,000-meter grid squares. A two-letter alphabetical identifier that is unique in the grid zone labels each 100,000-meter square. The first letter is the column designation; the second letter is the row designation (Figure 1.30).

Grid Coordinates. We have now divided the earth's surface into 6° by 8° quadrangles, and covered these with 100,000-meter squares. The military grid reference for a point consists of the numbers and letters that indicate in which areas the point lies, plus the coordinates that locate the point to the desired position within the 100,000-meter square. The next step is to tie in the coordinates of the point with the larger areas. To do this, you must understand the following:

- *Grid Lines.* The regularly spaced lines that make the UTM and the UPS grid on any large-scale maps are divisions of the 100,000-meter square. The lines are spaced at 10,000- or 1,000-meter intervals (Figure 1.31). Each of these lines is labeled at

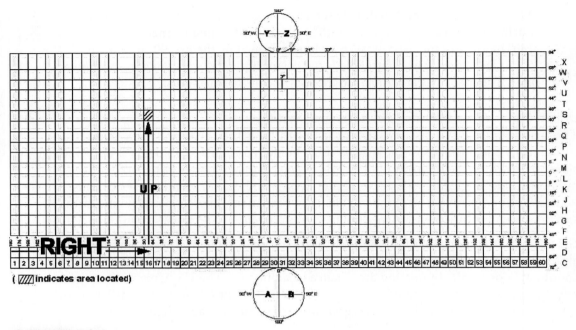

Figure 1.29 Grid Zone Designation for UTM and UPS Coordinate Grids

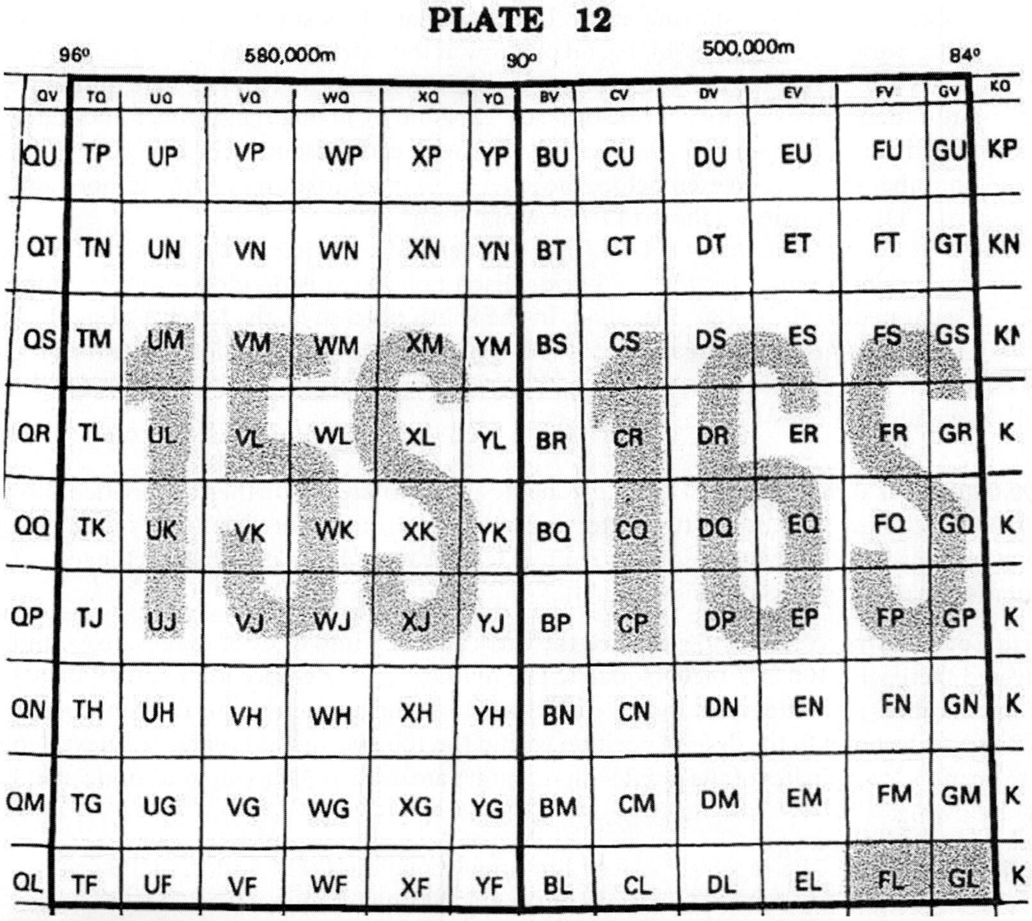

PLATE 12

	96°		580,000m			90°			500,000m			84°	
QV	TQ	UQ	VQ	WQ	XQ	YQ	BV	CV	DV	EV	FV	GV	KQ
QU	TP	UP	VP	WP	XP	YP	BU	CU	DU	EU	FU	GU	KP
QT	TN	UN	VN	WN	XN	YN	BT	CT	DT	ET	FT	GT	KN
QS	TM	UM	VM	WM	XM	YM	BS	CS	DS	ES	FS	GS	KM
QR	TL	UL	VL	WL	XL	YL	BR	CR	DR	ER	FR	GR	K
QQ	TK	UK	VK	WK	XK	YK	BQ	CQ	DQ	EQ	FQ	GQ	K
QP	TJ	UJ	VJ	WJ	XJ	YJ	BP	CP	DP	EP	FP	GP	K
QN	TH	UH	VH	WH	XH	YH	BN	CN	DN	EN	FN	GN	K
QM	TG	UG	VG	WG	XG	YG	BM	CM	DM	EM	FM	GM	K
QL	TF	UF	VF	WF	XF	YF	BL	CL	DL	EL	FL	GL	K

Figure 1.30 Grid Zone Designation Subdivided Into 100,000-Meter Grid Squares

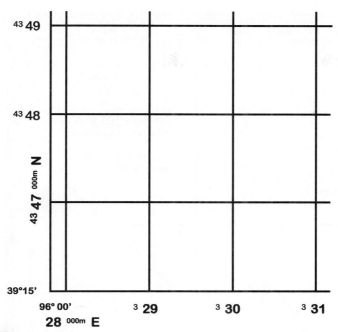

Figure 1.31 Grid Lines

both ends of the map with its false easting or false northing value, showing its relation to the origin of the zone. Two digits of the values are printed in large type. These same two digits appear at intervals along the grid lines on the face of the map. These are the *principal digits*, and represent the 10,000 and 1,000 digits of the grid value. They are very important to the map reader because they are the numbers you will use most often for referencing points. The smaller digits complete the UTM grid designation.

- *Grid Squares.* The north–south and east–west grid lines intersect at 90°, forming grid squares. On large-scale maps, one of these grid squares is normally 1,000 meters (1 kilometer).

Grid Coordinate Scales. Your primary tool for plotting grid coordinates is the grid coordinate scale. The grid coordinate scale divides the grid square more accurately than you can do by estimating, and the results are more consistent. When used correctly, it presents fewer chances for error.

- You can use the 1:25,000/1:250,000 scale (lower right in Figure 1.32) in two different scale maps, 1:25,000 or 1:250,000. The 1:25,000 scale subdivides the 1,000-meter grid block into 10 major subdivisions, each equal to 100 meters. Each 100-meter block has five graduations, each equal to 20 meters. You can accurately read points falling between the two graduations by estimating. These values are the fourth and eighth digits of the coordinates. Likewise, the 1:250,000 scale is subdivided into 10 major subdivisions of 1,000 meters each. Each 1,000-meter block has five graduations of 200 meters each. You can approximately read points falling between two graduations by estimating.
- The 1:50,000 scale (upper left in Figure 1.32) subdivides the 1,000-meter block into 10 major subdivisions, each equal to 100 meters. Each 100-meter block is then divided in half. You must estimate points falling between the graduations to the nearest 10 meters for the fourth and eighth digits of the coordinates.
- The 1:100,000 scale (lower left in Figure 1.32) subdivides the 1,000-meter grid block into five major subdivisions of 200 meters each. Each 200-meter block is then divided in half at 100-meter intervals.

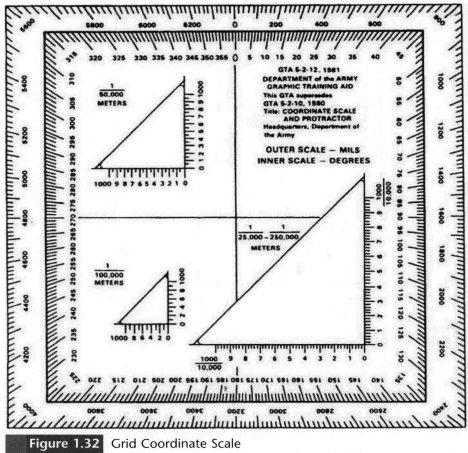

Figure 1.32 Grid Coordinate Scale

Locating a Point Using Grid Coordinates

Based on the military principle for reading maps (RIGHT and UP), you can determine locations on the map using grid coordinates. The number of digits represents the degree of precision to which a point has been located and measured on a map. The more digits you use, the more precise the measurement.

Locating a Point Without a Coordinate Scale. You can determine grids without a coordinate scale by referring to the north–south grid lines numbered at the bottom margin of any map. Then read RIGHT to the north–south grid line before the desired point (this first set of two digits is the RIGHT reading). Then by referring to the east–west grid lines numbered at either side of the map, move UP to the east–west grid line before the desired point (these two digits are the UP reading). Locate the point to the nearest 100 meters by estimation. Mentally divide the grid square in tenths, then estimate the distance from the grid line to the point in the same order (RIGHT and UP). Give the complete coordinate RIGHT, then the complete coordinate UP. Point X is about two-tenths or 200 meters to the RIGHT of 14 and is about seven-tenths or 700 meters UP from 84. You would read the coordinates to the nearest 100 meters, or "142847" (see Figure 1.33).

Locating a Point With a Coordinate Scale (1:25,000). To use the coordinate scale for determining grid coordinates, ensure that the appropriate scale appears on the corresponding map and that the scale is right side up. To ensure the scale is correctly aligned, place it with the zero–zero point at the lower left corner of the grid square. Keeping the horizontal line of the scale directly on top of the east–west grid line, slide it to the right until the vertical line of the scale touches the point for the coordinates you want (Figure 1.34). When you read coordinates, look at the two sides of the coordinate scale to ensure

> You must remember only one rule when reading or reporting grid coordinates: Always read to the RIGHT and then UP.

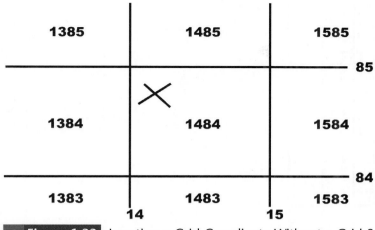

Figure 1.33 Locating a Grid Coordinate Without a Grid Scale

that the horizontal line of the scale is aligned with the east–west grid line, and the vertical line of the scale is parallel with the north–south grid line. Use the scale when you need precision of more than 100 meters. To locate the point to the nearest 10 meters, measure the hundredths of a grid square RIGHT and UP from the grid lines to the point. Point X is about 17 hundredths or 170 meters RIGHT and 84 hundredths or 840 meters UP. The coordinates to the nearest 10 meters are 14178484.

1:50,000 Coordinating Scale. The 1:50,000 coordinate scale has two sides: vertical and horizontal. These sides are each 1,000 meters in length. The point at which the sides meet is the zero-zero point. A long tick mark and a number divide each side into 10 equal 100-meter segments. A short tick mark divides each 100-meter segment into 50-meter segments (Figure 1.36). Mentally divide each 50-meter segment into tenths. For example, a point that lies after a whole number but before a short tick mark is identified as 10, 20, 30, or 40 meters. Any point that lies after the short tick mark but before the whole number is identified as 60, 70, 80, or 90 meters.

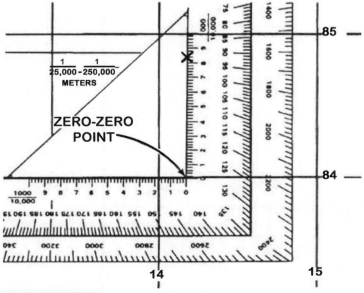

Figure 1.34 Locating a Grid Coordinate Using a Grid Scale (1:25,000)

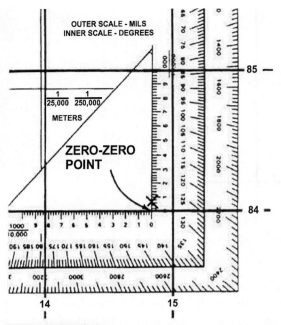

Figure 1.35 Locating a Grid Coordinate Using a Grid Scale Near the Zero-Zero Point

Recording and Reporting Grid Coordinates. Coordinates are written as one continuous number without spaces, parentheses, dashes, or decimal points. They must always contain an even number of digits. Therefore, the person who will use the written coordinates must know where to make the split between the RIGHT and UP readings. It is a military requirement that the 100,000-meter square identification letters be included in any point designation. Normally, you determine grid coordinates to the nearest 100 meters (six digits) for reporting locations. With practice, you can do this without using plotting scales. You determine the location of targets and other point locations for fire support to the nearest 10 meters (eight digits).

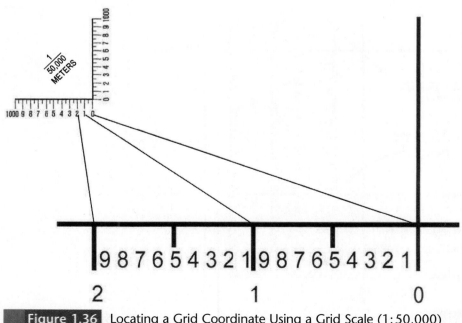

Figure 1.36 Locating a Grid Coordinate Using a Grid Scale (1:50,000)

Locating a Point Using the US Army Military Grid Reference System

You must remember only one rule when reading or reporting grid coordinates: Always read to the RIGHT and then UP. The first half of the reported set of coordinate digits represents the left-to-right (easting) grid label. The second half represents the label as read from the bottom to top (northing). The grid coordinates may represent the location to the nearest 10-, 100-, or 1,000-meter increment.

- *Grid Zone.* (NUMBER/NUMBER) The number 16 locates a point within Zone 16, which is an area 6° wide and extends between 80°S latitude and 84°N latitude (Figure 1.29)
- *Grid Zone Designation.* (NUMBER/LETTER) The number and letter combination, 16S, further locates a point within grid zone 16S, which is a quadrangle 6° wide by 8° high. Grid zone 16 contains 19 of these quads. Quad X, located between 72°N and 84°N latitude, is 12° high.
- *100,000-Meter Square Identification.* (LETTER/LETTER) The addition of two more letters locates a point within the 100,000-meter grid square. Thus 16SGL (Figure 1.30) locates the point within the 100,000-meter square GL in grid zone 16S.
- *10,000-Meter Square.* (NUMBER/NUMBER) The breakdown of the US Army military grid reference system continues as each side of the 100,000-meter square is divided into 10 equal parts. This division produces lines that are 10,000 meters apart. Thus the coordinates 16SGL08 would locate the point shown in Figure 1.37. The 10,000-meter grid lines appear as index (heavier) grid lines on maps at 1:100,000 and larger.

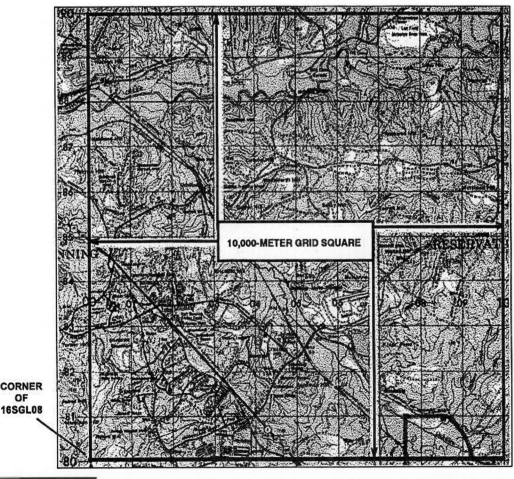

Figure 1.37 Coordinate (16SGL08) Localization to 10,000 Meter Square

- *1,000-Meter Square.* To obtain 1,000-meter squares, each side of the 10,000-meter square is divided into 10 equal parts. This division appears on large-scale maps as the actual grid lines; they are 1,000 meters apart. On the Columbus, Ga., map, using coordinates 16SGL0182, the easting 01 and the northing 82 give the location of the southwest corner of grid square 0182 or to the nearest 1,000 meters of a point on the map (Figure 1.38).
- *100-Meter Identification.* To locate to the nearest 100 meters, you can use the grid coordinate scale to divide the 1,000-meter grid squares into 10 equal parts (Figure 1.39).
- *10-Meter Identification.* The grid coordinate scale has divisions every 50 meters on the 1:50,000 scale and every 20 meters on the 1:25,000 scale. You can use these to estimate to the nearest 10 meters and give the location of a point on the earth's surface to the nearest 10 meters.
- *Precision.* The precision of a point's location is shown by the number of digits in the coordinates; the more digits, the more precise the location (Figure 1.40). **Example:** 16SGL01948253 (gas tank) (Figure 1.39, insert).

Other Grid Systems

Not everyone uses the military grid reference system. You and your Soldiers must be prepared to interpret and use other grid systems, depending on the area of operations or the personnel with whom you are operating.

British Grids

In a few areas of the world, you will find British grids on military maps. The British grid systems are being phased out, however. Eventually all military mapping will convert to the UTM grid.

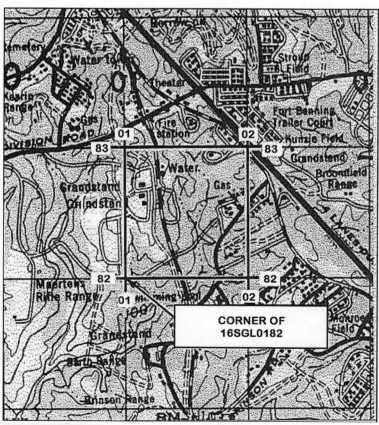

Figure 1.38 Coordinate (16SGL0182) Localization to 1,000 Meter Square

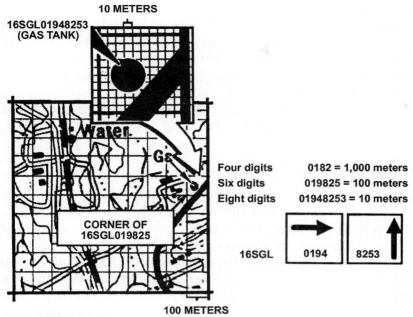

Figure 1.39 Coordinate Localization Within 10 Meters Using Grid Coordinate Scale

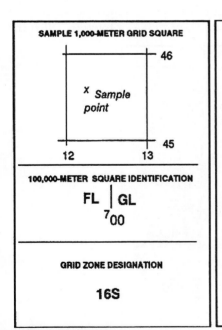

SAMPLE 1,000-METER GRID SQUARE

x Sample point

100,000-METER SQUARE IDENTIFICATION

FL | GL
7 00

GRID ZONE DESIGNATION

16S

100-METER REFERENCE

1. Read large numbers labeling the VERTICAL grid line left of point and estimate tenths (100-meters) from grid line to point.

2. Read large numbers labeling the HORIZONTAL grid line below point and estimate (100-meters) from grid line.

Example: 123456

WHEN REPORTING ACROSS A 100,000-METER LINE, PREFIX THE 100,000-METER SQUARE IDENTIFICATION, IN WHICH THE POINT LIES.

Example: FL123456

WHEN REPORTING OUTSIDE THE GRID ZONE DESIGNATION AREA, PREFIX THE GRID ZONE DESIGNATION.

Example: 16SFL123456

Figure 1.40 Coordinate Precision

Critical Thinking

Explain how the Military Grid Reference System relates to GPS technology.

World Geographic Reference System (GEOREF)

This worldwide position reference system is used primarily by the US Air Force. You can use it with any map or chart that shows latitude and longitude. Instructions for using GEOREF data are printed in blue and are found in the margin of aeronautical charts (Figure 1.41). This system is based upon a division of the earth's surface into quadrangles of latitude and longitude; each has a systematic identification code. The system expresses latitude and longitude in a form suitable for rapid reporting and plotting. Figure 1.41 illustrates a sample grid reference box using GEOREF.

Measuring Distances on a Map

From marginal information to symbols, from legend to grid coordinates, and from contour lines to colors, you can see how important it is to understand the "instructions" when using a map. But you must know another bit of important information if you are going to be proficient at navigation—how to measure distances on a map.

A map is a scaled representation of part of the earth's surface. The scale of the map permits you to convert distance on the map to distance on the ground or vice versa. You must be able to determine distance on a map, as well as on the earth's surface, to plan and execute military missions.

Representative Fraction

The numerical scale of a map indicates the relationship between distance measured on a map and the distance on the ground. This scale is usually written as a fraction called the

> **Example**
>
> *The map scale is 1:50,000*
>
> *RF = 1/50,000*
>
> *The map distance from point A to point B is 5 units*
>
> *5 × 50,000 = 250,000 units of ground distance*

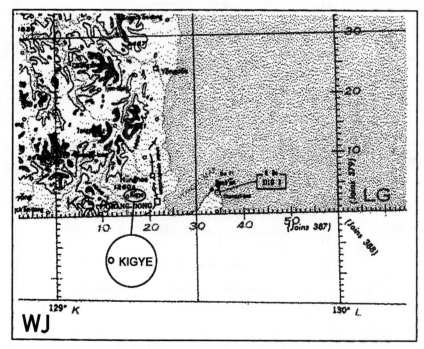

TO REFERENCE BY GEOREF (SHOWN IN BLUE) TO MINUTES
Select nearest intersection south and west of point.
Sample Point: KIGYE
1. WJ identifies basic 15° quadrangle.
2. KG identifies 1° quadrangle.
3. 15 identifies Georef minute of longitude.
4. 03 identifies Georef minute of latitude.
5. Sample reference: WJKG 1503.

Figure 1.41 World Geographic Reference System (GEOREF)

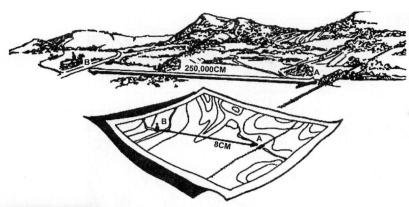

Figure 1.42 Converting Map Distance to Ground Distance

representative fraction (RF). The RF is always written with the map distance as the numeral 1 and is independent of any unit of measure. (It could be yards, meters, inches, and so forth.) An RF of 1/50,000 or 1:50,000 means that one unit of measure on the map is equal to 50,000 units of the same measure on the ground.

You determine the ground distance between two points by measuring between the same two points on the map and then multiplying the map measurement by the denominator of the RF or scale (Figure 1.42).

Since the distance on most maps is marked in meters and the RF in most cases is expressed in meters, let's briefly review the **metric system**. In the metric system, the standard unit of measurement is the meter.

- 1 meter contains 100 centimeters (cm)
- 100 meters is a regular football field plus 10 meters
- 1,000 meters is 1 kilometer (km)
- 10 kilometers is 10,000 meters.

metric system

a decimal system of measurement designed in France in 1791 and used in most of the world—the basic unit is a meter

Graphic (Bar) Scales

A graphic scale is a ruler printed on the map and is used to convert distances on the map to actual ground distances. The graphic scale is divided into two parts. To the right of the zero, the scale is marked in full units of measure; this is the *primary scale*. To the left of the zero, the scale is divided into tenths; this is called the *extension scale*. Most maps have three or more graphic scales, each using a different unit of measure (Figure 1.43). When you use the graphic scale, be sure to use the correct scale for the unit of measure you want.

To determine straight-line distance between two points on a map, lay a straight-edged piece of paper on the map so that the edge of the paper touches both points and extends past them. Make a tick mark on the edge of the paper at each point (Figure 1.44).

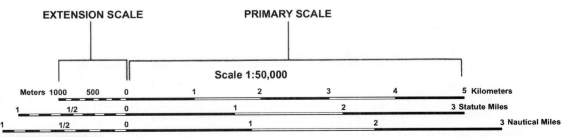

Figure 1.43 Graphic (Bar) Scale

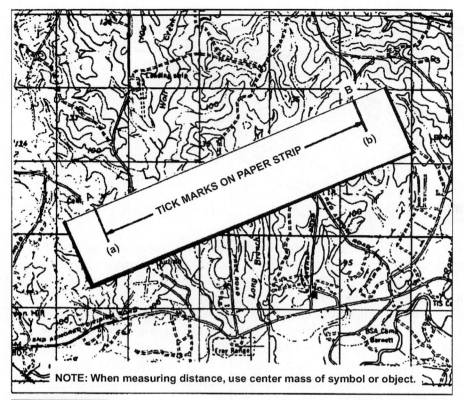

NOTE: When measuring distance, use center mass of symbol or object.

Figure 1.44 Measuring Map Distances Using the Graphic (Bar) Scale

To convert the map distance to ground distance, move the paper down to the graphic bar scale, and align the right tick mark with a printed number in the primary scale so that the left tick mark is in the extension scale (Figure 1.45).

To measure distance along a road, stream, or other curved line, use the straight edge of a piece of paper. In order to avoid confusion over the point to measure from and the ending point, get the eight-digit coordinate for both points. Place a tick mark on the paper and map at the beginning point from which you will measure the curved line. Align the edge of the paper along a straight portion and make a tick mark on both map and paper when the edge of the paper leaves the straight portion of the line being measured (Figure 1.46, upper). Keeping both tick marks together (on paper and map), place the point of the pencil close to the edge of the paper on the tick mark to hold it in place and pivot the paper until another straight portion of the curved line is aligned with the edge of the paper. Continue in this manner until you complete the measurement (Figure 1.46, lower). When you have completed measuring the distance, move the paper to the graphic scale to determine the ground distance.

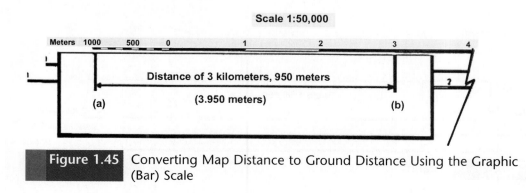

Figure 1.45 Converting Map Distance to Ground Distance Using the Graphic (Bar) Scale

When you measure distance on a map you do not take into consideration the rise and fall of the land. All distances you measure using the map and graphic scales are flat distances. Therefore, the distance measured on a map will increase when you travel it on the ground. You must take this into consideration when navigating across rough country (FM 3-25.26).

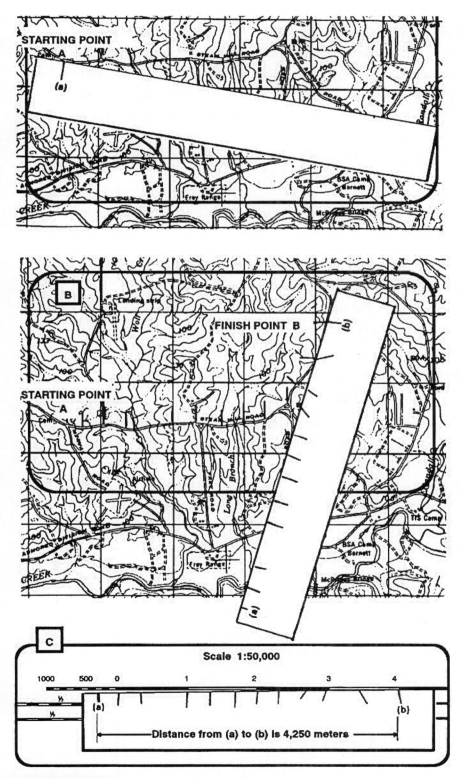

Figure 1.46 Measuring Distances Around a Curve

CONCLUSION

With the military advancing technologically almost daily, it's very easy to forget how to do things the old-fashioned way. When the military started to use GPS systems, some wanted to do away with teaching navigation by map and compass. They believed it was not needed anymore. Fortunately, they lost the argument. As long as the military must travel over land, Soldiers will need to know how to use a map and compass. To be proficient in navigation you need a thorough knowledge of the map, the coordinate and grid reference systems, and how to measure distance.

Learning Assessment

1. Find and identify five common symbols on your map.
2. Give examples of how different colors are used on the map.
3. Identify the symbols used on a military map and how they represent certain objects and physical surroundings.
4. Identify the information you can find in a map's legend.
5. Determine the elevation and slope of selected points on a map.
6. Identify the major, minor, and supplemental terrain features on a map.
7. Give military grid coordinates for points on the map.
8. Measure distances between selected locations on a map.

Key Words

marginal information
topographic symbols
contour lines
terrain features
latitude
longitude
grid coordinates
metric system

References

De Mar, G. (n.d.). *Christopher Columbus and the Flat Earth Myth* (Part 7). Retrieved 8 February 2005 from http://www.americaninvasion.org/articlearchive/10-12-04.asp

Field Manual 3–25.26, *Map Reading and Land Navigation*. Change 1. 30 August 2006.

Field Manual 21–31, *Topographic Symbols*. 31 December 1968.

Scarborough, Rowan. (2003, July 11). Lynch convoy plagued by map error, fatigue. *The Washington Times*.

US Army Official Report on 507th Maintenance Co.: An Nasariyah, Iraq. (2003). Washington, DC: Department of the Army.

MAP READING II

Key Points

I have never been lost, but I will admit to being confused for several weeks.

Daniel Boone

Introduction

In the last chapter you were introduced to the map, the information on it, and how best to read it. This chapter will teach you how to use the map to navigate terrain by orienting your map, using a compass and azimuths, and locating known and unknown points using azimuths. With this knowledge you can determine your location if you are lost, shoot an azimuth to where you want to go, determine distance and direction, and plan a route to navigate by **dead reckoning**.

dead reckoning

a technique in which you use a protractor and graphic scales to determine the direction and distance from one point to another on a map, then use a compass and some means of measuring distance to apply this information on the ground—in other words, it begins with the determination of a polar coordinate on a map and ends with the act of finding the coordinate on the ground

Lensatic Compass

Compasses are the primary navigation tools to use when moving outdoors when there is no other way to find directions. Soldiers should be thoroughly familiar with the compass and its uses. The lensatic compass is the most common and simplest instrument for measuring direction.

The lensatic compass (Figure 2.1) has three major parts: the cover, the base, and the lens.

1. *Cover.* The compass cover protects the floating dial. It contains the sighting wire (front sight) and two luminous sighting slots or dots used for night navigation.

2. *Base.* The body of the compass contains the following movable parts:

- The *floating dial* is mounted on a pivot so it can rotate freely when the compass is held level. Printed on the dial in luminous figures are an arrow and the letters E and W. The arrow always points to magnetic north and the letters fall at east (E) 90° and west (W) 270° on the dial. There are two scales—the outer scale denotes mils and the inner scale (normally in red) denotes degrees.
- Encasing the floating dial is a glass containing a *fixed black index line*.
- The *bezel ring* is a ratchet device that clicks when turned. When you rotate it fully, it clicks 120 times; each click is equal to 3°. The glass face of the bezel ring contains a *short luminous line* that is used in conjunction with the north-seeking arrow during navigation.
- The *thumb loop* is attached to the base of the compass.

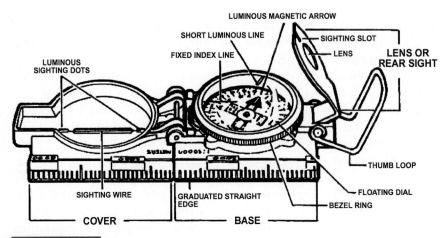

Figure 2.1 Lensatic Compass

3. *Lens.* You use the lens to read the dial. It contains the rear-sight slot used in conjunction with the front for sighting on objects. The rear sight also serves as a lock and clamps the dial when closed for its protection. You must open the rear sight more than 45° to allow the dial to float freely.

Compass Handling

Compasses are delicate instruments and you should care for them accordingly.

Inspection. A detailed inspection is required when you first obtain and use a compass. One of the most important parts to check is the floating dial, which contains the magnetic needle. You must also make sure that the sighting wire is straight, the glass and crystal parts are not broken, the numbers on the dial are readable, and most important, that the dial does not stick.

Effects of Metal and Electricity. Metal objects and electrical sources can affect the performance of a compass. Nonmagnetic metals and alloys do not affect compass readings, however. The following separation distances are suggested to ensure your compass functions properly:

High-tension power lines	55 meters
Field gun, truck, or tank	18 meters
Telegraph or telephone wires and barbed wire	10 meters
Machine gun	2 meters
Steel helmet or rifle	½ meter

Accuracy. A compass in good working condition is very accurate. You must check a compass periodically, however, on a known line of direction, such as a surveyed azimuth using a declination station. Do not use compasses with more than 3° variation.

Protection. If you are traveling with the compass unfolded, make sure the rear sight is fully folded down onto the bezel ring. This will lock the floating dial and prevent vibration, as well as protect the crystal and rear sight from damage.

Methods of Expressing Direction

Military personnel need a way of expressing direction that is accurate, adaptable to any part of the world, and has a common unit of measure. Directions are expressed as units of angular measure in degrees, mils, or grads:

- *Degree.* The most common unit of measure is the degree (°) with its subdivisions of minutes (') and seconds ("). There are 360 degrees in a circle, 60 minutes in a degree, and 60 seconds in a minute.
- *Mil.* Another unit of measure, the mil (abbreviated **m**), is used mainly in artillery, tank, and mortar gunnery, to provide a more accurate form of measure. The mil expresses the size of an angle formed when a circle is divided into 6,400 angles, with the vertexes of the angles at the center of the circle. A relationship can be established between degrees and mils. A circle equals 6,400 mils divided by 360 degrees, or 17.78 mils per degree. To convert degrees to mils, multiply degrees by 17.78.
- *Grad.* The grad is a metric unit of measure found on some foreign maps. There are 400 grads in a circle (a 90° right angle equals 100 grads). The grad is divided into 100 centesimal minutes (centigrads) and the minute into 100 centesimal seconds (milligrads).

Base Lines

In order to measure something, you always need a starting point, or zero measurement. To express direction as a unit of angular measure, you must have a starting point, or zero measure, and a point of reference. These two points designate the *base* or *reference line*. There are three base lines—true north, magnetic north, and grid north. The most commonly used are magnetic and grid.

True North. A line from any point on the earth's surface to the North Pole. All lines of longitude are true north lines. True north is usually represented by a star (Figure 2.2).

Magnetic North. The direction to the north magnetic pole, as indicated by the north-seeking needle of a magnetic instrument. Magnetic north is usually symbolized by a line ending with half of an arrowhead (Figure 2.2). You obtain magnetic readings with magnetic instruments, such as lensatic and M2 compasses.

Grid North. The north that is established using the vertical grid lines on the map. Grid north may be symbolized by the letters GN or the letter "y" (Figure 2.2).

Azimuths

An **azimuth** is a horizontal angle measured clockwise from a north base line. The azimuth is the most common military method to give direction from Point A (starting point) to Point B (ending point). When you use an azimuth, the starting point of the azimuth is the center of an imaginary circle (Figure 2.3).

Magnetic Azimuth

You determine magnetic azimuths with magnetic instruments, such as lensatic and M2 compasses.

Finding Azimuth Using the Centerhold Technique

First, open the compass to its fullest so that the cover forms a straightedge with the base. Move the lens (rear sight) to the rearmost position, allowing the dial to float freely. Next, place your thumb through the thumb loop, form a steady base with your third and fourth fingers, and extend your index finger along the side of the compass. Place the thumb of the other hand between the lens (rear sight) and the bezel ring. Extend the index finger along the remaining side of the compass, and the remaining fingers around the fingers of the other hand. Pull your elbows firmly into your sides; this will place the compass between

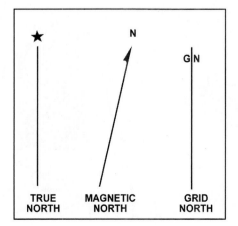

Figure 2.2 North

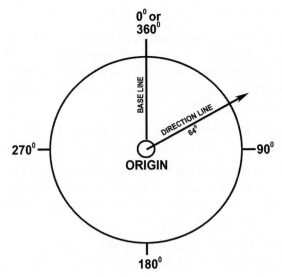

Figure 2.3 Azimuth

your chin and your belt. To measure an azimuth, simply turn your entire body toward the object, pointing the compass cover directly at the object. Once you are pointing at the object, look down and read the azimuth from beneath the fixed black index line (Figure 2.4). This preferred method offers the following advantages over the sighting technique:

1. It is faster and easier to use.
2. You can use it regardless of visibility.
3. You can use it when navigating over any type of terrain.
4. You can use it without putting down the rifle; however, you must sling the rifle well back over either shoulder.
5. You can use it without removing eyeglasses.

Finding Azimuth Using the Compass-to-Cheek Technique

Fold the cover of the compass containing the sighting wire to a vertical position; then fold the rear sight slightly forward. Look through the rear-sight slot and align the front-sight hairline with the desired object in the distance. Then glance down at the dial through the eye lens to read the azimuth (Figure 2.5).

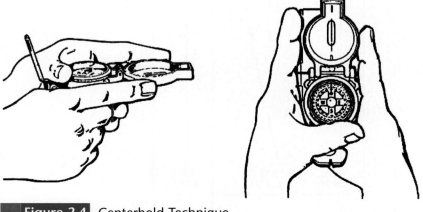

Figure 2.4 Centerhold Technique

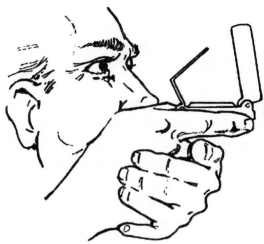

Figure 2.5 Compass-to-Cheek Technique

Setting a Compass Azimuth

Although different models of the lensatic compass vary somewhat in the details of their use, the principles are the same.

In Daylight or with Light Source

1. Hold the compass level in the palm of the hand.
2. Rotate it until the desired azimuth falls under the fixed black index line (for example, 320°), maintaining the azimuth as prescribed (Figure 2.6).
3. Turn the bezel ring until the luminous line is aligned with the north-seeking arrow. Once the alignment is obtained, the compass is preset.

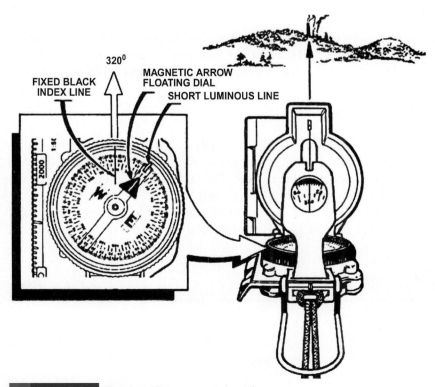

Figure 2.6 Setting Compass Azimuth

4. To follow an azimuth, assume the centerhold technique and turn your body until the north-seeking arrow is aligned with the luminous line. Then move forward in the direction of the front cover's sighting wire, which is aligned with the fixed black index line that contains the desired azimuth.

In Limited Visibility

During limited visibility, an azimuth may be set on the compass by the click method. Remember that the bezel ring clicks represent 3° intervals.

1. Rotate the bezel ring until the luminous line is over the fixed black index line.

2. Find the desired azimuth and divide it by three. The result is the number of clicks that you must rotate the bezel ring.

3. Count the desired number of clicks. If the desired azimuth is smaller than 180°, the number of clicks on the bezel ring should be counted in a counterclockwise direction. For example, the desired azimuth is 51°. Desired azimuth is 51° ÷ 3 = 17 clicks counterclockwise. If the desired azimuth is larger than 180°, subtract the number of degrees from 360° and divide by 3 to obtain the number of clicks. Count them in a clockwise direction. For example, the desired azimuth is 330°: 360° − 330° = 30 ÷ 3 = 10 clicks clockwise.

4. With the compass preset as described above, assume a centerhold technique and rotate your body until the north-seeking arrow is aligned with the luminous line on the bezel. Then move forward in the direction of the front cover's luminous dots, which are aligned with the fixed black index line containing the azimuth.

5. When you are going to use the compass in darkness, set an initial azimuth while light is still available, if possible. With the initial azimuth as a base, you can establish any other azimuth that is a multiple of three by using the clicking feature of the bezel ring.

Grid Azimuth

When an azimuth is *plotted on a map* between Point A (starting point) and Point B (ending point), the points are joined together by a straight line. You use a *protractor* to measure the angle between grid north and the drawn line, and this measured azimuth is the grid azimuth (Figure 2.7).

Protractor

There are several types of protractors—full circle, half circle, square, and rectangular (Figure 2.8). All of them divide the circle into units of angular measure, and each has a scale around the outer edge and an index mark. The index mark is the center of the protractor circle from which you measure all directions.

The military protractor, GTA 5-2-12, contains two scales: one in degrees (inner scale) and one in mils (outer scale) (Figure 2.8). This protractor represents the azimuth circle.

Sometimes the desired azimuth is not exactly divisible by three, which means you must round up or round down. If you round the azimuth up, this increases the value of the azimuth and you will find you are navigating to the left. If you round the azimuth down, this decreases the value of the azimuth, and you will find you are navigating to the right.

The index mark is the center of the protractor circle from which you measure all directions.

Critical Thinking

Summarize the different ways to use a compass in varying conditions of light, fog, and darkness.

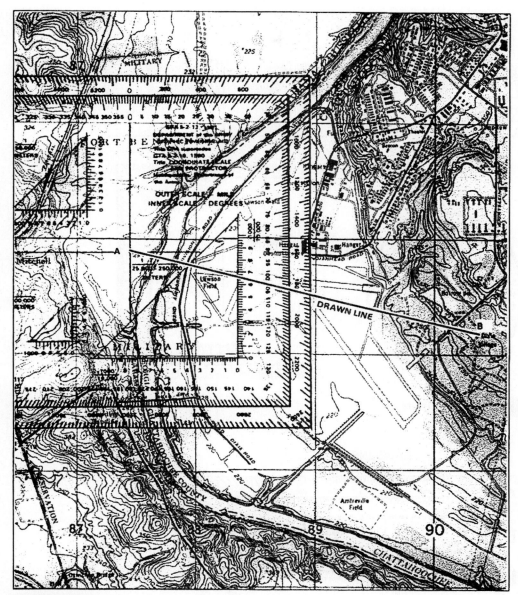

Figure 2.7 Measuring an Azimuth

The degree scale is graduated from 0° to 360°; each tick mark on the degree scale represents one degree. A line from 0° to 180° is called the *base line* of the protractor. Where the base line intersects the *horizontal line*, between 90° and 270°, is the *index* or center of the protractor (Figure 2.9).

When you use the protractor, always orient the base line parallel to a north–south grid line (Figure 2.8). The 0° or 360° mark is always toward the top or north on the map and the 90° mark is to the right.

Measuring Azimuth with a Protractor

To measure a grid azimuth with a protractor:

1. Draw a line connecting the two points (A and B).
2. Place the index of the protractor at the point where the drawn line crosses a vertical (north–south) grid line.

When you use the protractor, always orient the base line parallel to a north–south grid line.

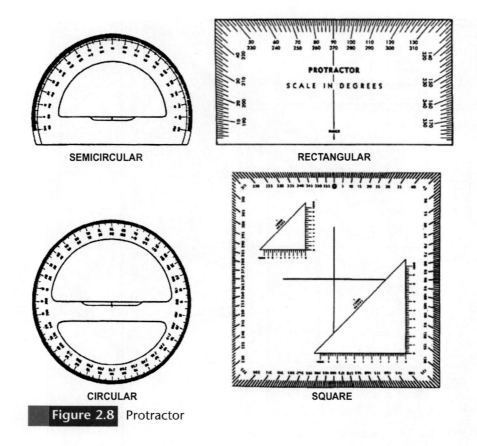

SEMICIRCULAR

RECTANGULAR

CIRCULAR

SQUARE

Figure 2.8 Protractor

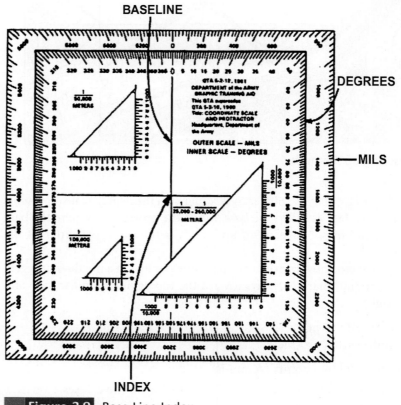

Figure 2.9 Base Line Index

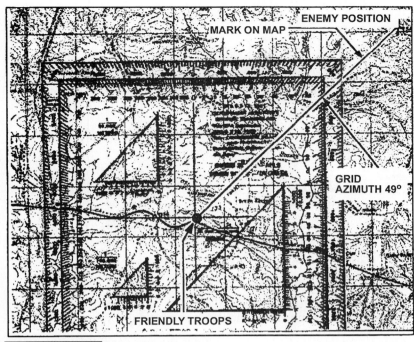

Figure 2.10 Grid Azimuth 49

3. Keeping the index at this point, align the 0° to 180° line of the protractor on the vertical grid line.

4. Read the value of the angle from the scale; this is the grid azimuth from Point A to Point B (Figure 2.7).

Plotting Azimuth with a Protractor

To "plot" or draw an azimuth from a known point on a map with a protractor (Figure 2.10):

1. Place the protractor on the map with the index mark at the center of mass of the known point and the base line parallel to a north–south grid line.

2. Make a mark on the map at the desired azimuth (angle) located on the protractor.

3. Remove the protractor and draw a line connecting the known point and the mark on the map. This is the grid direction line (azimuth).

Converting Map and Compass Directions

Grid north lines depicted on a grid reference map deviate from magnetic north on a compass. With simple calculations, you can convert between map and compass directions to ensure precise navigation.

Declination

Declination is the angular difference between any two norths. If you have a map and a compass, the declination of most interest to you will be the declination between magnetic and grid north. The declination diagram (Figure 2.11) shows the angular relationship between prongs (lines) representing true north, magnetic north, and grid north. While the relative positions of the prongs are correct, they are seldom plotted to scale. Do not use the diagram to measure a numerical value. You will find this value in the map margin (in both degrees and mils) beside the diagram.

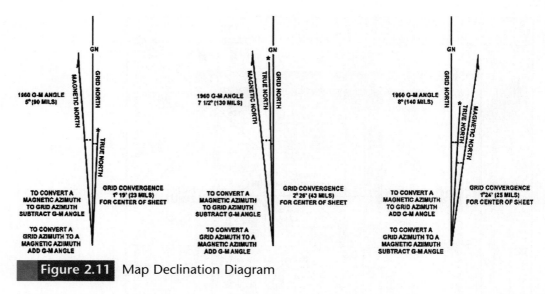

Figure 2.11 Map Declination Diagram

Conversion

Use declination to convert a grid azimuth to a magnetic azimuth and vice versa:

1. *Find the Grid-Magnetic Angle.* The G-M angle value is the angular difference between grid north and magnetic north. On a declination diagram it is an arc, indicated by a dashed line that connects the grid north and magnetic north prongs. This value is expressed to the nearest one-half degree, with mil equivalents shown to the nearest 10 miles.

2. *Observe the Relation of Magnetic North to Grid North.* Locate the magnetic north prong on the declination diagram. Note whether it is left (west) or right (east) of the grid north prong.

3. *If Magnetic North Is Left (West) of Grid North:*
   - To convert a magnetic azimuth to a grid azimuth subtract the G-M angle
   - To convert a grid azimuth to a magnetic azimuth add the G-M angle.

4. *If Magnetic North Is Right (East) of Grid North:*
   - To convert a magnetic azimuth to a grid azimuth add the G-M angle
   - To convert a grid azimuth to a magnetic azimuth subtract the G-M angle.

> *The G-M angle is important to you because azimuths translated between map and ground will be in error by the size of the declination angle if you don't adjust for it.*

Orienting a Map

The first step for a navigator in the field is to orient the map. You have oriented your map when it is in a horizontal position with its north and south corresponding to the north and south on the ground. Here are some ways to orient your map:

Using a Compass. When you orient a map with a compass, remember that the compass measures magnetic azimuths. Since the magnetic arrow points to magnetic north, pay special attention to the declination diagram. You can use either of two techniques:

FIRST TECHNIQUE. Determine the direction of the declination and its value from the declination diagram.

1. With the map in a horizontal position, take the straightedge on the left side of the compass and place it alongside the north–south grid line with the cover of the compass pointing toward the top of the map. This places the fixed black index line of the compass parallel to north–south grid lines of the map.

2. Keeping the compass aligned as directed above, rotate the map and compass together until the magnetic arrow is below the fixed black index line on the compass. At this time, you are close to orienting your map.

3. Rotate the map and compass in the direction of the declination diagram.

4. If the magnetic north arrow on the map is to the left of the grid north, check the compass reading to see if it equals the G-M angle given in the declination diagram. You have now oriented your map (Figure 2.12).

5. If the magnetic north is to the right of grid north, check the compass reading to see if it equals 360 degrees minus the G-M angle (Figure 2.13).

SECOND TECHNIQUE. Determine the direction of the declination and its value from the declination diagram.

1. Using any north–south grid line on the map as a base, draw a magnetic azimuth with the protractor equal to the G-M angle given in the declination diagram.

2. If the declination is easterly (right), the drawn line is equal to the value of the G-M angle. Then align the straightedge on the left side of the compass alongside the drawn line on the map. Rotate the map and compass until the magnetic arrow of the compass is below the fixed black index line. You have now oriented your map (Figure 2.14).

3. If the declination is westerly (left), the drawn line will equal 360 degrees minus the value of the G-M angle. Then align the straightedge on the left side of the compass alongside the drawn line on the map. Rotate the map and compass until the magnetic arrow of the compass is below the fixed black index line. You have now oriented your map (Figure 2.15).

1. Once the map is oriented, you determine magnetic azimuths using your compass. Do not move the map from its oriented position, since any change in its position moves it out of line with magnetic north.

2. Take special care when you orient your map with a compass. A small mistake can cause you to navigate in the wrong direction.

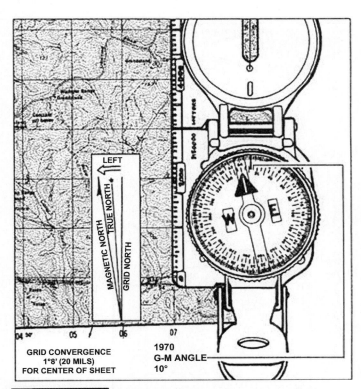

Figure 2.12 Map Oriented With 10 Degrees West Declination

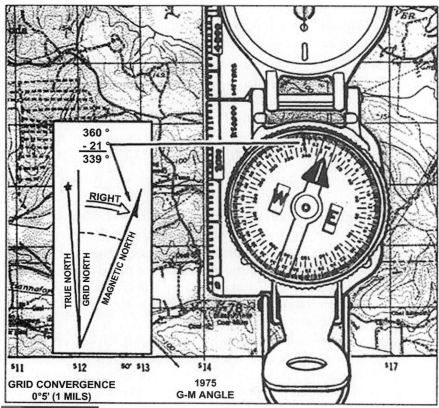

Figure 2.13 Map Oriented With 21 Degrees East Declination

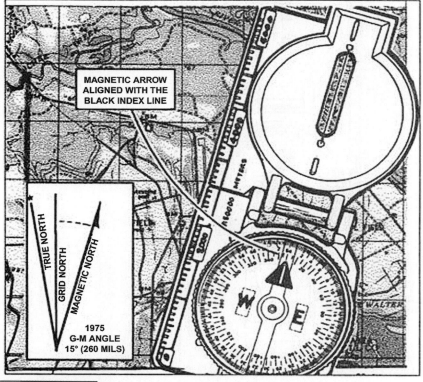

Figure 2.14 Map Oriented With 15 Degrees East Declination

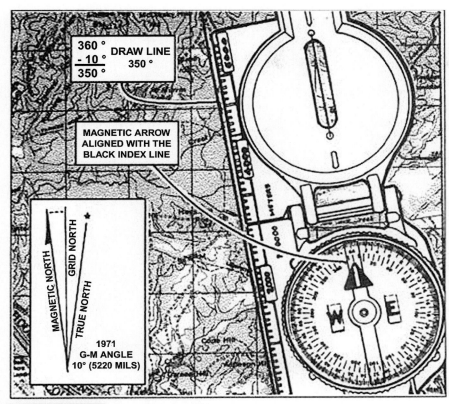

Figure 2.15 Map Oriented With 10 Degrees West Declination

Using Terrain Association. You can orient your map by terrain association when a compass is not available or when you have to make many quick references as you move across country. Using this method requires you to carefully examine the map and the ground, and to know your approximate location (Figure 2.16).

Intersection

Intersection is locating an unknown point by successively occupying at least two (preferably three) known positions on the ground and then map sighting on the unknown location. You use it to locate distant or inaccessible points or objects such as enemy targets and danger areas. There are two methods of intersection: the map and compass method and the straightedge method for when a compass is not available.

Using the Map and Compass Method

1. Orient the map using the compass.
2. Locate and mark your position on the map.
3. Determine the magnetic azimuth to the unknown position using the compass.
4. Convert the magnetic azimuth to grid azimuth.
5. Draw a line on the map from your position on this grid azimuth.
6. Move to a second known point and repeat steps 1, 2, 3, 4, and 5.
7. The unknown position is located where the lines cross (intersect) on the map. Determine the grid coordinates to the desired accuracy (Figure 2.17).

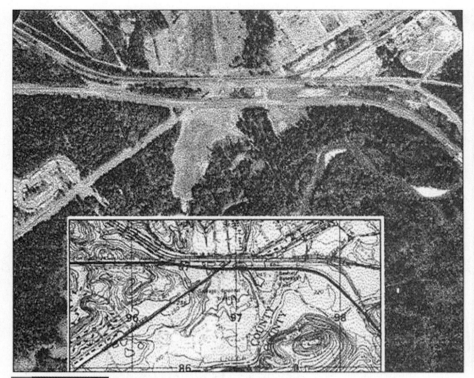

Figure 2.16 Terrain Association

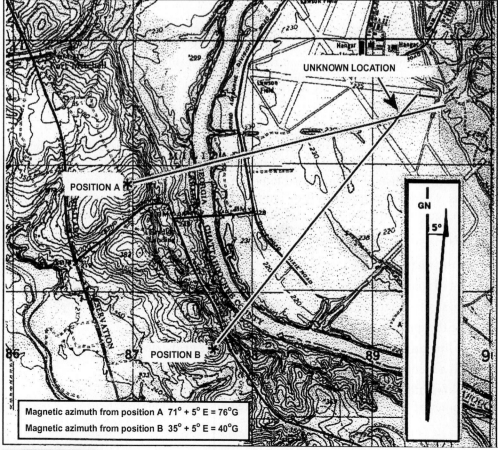

Magnetic azimuth from position A 71° + 5° E = 76°G
Magnetic azimuth from position B 35° + 5° E = 40°G

Figure 2.17 Intersection Using a Map and Compass

Using the Straightedge Method

1. Orient the map on a flat surface by the **terrain-association** method.
2. Locate and mark your position on the map.
3. Lay a straightedge on the map with one end at your position (A) as a pivot point; then rotate the straightedge until the unknown point is sighted along the edge.
4. Draw a line along the straight edge.
5. Repeat the above steps at position (B) and check for accuracy.
6. The intersection of the lines on the map is the location of the unknown point (C). Determine the grid coordinates to the desired accuracy (Figure 2.18).

Resection

Resection is the method of locating your position on a map by determining the grid azimuth to at least two well-defined locations that you can pinpoint on the map. For greater accuracy, you should use three or more well-defined locations.

Using the Map and Compass Method

1. Orient the map using the compass.
2. Identify two or three known distant locations on the ground and mark them on the map.
3. Measure the magnetic azimuth to one of the known positions from your location using a compass.
4. Convert the magnetic azimuth to a grid azimuth.
5. Convert the grid azimuth to a **back azimuth**. Using a protractor, draw a line for the back azimuth on the map from the known position back toward your unknown position.
6. Repeat 3, 4, and 5 for a second position and a third position, if desired.
7. You are located where the lines intersect. Determine the grid coordinates to the desired accuracy (Figure 2.19).

terrain association

a technique of orienting a map in which the Soldier constantly compares what he or she sees on the map to what he or she sees on the ground—this technique requires the Soldier to know his or her approximate starting location

resection

using two or more azimuths to determine your position on a map

back azimuth

the opposite direction of an azimuth—to obtain a back azimuth from an azimuth, add 180 degrees if the azimuth is 180 degrees or less, or subtract 180 degrees if the azimuth is 180 degrees or more

warning

You should exercise extreme care when adding or subtracting the 180 degrees. A simple mathematical mistake could have disastrous consequences.

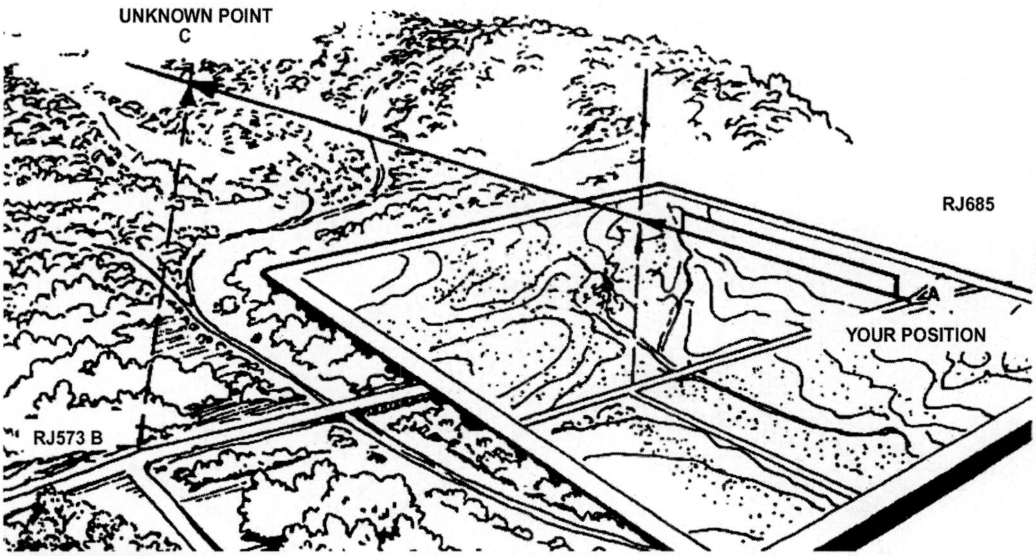

Figure 2.18 Intersection Using a Map and Straightedge

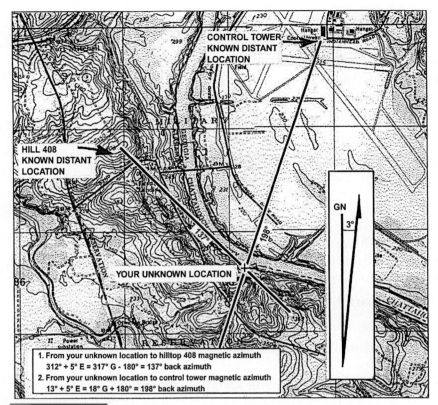

Figure 2.19 Resection Using a Map and Compass

Using the Straightedge Method

1. Orient the map on a flat surface by the terrain-association method.

2. Locate at least two known distant locations or prominent features on the ground and mark them on the map.

3. Lay a straightedge on the map using a known position as a pivot point. Rotate the straightedge until the known position on the map is aligned with the known position on the ground.

4. Draw a line along the straightedge away from the known position on the ground toward your position.

5. Repeat 3 and 4 using a second known position.

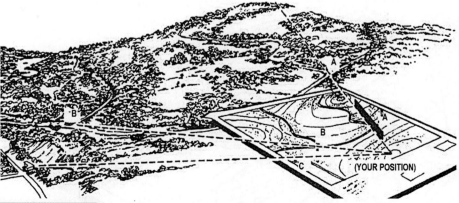

Figure 2.20 Resection Using a Map and Straightedge

6. The intersection of the lines on the map is your location. Determine the grid coordinates to the desired accuracy (Figure 2.20).

Modified Resection

Modified resection is the method of locating your position on the map when you are located on a linear feature on the ground, such as a road, canal, or stream (Figure 2.21). Proceed as follows:

1. Orient the map using a compass or by terrain association.
2. Find a distant point that you can identify on the ground and on the map.
3. Determine the magnetic azimuth from your location to the distant known point.
4. Convert the magnetic azimuth to a grid azimuth.
5. Convert the grid azimuth to a back azimuth. Using a protractor, draw a line for the back azimuth on the map from the known position back toward your unknown position.
6. Your location is where the line crosses the linear feature. Determine the grid coordinates to the desired accuracy.

Polar Plot

A polar plot is a method of locating or plotting an unknown position from a known point by giving a direction and a distance along that direction line. You must know the following when using polar plot (Figure 2.22):

- Your present known location on the map
- Azimuth (grid or magnetic)
- Distance (in meters).

If you use the laser range finder to determine the range you will be more accurate in determining the unknown position's location.

Locations

The key to success in land navigation is to know your location at all times. With this basic knowledge, you can decide which direction and how far to travel.

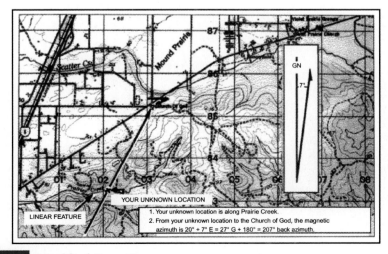

Figure 2.21 Modified Resection

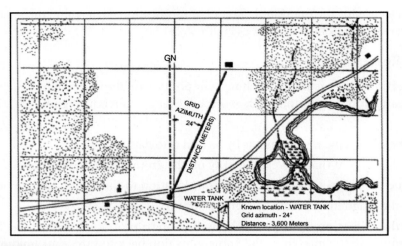

Known location - WATER TANK
Grid azimuth - 24°
Distance - 3,600 Meters

Figure 2.22 Polar Plot

Known Position. Most important of all is your initial location before starting any movement in the field. If you move without establishing your initial location, everything that you do in the field from there on is a gamble. Determine your initial location by referring to your last known position, by grid coordinates and terrain association, or by locating and orienting your position on the map and on the ground, by resection, modified resection, or polar plot.

Known Point/Known Distance (Polar Plot). You can determine this location if you know the starting point, the azimuth to the desired objective, and the distance to it.

Resection, Modified Resection, and Intersection. You read about these earlier in the section.

Indirect Fire. You find a location by indirect fire using smoke. Use the point of impact of the round as a reference point from which to obtain distances and azimuth, from modified resection or polar plot.

CONCLUSION

You now have learned the basic skills of map reading, such as how to read a map, measure distance, identify symbols and terrain features, shoot an azimuth, find an unknown point on a map by intersection and resection, and determine elevation of a point on a map. This information is critical to all Soldiers. Map reading and navigation is a perishable skill that Soldiers must constantly practice and apply, regardless of their rank or military occupational specialty. Failure to do so may result in the loss of your Soldiers' lives in combat.

Learning Assessment

1. What are the steps needed to determine a grid azimuth?
2. What are the steps needed to determine a magnetic azimuth?
3. Using intersection, find an unknown point on a map.
4. Using resection, find your point on a map.

Key Words

dead reckoning
azimuth
terrain association
resection
back azimuth

Reference

Field Manual 3-25.26, *Map Reading and Land Navigation*. Change 1. 30 August 2006.

TERRAIN ANALYSIS

Key Points

1 Intelligence Preparation of the Battlefield

2 Analyzing the Military Aspects of the Terrain

3 Weather Analysis

When I took a decision or adopted an alternative,
it was after studying every relevant—and many an
irrelevant—factor. Geography, tribal structure, religion,
social customs, language, appetites, standards—all
were at my finger-ends. The enemy I knew almost like
my own side.

T. E. Lawrence (Lawrence of Arabia), 1933

Introduction

The previous chapters introduced you to Map Reading I and II, focusing on how to apply those skills to navigate from one point to another. This chapter will introduce you to a completely new way of thinking about maps and terrain. The previous chapters taught you to open a map, read marginal information, and in one quick viewing determine terrain features, contour lines, elevation, and slope. You also learned how to navigate on the ground using three simple tools—a map, a protractor, and a compass. You gained an understanding that your map serves a useful purpose. After completing this chapter, you will never again look at a map as a simple two-dimensional tool to help you navigate from one point to the next. You will learn how to analyze terrain using steps from the Intelligence Preparation of the Battlefield (IPB) process. Future chapters, such as Troop Leading Procedures and Tactical Orders, require you to have a firm understanding of the information covered in this chapter. You will apply the knowledge from this day forward while in ROTC and at all levels during your career as a military officer.

Hamburger Hill, 1969

The battle took place on Dong Ap Bia (Ap Bia Mountain) in the rugged, jungle-shrouded mountains along the Laotian border of South Vietnam. Rising from the floor of the western A Shau Valley, Ap Bia Mountain is a looming, solitary massif, unconnected to the ridges of the surrounding Annamite range. It dominates the northern valley, towering some 937 meters above sea level. Snaking down from its highest peak are a series of ridges and fingers, one of the largest extending southeast to a height of 900 meters, another reaching south to a 916-meter peak. The entire mountain is a rugged, uninviting wilderness blanketed in double- and triple-canopy jungle, dense thickets of bamboo, and waist-high elephant grass. Local Montagnard tribesmen called Ap Bia "the mountain of the crouching beast." LTC Weldon Honeycutt, commander of the 3d Battalion, 187th Infantry (the "Rakkasans"), called it "Hill 937." The Soldiers who fought there dubbed it "Hamburger Hill."

The fight on Hamburger Hill occurred during Operation Apache Snow, the second part of a three-phased campaign intended to destroy North Vietnam Army (NVA) bases in the treacherous A Shau Valley. The American and South Vietnamese units participating in Apache Snow knew, based on existing intelligence and previous experiences in the A Shau, that they were in for a tough fight. Beyond that, however, they had little evidence as to the enemy's actual strength and dispositions. Masters of camouflage, the NVA completely concealed their bases from aerial surveillance. When the NVA moved, they did so at night along trails covered by triple-canopy jungle, again confounding observation from above. They effected their command and control mainly by runner and wire, leaving no electronic signature for the Americans to monitor or trace. Technology, therefore, provided scant assistance to the American battalion commander trying to "see the enemy" during Apache Snow. He had to generate his own tactical intelligence. Patrols, captured equipment, installations, documents, and occasionally prisoners provided combat commanders with the raw data from which to draw their assessment of the enemy order of battle and dispositions. Gathering this information took time, though. Moreover, intelligence about the enemy's strength and dispositions did not necessarily illuminate his commander's intent. It took days to ascertain this, and the learning experience proved decidedly unpleasant for the Americans.

On 11 May, Honeycutt dispersed his Rakkasans and scoured the vicinity to the north and northwest of Ap Bia Mountain. When Bravo Company made heavy contact with some NVA late in the day, Honeycutt adjusted his estimate of the enemy's strength from "a few trail watchers" to a reinforced platoon or even a company. The Rakkasans could still deal with a force that size, but they would have to concentrate to do so. For the next three days, Honeycutt fought the mountain and the NVA to bring his scattered companies together for a coordinated battalion attack. Despite the fact that, since the initial assault, no company was more than about 1,500 meters from the crest of the mountain, it took two days to consolidate the battalion for a three-company assault. Time and again, the American infantrymen found themselves hampered as much by the topography as by the enemy. The rugged terrain slowed dismounted movement to a crawl. Between 12 and 14 May, for example, Delta Company was virtually immobilized when it went down a steep ravine and was caught there by the enemy. In one grueling five-hour period, the company labored to advance a total of only 500 meters. The steep, mud-covered slopes, more than the enemy, kept this company from fulfilling Honeycutt's intent. In the end, the troops had to abandon their attack and withdraw the way they had come.

These three days were a period of intensely unpleasant "discovery learning" for Honeycutt and his men. Map reconnaissance and helicopter over-flights did not indicate that his initial scheme of maneuver was impractical. It took Delta Company's three-day ordeal to do so. Though Honeycutt had a long and distinguished record as a combat commander in both Vietnam and Korea, he underestimated Ap Bia Mountain and the NVA facing him. Although his estimate of the enemy strength was incorrect, his miscalculation was not immediately apparent to him or to any of the American leadership. It took three days of assaults by Bravo and Charlie Companies, each bloodily repulsed, before the situation became clearer. The enemy was stronger than anticipated, much stronger than company strength, and he grew more powerful every night as he received reinforcements from Laos. The NVA commander's demonstrated tenacity and willingness to replace heavy losses indicated he intended to put up a stiff fight for Hill 937 (Scalard).

Intelligence Preparation of the Battlefield

Intelligence Preparation of the Battlefield (IPB) is the best process the Army has for understanding the battlefield and the options it presents to friendly and enemy forces. IPB is a systematic and continuous process of analyzing the enemy and environment in a specific geographical area. IPB is designed to support military decision making. It helps leaders selectively apply and maximize combat power at critical points in time and space on the battlefield. IPB consists of four steps:

- Define the battlefield environment
- Describe the battlefield's effects
- Evaluate the threat
- Determine threat courses of action (COA).

In this chapter, you will learn the basics of describing the battlefield's effects on military operations. Under Army doctrine, the intelligence officer (S-2 or G-2) is responsible for preparing and briefing the IPB to the commander. IPB is a lengthy and detailed process and all steps are not applicable to you as a small unit leader. Knowledge of the IPB process, however, gives an advantage to any leader on the ground. This is especially true in today's Contemporary Operating Environment (COE), where the enemy operates in an asymmetric manner and missions are decentralized down to the smallest maneuver elements.

Analyzing the Military Aspects of the Terrain

The best way to analyze the terrain is to conduct a personal reconnaissance on the ground your platoon will operate on. When you don't have time to conduct a personal ground reconnaissance, then you must conduct the **terrain analysis** using maps or aerial photos. Before you can analyze the effects of terrain and weather on military operations, you must know your **area of operation** (AO).

Identifying Your Area of Operations: When you analyze the military aspects of terrain, you identify the effects of terrain and weather on military operations—including troops, weapons, weapon systems, vehicles, and equipment. Your AO is the area where your platoon will conduct your current and future missions. The battalion commander receives the battalion AO from higher up and breaks the battalion AO down into company AOs. Each company commander further breaks down the company's AO into platoon AOs. In hasty planning, you may receive your AO in the form of four or more grid coordinates. When you plot and connect these coordinates on your map, you have your platoon AO. In deliberate planning, your AO will be defined on the company commander's map overlay. You will be expected to make a copy of the company map overlay for use in developing your platoon operations orders (OPORD) as part of the Troop Leading Procedures (TLP) and mission planning. Once you have identified your AO, you can begin to analyze the terrain in your AO and the effects of weather in your AO. Figure 3.1 illustrates graphic control measures and operational symbols that depict a platoon's AO within a company AO.

Intelligence Preparation of the Battlefield

a systematic and continuous process that describes the tactical environment and the effects of that environment on operations and what the enemy can accomplish

This chapter intentionally limits the scope of the IPB process to analyzing the effects of terrain and weather on small-unit operations.

terrain analysis

the process of interpreting natural and man-made features of a geographic area to determine their effects on military operations

area of operation

geographical area assigned to an Army commander by a higher commander—an AO has lateral and rear boundaries that usually define it within a larger joint geographical area

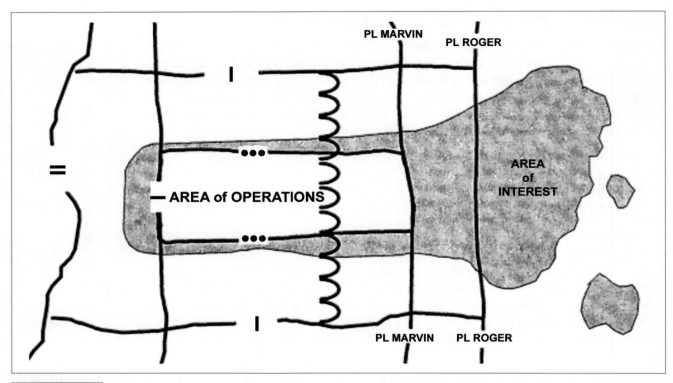

Figure 3.1 Platoon Area of Operations

Your platoon AO is essentially "the box" that your platoon must operate within.

You can learn more about unit boundaries and graphic control measures by studying FM 1-02, Operational Terms and Graphics.

OAKOC

acronym that a leader uses to determine the effect of terrain and weather on enemy and friendly forces

Your platoon AO is essentially "the box" that your platoon must operate within. Both your platoon's maneuver and its fires must remain in your AO unless previously coordinated and approved. As with the figure above, graphic control measures assist in preventing fratricide (friendly-fire incidents). At the small-unit level, defining the AO is probably the easiest step of the process, as the AO is directed by higher levels of command. At the tactical level, the platoon leader must be able to analyze terrain primarily to determine objectives, specific avenues of approach (AA), routes or infiltration lanes that support attacks, and terrain that supports the defense. The military aspects of terrain are: 1) observation and fields of fire; 2) cover and concealment; 3) obstacles; 4) key terrain; 5) avenues of approach. You can use the acronym **OAKOC** to analyze the military aspects of terrain in the order that best supports your operation:

Observation and Fields of Fire—Observation refers to the ability of a force to exercise surveillance over a given area using personnel or sensors. Fields of fire includes considering the characteristics of the weapons available when conducting a defense— for example, maximum effective range; the requirement for grazing fire; and the arming range and time of flight for antiarmor weapons.

Avenues of Approach—Air or ground routes by which a force may reach an objective.

Key and Decisive Terrain—Area that provides a marked advantage to whichever opposing force seizes or controls it.

Obstacles—Any object that disrupts, turns, fixes, or blocks an enemy force.

Cover and Concealment—Cover is terrain that will protect from direct and indirect fires. Concealment is terrain that will protect from aerial and ground observation.

Observation and Fields of Fire

As platoon leader you analyze areas surrounding key terrain, objectives, avenues of approach, and obstacles to determine if they provide clear observation and fields of fire for both friendly and enemy forces. You locate intervisibility lines (terrain that inhibits observation from one point to another) that the commander has not identified and determine where visual contact occurs between the two forces. When analyzing fields of fire, you focus on both friendly and enemy direct-fire capabilities. Additionally, you identify positions that enable artillery observers to call for indirect fires and permit snipers to engage targets. Whenever possible, you conduct a ground reconnaissance from both friendly and enemy perspectives.

Characteristics of the offense: Surprise, concentration, tempo, audacity.

Characteristics of the defense: Preparation, security, disruption, massing effects, flexibility.

Critical Thinking

Consider the characteristics of the offense and defense. Why does the defensive force benefit more by good observation and fields of fire than the offensive force?

Critical Thinking

What can the defender do to negate the effects of the masked terrain on his or her observation and fields of fire on the approaching attacker?

Critical Thinking

What is the relationship between a) observation and fields of fire and b) cover and concealment?

Cover and Concealment

Cover is protection from the effects of fires. *Concealment* is protection from observation but not from direct or indirect fires. Considering these elements can lead you to identify areas that can, at best, achieve both. As platoon leader, you look at the terrain, foliage, structures, and other features on the key terrain, objective, and avenues of approach to identify sites that offer both cover and concealment.

Critical Thinking

Consider the characteristics of the offense and defense. Who would benefit more from good cover and concealment, the attacker or defender? Which characteristics of the offense can the attacker benefit from by using good cover and concealment? Which characteristics of the defense can the defender benefit from by using good cover and concealment?

How well a position provides cover and concealment depends on the capabilities of the weapons or equipment available to the Soldier. In the example of a Soldier behind a tree, the tree would offer little cover from indirect fire, and the Soldier's thermal signature emitting from behind the tree would not provide him or her concealment from a thermal imagery device.

Cover and concealment generally favor the offense because the attacker can use a covered and concealed route to maintain tempo and surprise the defender. As a platoon leader, you must also look for ways to use cover and concealment to aid you in the defense. A well-covered and concealed platoon defense may result in your attackers entering your platoon's **engagement area** or **kill zone** before they observe your platoon's location. You can also place listening posts and observation posts (LP/OP) in well-covered and concealed locations to improve your defense through early warning. You can also plan well-covered and concealed routes to use in counterattacking the enemy. It is important for you to always consider how the effects of cover and concealment affect you and the enemy in both the offense and defense.

Line of Sight (LOS) Analysis: As a platoon leader, you will conduct **line of sight analysis** to determine the observation, fields of fires, and cover and concealment that the terrain provides both you and the enemy. You will use your knowledge of contour lines, elevation, and slope from your previous map-reading lessons to conduct a line of sight (LOS) analysis of the terrain in your AO. Consider the simple illustration in Figure 3.2. The masked area all lies behind terrain that is level with or higher than your defensive position. From your defensive position, you cannot see into the masked area and you cannot fire your direct fire weapons into the masked area. In short, you do not have observation or fields of fire behind the terrain that produces the masked area. Indirect fire systems (M203 grenade launchers, mortars, artillery) may range the masked area, but unobserved indirect fires are generally ineffective if you can't see their effects on the enemy. As discussed above, observation and fields of fire are related. In the illustration, the masked area will provide the attacker cover from the defender's direct fire and will provide the attacker concealment from the defender's observations.

engagement area

an area where the commander intends to trap and destroy an enemy force using the massed fires of all available weapons

kill zone

an area where the defender ideally wants to destroy and defeat an attacker

line of sight analysis

the analysis of the intervisibility between two points located on the earth's surface

Conducting LOS analysis of the terrain in your AO is more difficult if you are conducting offensive operations, especially if you do not know your enemy's location. In the offense, you must conduct an LOS analysis throughout your AO to determine a route that will give you the best cover and concealment to your objective while also denying the enemy observation and fields of fire on your movement.

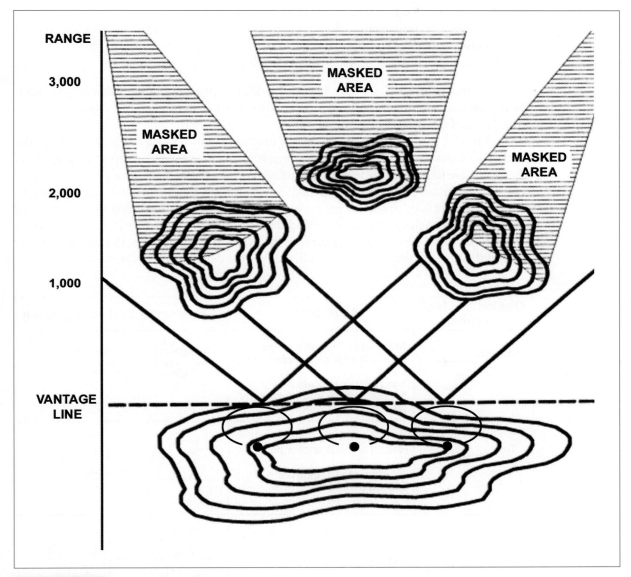

Figure 3.2 Platoon Defense LOS Analysis

Obstacles

As platoon leader you first identify existing and reinforcing obstacles in your AO that limit your mobility with regards to the mission. Existing obstacles are typically natural terrain features on the battlefield. These may include:

- ravines, gaps, or ditches more than three meters wide
- tree stumps and large rocks more than 18 inches high
- forests with trees eight inches or greater in diameter and with less than four meters between trees
- man-made obstacles such as towns or cities.

Reinforcing obstacles are typically man-made obstacles that augment existing obstacles. These may include minefields, antitank ditches, road craters, abatis and log cribs, wire obstacles, and infantry strong points.

Before you can consider the effects of obstacles, you will first need to identify the existing obstacles within your AO to determine if you can use them to support your mission. After you have identified the terrain that affords good existing obstacles, you must decide how you can install mines, wire, and ditches to reinforce the existing terrain obstacles. To analyze the effects of obstacles on military operations, you must first understand the purposes of obstacles in the offense and defense. You must also keep in mind that all obstacles must be observed or covered with direct fire or indirect fire in order to be successful. There are four purposes of obstacles in the defense: to *disrupt, turn, fix,* or *block.*

Obstacle Effect Graphic	Application	Examples Conveying Intent
Disrupt 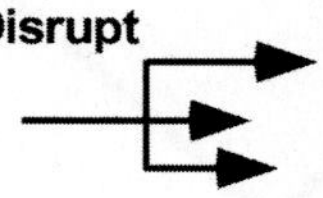	Short arrow indicates where enemy is attacked by obstacles. Long arrows indicate where bypass is allow and attacked by fires.	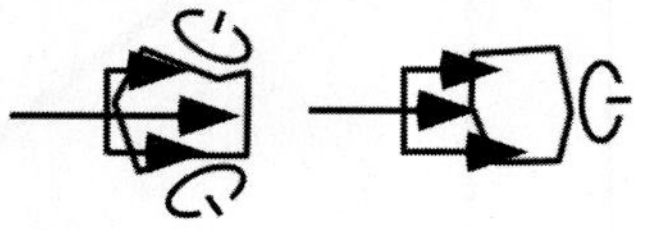
Turn 	Heel of arrow is anchor point. Direction of arrow indicates desired direction of turn.	
Fix 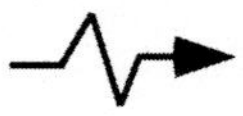	Irregular part of arrow indicates where enemy advance is slowed by obstacles.	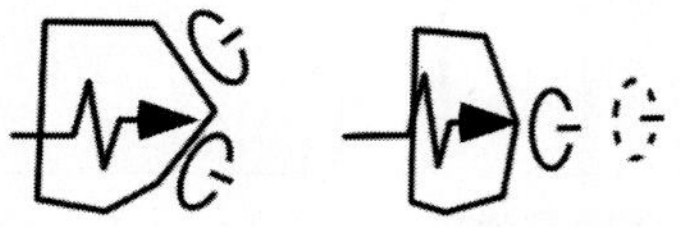
Block 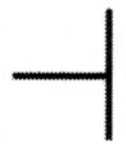	The ends of the verticle line indicate the limit of enemy advance. The ends of the vertical line also indicate where obstacles tie in to NO-GO terrain.	
		Direction of Enemy Attack →

Figure 3.3 Obstacle Effect Graphics

Purposes of Obstacles

Blocking obstacles deny the attackers access to an area, route, or avenue of approach. The best blocking obstacles tie reinforcing obstacles to impassable terrain in a depth and concentration that prevents the attackers from defeating the obstacle or bypassing it. A properly placed blocking obstacle will block the enemy from moving beyond the engagement area and gives the defender the opportunity to counterattack the attacker's flanks.

In the defense, you use **fixing obstacles** with engagement areas, **fire sacks,** or kill zones. Unlike a blocking obstacle, the fixing obstacle does not have to prevent the enemy's movement in order to succeed. The fixing obstacle slows, harasses, or interdicts the enemy's movement so that the defender has time to concentrate and mass direct and indirect fires on the enemy in the engagement area. The defender begins depleting the attacking force as far forward as possible: first, using close air support (CAS); then indirect fire; and then using organic weapons. A fixing obstacle can also give the defender the time needed to break contact or fire and maneuver on the attacker's unprotected flanks.

blocking obstacle

an obstacle that denies the attackers access to an area, route, or avenue of approach

fixing obstacle

an obstacle that slows, harasses, or interdicts the enemy's movement—it does not have to prevent the enemy's movement in order to succeed

fire sack

an area where a high density of preplanned flanking and frontal fires are placed on the attacking force by all available fire means— these fires are designed to produce high casualties among the attacker in a short period of time

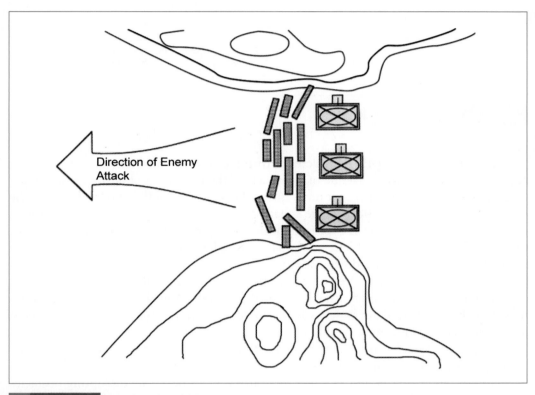

Figure 3.4 Block Obstacle Effect

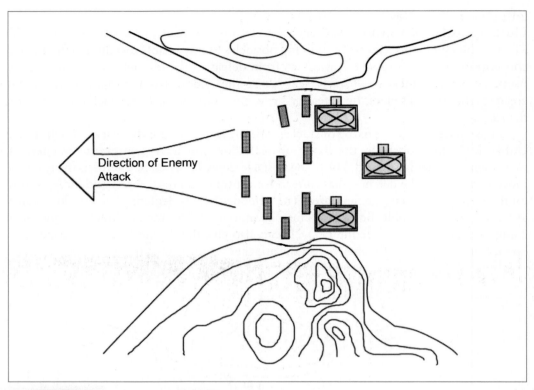

Figure 3.5 Fix Obstacle Effect

turning obstacle

an obstacle that turns the attackers off their current avenue of approach onto an avenue of approach of the defender's choosing

disrupting obstacle

an obstacle that breaks up the enemy forces' formation and tempo, interrupts their timetables, makes them commit breaching assets prematurely, and causes them to launch their attack piecemeal

The defender uses **turning obstacles** to turn the attackers off their current avenue of approach or route onto an avenue of approach of the defender's choosing. You employ turning obstacles in a manner that turns the attacking forces subtly—not giving away the obstacle's intent until the attackers are already committed to departing from their avenue of approach onto the avenue of approach the defender prefers. In order to accomplish this, the obstacles at the start of the turn are visibly complex and the attackers cannot bypass them. The obstacles farther down the turning obstacle are less difficult and the enemy believe they are successfully bypassing the obstacle, unaware that they are being turned onto a route or avenue of approach that favors the defender. You also use turning obstacles to expose the attackers' flank to defensive fires and channel the attackers into engagement areas, fire sacks, or kill zones.

As a platoon leader, you will employ **disrupting obstacles** to break up the enemy forces' formation and tempo, interrupt their timetable, make them commit breaching assets prematurely, and cause them to launch their attack piecemeal. The disrupting obstacles should be concealed at a distance, but the attackers should be able to easily identify them as they approach the obstacle. By not identifying the obstacles too early, the attackers do not have the time to react and bypass. By allowing the enemy to see the obstacle at approach, you force them to slow to deploy their forces and equipment to defeat the obstacle. You will employ fires as far forward of your position as possible to deplete the enemy as they move forward through the disrupting obstacle.

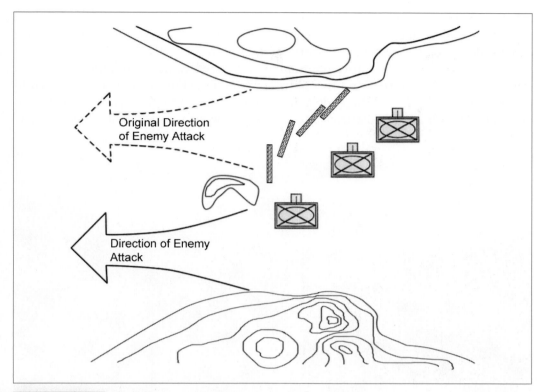

Figure 3.6 Turn Obstacle Effect

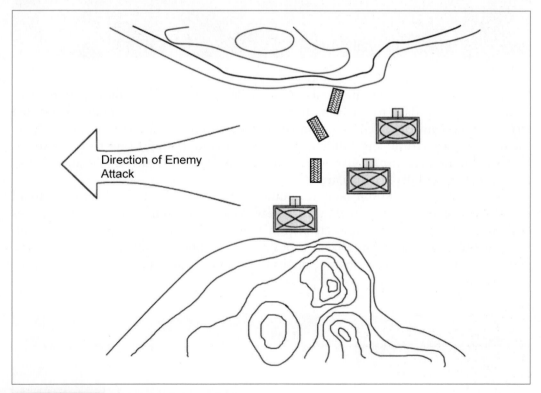

Figure 3.7 Disrupt Obstacle Effect

Levels of Restrictive Terrain

After you have identified existing and reinforcing obstacles in your platoon's AO, you must classify the terrain in your AO by one of three levels of restriction to movement: 1) unrestricted terrain; 2) restricted terrain; or 3) severely restricted terrain. *Unrestricted terrain* is free of any restriction to mounted or dismounted movement and offers flat to moderately sloping terrain and wide maneuver areas supported by well-developed road networks. An example of unrestricted terrain would be fields, pastures, and open desert.

Restricted terrain hinders movement to some degree. Restricted terrain interferes with a maneuver unit's ability to maintain speed, formation, or traveling techniques. Restricted terrain for mechanized forces would consist of moderate to steep slopes; moderate to dense rocks, trees, vegetation, and buildings; and little or poor supporting road networks. Restricted terrain for dismounted forces would include swamps, dense vegetation, steep, rugged terrain, and dense urban areas.

Severely restricted terrain includes minefields, unfordable rivers, road or railroad embankments, or extremely dense urban areas. As a rule of thumb, light infantry forces can traverse the most severely restricted terrain if they have the time and special equipment.

Remember to analyze the effects of obstacles from both the offensive and defensive perspective, to continuously observe all obstacles, and to cover all obstacles by direct or indirect fires.

Critical Thinking

How would a platoon use existing or reinforcing obstacles while conducting offensive operations?

Key Terrain

Key terrain affords a marked advantage to the combatant who seizes, retains, or controls it. As platoon leader, you identify key terrain starting at the objective or main battle area and working backward to your current position. It is a conclusion rather than an observation. You must assess which terrain is key to accomplishing your mission. Key terrain may allow you to apply direct fire or achieve observation of the objective (or avenue of approach). Key terrain may also be *enemy oriented,* meaning that if the enemy controls the terrain it could prevent your platoon from accomplishing its mission.

An example of key terrain for a platoon could be a tree line on a hillside that provides overwatch of a high-speed avenue of approach. Controlling this tree line may be critical in allowing follow-on forces (perhaps the main effort) to pass to their objective. High ground is not necessarily key terrain. For example, a prominent hilltop may overlook an avenue of approach and offer clear observation and fields of fire, but if it is easily bypassed, it is not key terrain.

Although unlikely, you may identify *decisive terrain*—key terrain that holds such importance that seizing, retaining, and controlling it will be necessary for accomplishing the mission, and may decide the battle's outcome. Use the two military aspects of terrain—observation and fields of fire, and cover and concealment—to analyze each piece of key terrain.

Critical Thinking

Think of the effects that each of the four types of obstacles has on an attacking force. Which type of obstacle works best against an infiltration lane or route, a maneuver corridor, and an avenue of approach?

Avenues of Approach

An avenue of approach is an air or ground route an attacking force follows to its objective or key terrain. For each avenue of approach, you determine the type (mounted, dismounted, air, or subterranean), size, and formation and the speed of the largest unit that can travel along it. (Your commander may give you this information.) Mounted forces may move on avenues along unrestricted or restricted terrain (or both). Dismounted avenues and avenues that reconnaissance elements and infantry platoons use normally include terrain that is restricted and at times severely restricted to mounted forces. Your terrain analysis also must identify avenues of approach for both friendly and enemy units.

In analyzing avenues of approach from the defensive perspective, you must determine how you can position your defense to provide you:

1. Observation to provide early warning of enemy approach
2. Fields of fire to allow you to place direct and indirect fires in depth as they approach
3. Cover and concealment that gives you the element of surprise and protects you from their weapons, and
4. The ability to reinforce existing obstacles so that you can block, fix, turn, or disrupt their approach in order to disrupt their tempo, prevent them from concentrating forces onto your defense, and keep them in your engagement area.

Lastly, you must identify your own covered and concealed avenues of approach or routes that allow you to counterattack the enemy.

Critical Thinking

Describe the avenue(s) of approach that you see in the photo. What size element would use the avenue(s) of approach? What formation and movement technique would the attacker use?

Weather Analysis

Terrain and weather analysis are inseparable. Soon you will be able to evaluate the effects of weather concurrently as you consider OAKOC. As a platoon leader, you will receive your terrain and weather analysis from your company commander (who received it from the battalion S-2 during the battalion OPORD). If you lead a specialty platoon, such as the battalion scouts, mortars, support platoon, or medical platoon, you will receive this information from the S-2 during the battalion OPORD. The S-2 will provide you with the weather and light data and its effects on terrain; mobility; weapon and acquisition systems; nuclear, biological, or chemical weapons (NBC); CAS; combat service support (CSS); etc. The S-2 will analyze the battalion's AO. You, however, must analyze the S-2's assessment and apply it to your own AO and mission.

Analyzing the Military Aspects of Weather

At the tactical level, you as the platoon leader must be able to determine the weather's effects on personnel, weapon systems, force mobility, and the tactical operations. Weather has a huge impact on Soldiers' morale, so you must not forget to factor this into your analyses. The military aspects of weather are:

1. visibility
2. winds
3. precipitation
4. temperature and humidity

You must go beyond merely making observations. You must arrive at significant conclusions about how the weather will affect your platoon and the enemy. Your commander provides his or her conclusions, and you identify your own critical conclusions about the weather. Most importantly, you must apply these conclusions when you develop friendly and enemy COAs.

Beginning Morning Nautical Twilight (BMNT)

begins when the sun is 12 degrees below the eastern horizon—it is the start of that period during which—in good conditions and in the absence of other illumination—enough light is available to identify the general outlines of ground objects, conduct limited military operations, and engage in most types of ground movement without difficulty

End Evening Nautical Twilight (EENT)

occurs when the sun has dropped 12 degrees below the western horizon, and is the instant of last available daylight for the visual control of limited ground operations

Critical Thinking

What effects do the moonrise and moonset have on planning night operations?

Visibility: Low visibility conceals offensive movement while degrading the defense's ability to observe engagement areas or kill zones. Low visibility can hinder the attacker's ability to identify fighting positions until it is too late. Many environmental factors other than day and night can degrade visibility. Cloud cover, fog, smoke, dust, and heavy rain can reduce sunlight or moonlight and can also render night vision and thermal devices less effective. The amount of available light is the major factor in evaluating visibility. You must consider the phases of the moon and the available light during **Beginning Morning Nautical Twilight** (BMNT), **End Evening Nautical Twilight** (EENT), sunrise, sunset, moonrise, and moonset. Low or poor visibility makes Soldiers edgy in a combat environment. You can't see as well, and you wonder whether you will see the enemy before they see you. This is especially true when you wear glasses, as dust, dirt or fogging of your glasses can seriously reduce your visibility in a combat environment.

Winds: Strong winds generally favor the force that is located upwind. Forces located downwind can suffer from blowing dust, smoke, sand, precipitation, and NBC agents. Strong winds can hinder or prevent airborne, air-assault, or aviation operations and can disrupt or decrease radar and communication systems' effectiveness. But strong winds can also be a friend to small-unit movement. Wind-blown trees and vegetation make it more difficult for the defender to distinguish between a Soldier moving and the movement of the vegetation around him. Winds can also give the attacker the edge over the defender by masking the sounds of the attacker's movement.

Precipitation: Precipitation can make movement difficult, reduce visibility, and interfere with electro-optical systems. Generally speaking, poor weather conditions favor the attacking forces. The defender has a tendency to hunker down in order to get out of the elements, whereas the attacker must maneuver regardless of the rain, snow, or sleet. Precipitation causes optics to fog up, reducing the effectiveness of binoculars and optical sights. Heavy rains can impair or reduce the effectiveness of radio, radar, and satellite equipment. Flash flooding can erase your planned movement and supply routes and wash out your defensive positions. Constant exposure to wet conditions can result in casualties from trench foot. Extended exposure to snow can result in frostbite. You must consider the type of precipitation (snow, sleet, hail, and/or rain) and its effects on troop morale, equipment, and your ability to move.

Cloud Cover: Cloud cover can negate the effects of illumination rounds, flares, and moonlight. It can even reduce the light from the sun. Darker conditions from cloud cover can allow an attacking force to move undetected, benefiting the attacker over the defender, but they can also make it harder for the attacker to locate the enemy defense. Cloud cover can also degrade target acquisition systems, close air support, counter-indirect fire systems, radar, and communication systems. Cloud cover will help conceal the approach of air support. The force with the thermal or night vision capability is less affected by cloud cover than the force that does not have the optically aided technology. You must also consider environmental conditions unique to your AO that have the same effects as cloud cover, such as sand or dust storms, burning tires or buildings in an urban environment, or oil-well fires. Cloud cover can also be a morale booster: It can reduce temperatures and the strain on Soldiers' eyes from bright sunlight.

Temperature and Humidity: In general, high temperatures and humidity benefit the defender, and low temperatures benefit the attacker. Heat and humidity can sap a Soldier's strength and morale. Heat and humidity will affect the defender in a static and covered position less. A static defender requires less water and rest than the Soldier on the move does, but you must factor in the level of exertion required to dig in the defense. On the other hand, a moving Soldier stays warmer during cold weather than the static defender. Extreme cold weather can result in frostbite. Remember that frostbite can occur even when skin is not exposed.

Likewise, you must watch for hypothermia, even in warm climates. Your Soldiers are susceptible to hypothermia in hot desert environments because of the sudden and extreme drops in temperature at night. Consider the drop in a daytime temperature of 120 degrees down to 70 degrees at sunset. That's a drop of 50 degrees in a matter of hours. Soldiers operating in wet gear can also suffer hypothermia, even in warm weather, as the core body temperature drops from loss of heat due to the constant water evaporation off the skin.

Temperature and humidity can play havoc with vehicles and equipment. Extreme temperatures can cause vehicle and equipment failure. Tracked vehicles can freeze to the ground in colder climates. Engines can overheat in hotter climates. The effects of high humidity range from producing moisture in powdered munitions to decreasing lift in aircraft, thus reducing the payload the aircraft can carry. Thermal sights and targeting systems are particularly affected at "temperature crossovers"—the time of day or night when the target and the air temperature are the same. At thermal crossover, the thermal

signature of the target may blend in with the surface temperatures of surrounding natural and man-made objects, making it more difficult to observe and place fires on targets. Temperature crossover generally occurs twice in a 24-hour period and interferes with the defender and attacker who are looking for the opposing force's thermal signature. Temperature and humidity can also cause the optics to fog up on optical sights and equipment.

You must also consider the effects of **temperature inversion** and fog in selecting defensive positions and route selection. Temperature inversion and fog generally affect low-lying areas. Most NBC agents will gravitate to low-lying areas, and temperature inversion or fog will allow the NBC agents to persist longer. Fog will burn off more slowly in depressions, valleys, draws, and over bodies of water. Defenders must ensure that they do not plan engagement areas and kill zones in an area that is susceptible to dense or prolonged periods of fog. Attackers, on the other hand, will plan routes that take advantage of terrain with dense or persistent fog to cover their movement. The defenders can use fog to help conceal their positions, but must be able to use thermal devices to detect attackers who are also benefiting from the fog cover.

Analyzing the Effect of Light Data

When planning an operation, you must consider all aspects of light data. You must know what light you will have, the source, when you will have it, and for how long. You must understand how the light data will benefit you and the enemy. The light data most important to you will depend largely on the time and purpose of your mission. If you were conducting a mission that relies on stealth and concealment, then you would want to conduct your mission between EENT and BMNT, but at a point when the moon cycle offers the least light and closest to moonset. If you were planning a day raid that requires surprise but affords a degree of visibility, then you would want to plan to initiate the raid at or near BMNT. If you are in the defense and need to know the best times to conduct reconnaissance and security (R&S) patrols or place LP/OPs, then you would want to know the darkest time of night—because low visibility offers the attackers concealment.

temperature inversion

a reversal of the normal way air temperature near the surface of the Earth is warmer than the air above it—when this gradient is inverted, the air gets colder near the surface of the earth, resulting in "stillness" of the air so that dirty or foggy air is no longer pulled away from the ground—temperature inversion also can affect visibility and communication signals

Critical Thinking

If thermal crossover has the same effect on target thermal signature for both forces possessing thermal technology, which operation is most affected by thermal crossover: the defense or offense?

CONCLUSION

You should now have a level of understanding and respect for the many things you as a small-unit leader must consider when analyzing the effects of terrain and weather on military operations. Like map reading and land navigation, analyzing the effects of terrain and weather is a perishable skill that you must practice and master to be an effective leader. Soon, and throughout your time as an ROTC cadet, you will have the opportunity to improve your proficiency through further study and practical applications during labs and field-training exercises. This chapter outlines a limited portion of the IPB process. You will receive more in-depth formal training on the IPB process when you attend future Officer Education System courses as a commissioned officer.

Learning Assessment

1. Define the military aspects of terrain (OAKOC).
2. Describe the four purposes of military obstacles.
3. Describe how each of the following aspects of weather can affect military operations:
   a. Visibility
   b. Winds
   c. Precipitation
   d. Cloud cover
   e. Temperature and humidity
   f. Light

Key Words

Intelligence Preparation of the Battlefield
terrain analysis
area of operation
OAKOC
engagement area
kill zone
line of sight analysis
fire sack
Beginning Morning Nautical Twilight (BMNT)
End Evening Nautical Twilight (EENT)
temperature inversion

References

Field Manual 3-0, *Operations*. 27 February 2008.

Field Manual 3-21.8, *The Infantry Rifle Platoon and Squad*. 28 March 2007.

Field Manual 3-25.26, *Map Reading and Land Navigation*. Change 1. 30 August 2006.

Field Manual 34-130, *Intelligence Preparation of the Battlefield*. 8 July 1994.

Field Manual 5-33, *Terrain Analysis*. 11 July 1990.

Scalard, D. P. (n.d.). The Battle of Hamburger Hill: Battle Command in Difficult Terrain Against a Determined Enemy. *Studies in Battle Command*. Retrieved 24 March 2005 from http://www.ehistory.com/vietnam/essays/battlecommand/index.cfm

INTRODUCTION TO PROBLEM SOLVING

Key Points

1 Definition and Levels of Decision Making

2 The Seven Steps of the Army Problem Solving Process

3 The Roles of Knowledge, Intuition, Judgment, and Ethics

The good leader must have ethos, pathos, and logos. The ethos is his moral character, the source of one's ability to persuade. The pathos is the ability to touch feelings, to move people emotionally. The logos is the ability to give solid reasons for an action, to move people intellectually.

Mortimer Adler, American professor, author, philosopher, and educational theorist

Introduction

Good decision making is a fundamental leadership skill. Whether you are leading in a business, a government agency, a university, or on a battlefield, making good decisions is essential. Many of the key decisions leaders make involve problems they must solve. A **problem** is an existing condition or situation in which what you want to happen is different from what is happening.

problem

the difference between the current state or condition and a desired state or condition

When problems arise, leaders must analyze the cause of the problems and determine the best possible way to solve them. Every leader uses a system to help in the problem solving process. Leaders may not be conscious of the system they use, but they inevitably use some kind of problem solving process.

Unfortunately, many of the unconscious problem solving systems leaders use lead them to make poor decisions. The reason is simple: When leaders react to what they see on the surface, but don't take time to uncover the underlying factors at the root of many problems, their quick decisions may simply make the problem worse. A quick decision in response to superficial problems is often a poor decision. When a warning light goes off on your car's dashboard, the problem is not a red light on the dashboard. Something is wrong with the engine. If you react to the problem of the dashboard light and solve that problem by disconnecting a wire that leads to the dashboard—a quick, easy, inexpensive fix—you are far from solving the problem. The better way to address a problem is to systematically and logically analyze what is taking place and what you can do in response.

This lesson provides an overview of the Army problem solving process—a systematic, logical approach to problem solving and decision making that leads to better decisions. When you lead men and women in battle, good decision making is not a luxury.

The Battalion Dining In

Your battalion commander has tasked you to plan a dining in. Traditionally, such an event is held at the hotel and conference center on campus, but one week before the dining in, this hotel must close unexpectedly due to flooding from a broken water line. What will you do? Cancel or reschedule the dining in? Move it to another location? You must make a decision quickly, and you must be able to defend your decision to your battalion commander. What steps will you take to solve this problem?

Definition and Levels of Decision Making

decision making

a process that involves selecting the line of action you believe will most likely lead to successfully completing your mission – this involves sound judgment, logical reasoning, and wise use of resources

Decision making involves selecting the line of action you believe will most likely lead to successfully completing your mission. This involves sound judgment, logical reasoning, and wise use of resources. Decision making starts the process of solving the problem. Thus, decision making is knowing whether to decide, then when and what to decide. It includes understanding the consequences of your decisions.

Civilian authors have written extensively about problem solving and decision making, producing a number of models for both. For decision making, most Army leaders follow one of two processes, depending on the level of their authority. Lieutenants and other leaders at company level and below follow the **troop leading procedures** (TLP). The TLP are designed to solve tactical problems. Leaders at battalion level and above follow the **military decision making process** (MDMP). The MDMP is designed for organizations with staffs that help the commander make and implement decisions. Both TLP and MDMP are established and proven methods that combine elements of the planning and operating leadership actions to save time. Both follow the Army problem solving process discussed below.

troop leading procedures

a collection of analytical processes, tactics, techniques, and procedures a leader uses to plan and prepare his or her unit to accomplish a tactical mission

military decision making process

a single, established, analytical process that helps the commander and his or her staff examine a battlefield situation and reach logical decisions

The Seven Steps of the Army Problem Solving Process

Problem solving is a daily activity for Army leaders. Army problem solving is a systematic way to arrive at the best solution to a problem. It applies at all levels and includes the steps you need to develop well-reasoned, supportable solutions (see Figure 4.1). It incorporates risk management techniques appropriate to the situation.

You must remain as objective as possible when solving problems. The goal is to prepare an unbiased solution or recommendation based on the facts. Problem solving is an important Army leadership action. It is essential to good staff work.

The Army problem solving model has seven steps.

Army leaders usually follow one of two decision making processes. Leaders at company level and below follow the troop leading procedures (TLP). Leaders at battalion level and above follow the military decision making process (MDMP).

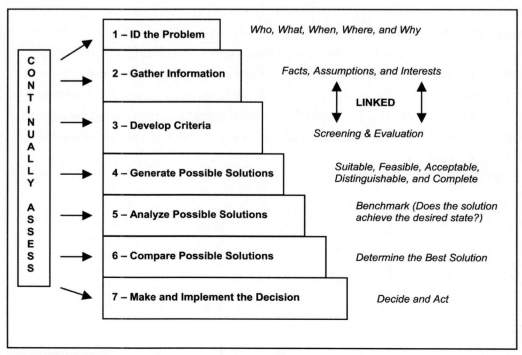

Figure 4.1 Seven Step Problem Solving Model

Step 1—Identify the Problem

The first step in problem solving is recognizing and defining the problem. This step is crucial, as the actual problem may not be obvious. Determine what the problem is by clearly defining its scope and limitations. Allow sufficient time and energy to clearly define the problem before you move on to other steps of the problem solving process.

A problem exists when there is a difference between the current state or condition and a desired state or condition. You should identify problems from a variety of sources. These include:

- Higher headquarters directives or guidance
- Decision maker guidance
- Subordinates
- Your personal observations.

When identifying the problem, actively seek to identify its root cause, not merely the symptoms on the surface. Symptoms may be the reason that the problem became visible. They are often the first things people notice and frequently require attention. But focusing only on a problem's symptoms may lead to false conclusions or inappropriate solutions. Using a systematic approach to identifying problems helps avoid the "solving symptoms" pitfall.

To identify the root cause of a problem, you should do the following:

- Compare the current situation to the desired end state
- Define the problem's scope or boundaries
- Answer the following questions:

  - Whom does the problem affect?
  - What is affected?
  - When did the problem occur?
  - Where is the problem?
  - Why did the problem occur?

- Determine the cause of obstacles between the present situation and the solution—many times a problem's causes are simply obstacles between the current situation and the desired end state
- Write a draft problem statement
- Redefine the problem as necessary as you gain and assess new information.

After identifying the root causes, develop a problem statement. You write a problem statement as an infinitive phrase, such as, "To determine the best location for constructing a multipurpose vehicle wash rack facility during this fiscal year." When the problem under consideration is based on a directive from a higher authority, it is best to submit the problem statement to the decision maker for approval. This ensures that you have understood the decision maker's guidance before you continue.

Once you have developed the problem statement, make a plan to solve the problem. Make the best possible use of available time, and allocate time for each problem solving step. Doing this provides you a series of deadlines to meet in solving the problem. Use reverse planning to prepare a problem solving timeline, then use this timeline to periodically assess your progress. Don't let real or perceived pressure cause you to abandon solving the problem systematically. You can change time allocations as necessary, but don't ignore them.

Step 2—Gather Information

After completing the problem statement, continue to gather information relevant to the problem. Gathering information begins with defining the problem and continues throughout the problem solving process. Never stop acquiring new or additional information and assessing its impact.

When gathering information, define unfamiliar terms. This is particularly important when dealing with technical information. Consider the intended audience in deciding what to define. For example, a product for an audience that includes civilians may require definitions of all Army terms. A technical report prepared for a decision maker unfamiliar with the subject should include definitions the reader needs in order to understand the report.

Gather information from primary sources whenever possible. Primary sources are people with first-hand knowledge of the subject under investigation, or documents they have produced. Methods of gathering information from primary sources include interviews, letters of request for specific information, and questionnaires.

You need two types of information to solve problems: facts and assumptions. Fully understanding these types of information is critical to understanding problem solving. In addition, you will need to know how to handle opinions and how to manage information when working in a group.

Facts

facts

verifiable pieces of information that are objectively real

Facts are verifiable pieces of information that are objectively real. They form the foundation on which you base the solution to a problem. Regulations, policies, doctrinal publications, commander's guidance, plans and orders, personal experience, and the Internet are just a few sources of facts.

Assumptions

assumptions

information you accept as true in the absence of facts

Assumptions are information you accept as true in the absence of facts. This information is probably correct, but you cannot verify it. Appropriate assumptions used in decision making have two characteristics:

- They are valid; that is, they are likely to be true
- They are necessary; that is, they are essential to continuing the problem solving process.

If you can continue the process without making a particular assumption, discard the assumption. So long as an assumption is both valid and necessary, treat it as a fact. You should continually seek to confirm or deny the validity of your assumptions.

Opinions

When gathering information, evaluate opinions carefully. An opinion is a personal judgment that you or other individuals make. You can't totally discount opinions. They are often the result of years of experience. Objectively evaluate opinions to determine whether to accept them as facts, include them as opinions, or reject them. You should neither routinely accept opinions as facts nor reject them as irrelevant—regardless of their source.

Organizing Information

Check each piece of information to verify its accuracy. If possible, two individuals should check and confirm the accuracy of facts and the validity of assumptions.

The ability to establish whether a piece of information is a fact or an assumption is of little value if those working on the problem don't know the information exists. Always share information with the decision maker, subordinates, and peers, as appropriate. A proposed solution to a problem is only as good as the information that forms the basis of the solution. Sharing information among members of a problem solving team increases the likelihood that a team member will uncover the information that leads to the best solution.

Organizing information includes coordination with units and agencies that may be affected by the problem or its solution. Determine who these are as you gather information. Coordinate with other leaders as you solve problems, both to obtain assistance and to keep others informed of situations that may affect them. Such coordination may be informal and routine: For example, a squad leader checking with the squad on his right to make sure their fields of fire overlap. Or it may be formal, as when a division action officer staffs a decision paper with the major subordinate commands. At a minimum, always coordinate with units or agencies that your solution might affect.

Step 3—Develop Criteria

The next step in the problem solving process is developing criteria. A criterion is a standard, rule, or test by which you can judge something—a measure of value. You develop criteria to assist you in formulating and evaluating possible solutions to a problem. Criteria are based on facts or assumptions. You should develop two types: screening criteria and evaluation criteria.

Screening Criteria

Use screening criteria to ensure the solutions you are considering can solve the problem. Screening criteria define the limits of an acceptable solution. As such, they are tools to establish the baseline products for analysis. You may reject a solution based solely on applying your screening criteria. Five categories of screening criteria are commonly applied to test a possible solution:

- *Suitability* – solves the problem and is legal and ethical
- *Feasibility* – fits within available resources
- *Acceptability* – worth the cost or risk
- *Distinguishability* – differs significantly from other solutions
- *Completeness* – contains the critical aspects of solving the problem from start to finish.

Evaluation Criteria

After developing your screening criteria, develop your evaluation criteria in order to differentiate among possible solutions. Well-defined evaluation criteria have five elements:

- *Short Title* – the criterion name
- *Definition* – a clear description of the feature you are evaluating
- *Unit of Measure* – a standard element used to quantify the criterion. Examples of units of measure are US dollars, miles per gallon, and feet
- *Benchmark* – a value that defines the desired state, or "good" for a solution in terms of a particular criterion
- *Formula* – an expression of how changes in the value of the criterion affect the desirability of the possible solution. State the formula in comparative terms (for example, more is better) or absolute terms (for example, a night movement is better than a day movement).

A well-thought-out benchmark is critical for meaningful analysis. Analysis judges a solution against a standard, telling you whether that solution is good in an objective sense. It differs from comparison, which judges possible solutions against each other, telling you which is better or worse in a relative sense.

Benchmarks are the standards you use in analysis. They may be set down by regulations or guidance from the decision maker. Sometimes you can infer the benchmark from the tangible return expected from the problem's solution. Often, however, you will establish benchmarks yourself. Four common methods for doing this are:

- *Reasoning* – the benchmark is based on personal experience and your judgment as to what would be good
- *Historical precedent* – the benchmark is based on relevant examples of prior success
- *Current example* – the benchmark is based on an existing condition, which is considered desirable
- *Averaging* – the benchmark is based on the mathematical average of the solutions you are considering. Averaging is the least preferred of all methods because it essentially duplicates the comparison process.

In practice, the criteria by which you make choices are almost never equally important. Because of this it is often convenient to assign weights to each evaluation criterion. Weighting criteria establishes the relative importance of each with respect to the others. Weighting should reflect as closely as possible the judgment of the decision maker or acknowledged experts. For example, you might judge that two criteria are *equal* in importance, or that one criterion is *slightly favored* in importance, or *moderately* or *strongly favored*. If you assign these verbal assessments numerical values, say from 1 to 4 respectively, you could use mathematical techniques to produce meaningful numerical criteria weights.

Additionally, pair-wise comparison is an analytical tool that brings objectivity to the process of assigning criteria weights. In performing a pair-wise comparison, you methodically assess each evaluation criterion against each of the others and judge its relative importance. A computer equipped with simple software easily performs the mathematical algorithms.

This process does not in any way diminish the importance of your judgment. Rather it enables you to bring that judgment to bear with greater precision and in problems of greater complexity than might otherwise be possible. Regardless of the method you use to assign criteria weights, you should state the rationale for each when recommending or making a solution.

Step 4—Generate Possible Solutions

After gathering information relevant to the problem and developing criteria, you formulate possible solutions. Carefully consider the guidance the commander or your superiors have provided, and develop several alternative solutions. You should consider several alternatives, but too many possible solutions may result in time wasted on similar options. Experience and time available determine how many solutions to consider, but you should consider at least two solutions. Doing this will enable you to use both analysis and comparison as problem solving tools. Developing only one solution to "save time" may produce a faster solution but risks creating more problems from factors you didn't consider.

You should follow two steps when developing solutions:

- Generate options
- Summarize the solution in writing, sketches, or both.

Generate Options

Creativity is key to developing effective solutions. Often, groups are more creative than individuals. Those working on solutions should have some knowledge of or background in the problem area, however.

The basic technique for developing new ideas in a group setting is *brainstorming*. In brainstorming, everyone present participates freely in the discussion. Its rules include:

- State the problem and make sure all participants understand it
- Appoint someone to record all ideas
- Withhold judgment of ideas
- Encourage independent thoughts
- Aim for quantity, not quality
- "Hitchhike" ideas—combine your thoughts with those of others.

At the conclusion of brainstorming, discard solutions that clearly do not approach the standards described by your screening criteria. If this informal screen leaves only one solution or none, then the group must generate more options.

Summarize the Solution in Writing and Sketches

After generating options, accurately record each possible solution. The solution statement must clearly portray how the action or actions will solve the problem. In some circumstances the solution statement may be a single sentence (for example, "Purchase Model XYZ computers"). In other circumstances the solution statement may require more detail, including sketches or concept diagrams. For example, if the problem is to develop a multipurpose small-arms range, you may choose to portray each solution with a narrative and a separate sketch or blueprint of each proposed range.

Step 5—Analyze Possible Solutions

Having identified possible solutions, analyze each one to determine its merits and drawbacks. If criteria are well defined and include careful selection of benchmarks, your analysis is greatly simplified.

Use screening criteria and benchmarks to analyze possible solutions. Apply screening criteria to judge whether a solution meets minimum requirements. For quantitative criteria, measure, compute, or estimate the raw data values for each solution and each criterion. In analyzing solutions, which involves predicting future events, it's useful to have a process for visualizing those events. Wargaming, models, and simulations are examples of tools that can help you visualize events and estimate raw data values for use in analysis. Once you have determined the raw data values, judge them against applicable screening criteria to determine if a possible solution merits further consideration. Screen out any solution that fails to meet or exceed the set threshold of one or more screening criteria.

After applying the screening criteria to all possible solutions, use benchmarks to judge them with respect to the desired state. Data values that meet or exceed the benchmark indicate that the possible solution achieves the desired state and thus is "good" with respect to that criterion. Data values that fail to meet the benchmark indicate a solution that is not good in terms of the criterion you have identified.

For each solution, list the respects in which analysis reveals it to be good or not good. It is quite possible that every solution you are considering will fail to reach the benchmark, and so be considered not good in terms of a particular criterion. When this occurs, you must acknowledge that there are no good solutions under consideration in that particular respect.

Be careful not to compare solutions during analysis. To do so undermines the integrity of the process and may tempt you to jump to conclusions. Examine each possible solution independently to identify its strengths and weaknesses. Be careful also not to introduce new criteria.

Step 6—Compare Possible Solutions

During this step, compare each solution against the others to determine the best solution. Comparing solutions identifies which solution best solves the problem based on the evaluation criteria. Use any comparison technique that helps reach the best recommendation. The most common technique is a decision matrix. Table 4.1 shows a decision matrix you might develop in solving the Battalion Dining In problem at the beginning of this section.

TABLE 4.1	Decision Matrix			
Location	Cost	Distance from campus	Room size	Menu
Criterion weight	2	1	2	3
Banquet Hall A	$450	5 miles	Seating for 200	Unlimited
Banquet Hall B	$500	15 miles	Seating for 100	Limited
Banquet Hall C	$250	10 miles	Seating for 100	Limited and of questionable quality

You may use quantitative techniques (such as decision matrices, select weights, and sensitivity analyses) to support comparisons. But they are tools to support the analysis and comparison. They are not the analysis and comparison themselves. You should summarize the quantitative techniques clearly so a reader need not refer to an annex for the results.

Step 7—Make and Implement the Decision

After completing your analysis and comparison, identify the preferred solution. For simple problems, proceed straight to executing the solution. For more complex problems, you may need a leader plan of action or formal plan. If a superior assigned the problem, prepare the necessary products (verbal, written, or both) needed to present the recommendation to the decision maker. Before presenting findings and a recommendation, coordinate your recommendation with those whom the problem or solutions affect. In formal situations, you present your findings and recommendations to the decision maker as staff studies, decision papers, or decision briefings.

A good solution can be lost if you can't persuade the audience that it is correct. Every problem requires both a solution and the ability to communicate it. The writing and briefing skills you possess may ultimately be as important as good problem solving skills.

Based on the decision maker's decision and final guidance, refine the solution and prepare the necessary implementing instructions. A decision maker can issue formal implementing instructions as a memorandum of instruction, policy letter, or command directive. Once you have given instructions, monitor their implementation, and compare the results to the criteria of success and the desired end state established in the approved solution. When necessary, issue additional instructions.

You must also build into the implementation plan a feedback system that provides timely and accurate information, periodic review, and the flexibility to adjust. Stay involved, and be careful not to create new problems because of uncoordinated implementation of the solution.

Remember: Army problem solving does not end with identifying the best solution or obtaining approval of a recommendation. It ends when you solve the problem.

The Roles of Knowledge, Intuition, Judgment, and Ethics

Even following these steps, you may find that some decisions require you to take into account your knowledge, your intuition, and your best judgment. Intuition tells you what feels right—it comes from accumulated experience and is often referred to as "gut feeling." Don't be fooled into relying only on intuition, however, even if it has worked in the past. A leader who says, "Hey, I just do what feels right," may be hiding incompetence or may just be too lazy to do the homework needed to make a reasoned, thought-out decision. Don't let that be you. Use your experience, listen to your instincts, but do your research as well. Get the facts and generate alternatives. Analyze and compare as many as time allows. Then make your decision, and act.

Remember also that any decision you make must reflect Army Values. While most problems are not ethical problems, they often have ethical aspects. Taking leave, for example, is a right Soldiers and Department of the Army civilians enjoy, but leaders must balance mission requirements with their subordinates' desires and their own. Reconciling such issues may require ethical reasoning. As a leader, your superiors and subordinates expect you to take ethical aspects into account and make decisions that are right as well as good.

Critical Thinking

During your recent patrolling operation you (the patrol leader) and the assistant patrol leader (APL) are preparing to execute a reconnaissance mission in support of the commander's intent in your recent operations order. During the planning phase of your operation you discover that you and your unit are not in the correct position and that you have left behind a critical piece of equipment—the GPS. What will you do? What steps will you take to ensure that you can complete your assigned mission within the allotted time frame?

Critical Thinking

Explain the importance of ethical standards and setting priorities in the problem solving process.

As a leader, you must also set priorities. You may be trying to say something about urgency if you give your subordinates a list of things to do and say, "They're all important." But the message you actually send is, "I can't decide which of these is most important, so I'll just lean on you and see what happens."

Sometimes all courses of action may appear equally good (or bad), and any decision may appear equally right (or wrong). Situations like that may tempt you to sit on the fence, make no decision, and let things work themselves out. Occasionally, that may be appropriate. Remember that decision making involves judgment—knowing whether to decide. More often, though, problems left to themselves go from bad to worse. In such situations, making a decision may be less important than simply deciding to do something. Leaders must have the personal courage to say which tasks are more important than others. In the absence of a clear priority, you must set one. Not everything can be a top priority, and you can't make progress without making decisions.

> *Leaders must balance mission requirements with their people's desires and their own.*

> *Leaders must have the personal courage to say which tasks are more important than others.*

Critical Thinking

Describe a situation in which no decision would be the best decision.

Solving a Training Problem

A rifle platoon gets a new platoon leader and a new platoon sergeant within days of a poor showing in the division's military operations on urbanized terrain (MOUT) exercise. The new leaders assume the platoon's poor showing is a problem. Feedback from the evaluators is general and vague. The platoon's squad and fire team leaders are angry and not much help in assessing what went wrong, so the new leaders begin investigating. In their fact-finding step they identify the following facts: 1) The Soldiers are out of shape and unable to complete some of the physical tasks. 2) The fire team leaders don't know MOUT tactics, and some of the squad leaders are also weak. 3) Third Squad performed well, but didn't help the other squads. 4) The Soldiers didn't have the right equipment at the training site.

Pushing a bit further to get at the root causes of these problems, the new leaders uncover the following: 1) Platoon physical training (PT) emphasizes preparation for the Army Physical Fitness Test only. 2) Third Squad's leaders know MOUT techniques, and had even developed simple drills to help their Soldiers learn, but because of unhealthy competition encouraged by the previous leaders, Third Squad didn't share the knowledge. 3) The company supply sergeant has the equipment the Soldiers needed, but because the platoon had lost some equipment on the last field exercise, the supply sergeant didn't let the platoon sign out the equipment.

The new platoon leader and platoon sergeant set a goal of successfully meeting the exercise standard in two months. To generate alternatives, they meet with the squad leaders and ask for suggestions to improve training. They use all their available resources to develop solutions. Among the suggestions is to shuffle some of the team leaders to break up Third Squad's clique and spread some of the tactical knowledge around. When squad leaders complain, the platoon sergeant emphasizes that they must think as a platoon, not just a collection of squads. The platoon sergeant talks to the supply sergeant, who tells him the platoon's previous leadership had been lax about accounting for property. Furthermore, the previous leaders didn't want to bother keeping track of equipment, so they often left it in garrison. The platoon sergeant teaches his squad leaders how to keep track of equipment and says that, in the future, Soldiers who lose equipment will pay for it: "We wouldn't leave our stuff behind in war, so we're not going to do it in training."

Building on Third Squad's experience, the platoon leader works with the squad and fire team leaders to come up with some simple drills for the platoon's missions. He takes the leaders to the field and practices the drills with them so they'll be able to train their Soldiers to the new standard.

The platoon sergeant also goes to the battalion's fitness trainers and, with their help, develops a PT program that emphasizes skills the Soldiers need for their combat tasks. The new program includes rope climbing, running with weapons and equipment, and road marches. Finally, the leaders monitor how their plan is working. A few weeks before going through the course again, they decide to eliminate one of the battle drills because the squad leaders suggested it wasn't necessary after all.

The platoon leader and platoon sergeant followed the problem solving steps you just read about. Given a problem (poor performance), they identified the facts surrounding it (poor PT practices, poor property accountability, and unhealthy competition), developed a plan of action, and executed it. Where appropriate, they analyzed and compared different alternatives (Third Squad's drills). They included their subordinates in the process, but had the moral courage to make unpopular decisions (breaking up the Third Squad clique). Will the platoon do better the next time out? Probably, but before then the new leaders must assess the results of their actions to make sure they're accomplishing what their leaders want. Other aspects of this problem may crop up that were not apparent at first, and following this or any process doesn't guarantee success. The process is only a framework that helps you make a plan and act. Success depends on your ability to apply your attributes and skills to implementing your plan.

CONCLUSION

Every once in a while, you may come across a decision that's easy to make: yes or no, right or left, on or off. As you gain experience as a leader, some of the decisions you find difficult now will become easier. But you will always face difficult decisions that require imagination, that require rigorous thinking and analysis, or that require you to factor in your gut reaction. Those are the tough decisions, the ones the Army is paying you to make. As an experienced first sergeant once said to a brand new company commander, "We get paid the big bucks to make the hard calls."

Leaders make decisions. Making the right decision is not always easy. The Army problem solving process helps you make fact-based, logical decisions. Some problems, however, will offer competing solutions, in which case you may have to rely on intuition, values, and priorities to arrive at a final decision. The hallmark of a competent leader is the ability to make the tough calls and the right decisions.

Learning Assessment

1. List the seven steps of the Army Problem Solving Process.
2. How do ethics come into play when making a decision?
3. Which Army Problem Solving Process is used at company level and below?

Key Words

problem
decision making
troop leading procedures
military decision making process
facts
assumptions

References

Field Manual 5-0, *Army Planning and Orders Production*. 20 January 2005.
SH 21-76, *Ranger Handbook*. July 2006.

TROOP LEADING PROCEDURES

Key Points

1 The Eight Steps of the Troop Leading Procedures

2 Potential Challenges Associated With the Troop Leading Procedures

A competent leader can get efficient service from poor troops; while, on the contrary, an incapable leader can demoralize the best of troops.

GEN John J. "Blackjack" Pershing

Introduction

This section seeks to improve your confidence in leading troops and increase your skills in planning and preparing for tactical situations. It builds on previous experience in Army Operations and problem solving. It introduces the eight steps of the troop leading procedures, a method for applying the Army Problem Solving Process to tactical problems.

COL Chamberlain at Gettysburg

On 1 July 1863 the 20th Maine received word to press on to Gettysburg. The Union Army had engaged the Confederates there, and Union commanders were hurrying all available forces to the hills south of the little town.

The 20th Maine arrived at Gettysburg near midday on 2 July. The regiment was preparing to go into a defensive position as part of the brigade commanded by COL Strong Vincent when a staff officer rode up to COL Vincent and began gesturing towards a little hill at the extreme southern end of the Union line. The hill, Little Round Top, dominated the Union position and, at that moment, was unoccupied. If the Confederates placed artillery on it, they could force the entire Union Army to withdraw.

Realizing the danger, COL Vincent ordered his brigade to occupy Little Round Top. He positioned the 20th Maine, commanded by COL Joshua L. Chamberlain, on his brigade's left flank, the extreme left of the Union line. COL Vincent told COL Chamberlain to "hold at all hazards."

On Little Round Top, COL Chamberlain told his company commanders the purpose and importance of their mission. He ordered the left flank company to anchor on a large boulder. His thoughts turned to his left flank. There was nothing there except a small hollow and the rising slope of Big Round Top. The 20th Maine was literally at the end of the line.

COL Chamberlain then showed a skill common to good tactical leaders. He imagined threats to his unit, did what he could to guard against them, and considered what he would do to meet other possible threats. Since his left flank was open, COL Chamberlain sent B Company, commanded by CPT Walter G. Morrill, off to guard it and "act as the necessities of battle required." The captain positioned his men behind a stone wall that would face the flank of any Confederate advance.

The 20th Maine had been in position only a few minutes when the Soldiers of the 15th and 47th Alabama attacked. The Maine men held their ground, but then one of COL Chamberlain's officers reported seeing a large body of Confederate Soldiers moving laterally behind the attacking force. COL Chamberlain climbed on a rock—exposing himself to enemy fire—and saw a Confederate unit moving around his exposed left flank. If they outflanked him, his unit would be pushed off its position and destroyed. He would have failed his mission.

COL Chamberlain had to think fast. The tactical manuals he had so diligently studied called for a maneuver that would not work on this terrain. The colonel had to create a new maneuver, one that his Soldiers could execute, and execute now. The 20th Maine was in a defensive line, two ranks deep. It was threatened by an attack around its left flank. So the colonel ordered his company commanders to stretch the line to the left and bend it back to form an angle, concealing the maneuver by keeping up a steady rate of fire. The corner of the angle would be the large boulder he had pointed out earlier. The sidestep maneuver was tricky, but it was a combination of other battle drills his Soldiers knew. In spite of the terrible noise that made voice commands useless, in spite of the blinding smoke, the cries of the wounded, and the continuing Confederate attack, the Maine men were able to pull it off.

Now COL Chamberlain's thin line was only one rank deep. His units, covering twice their normal frontage, were bent back into an L shape. Minutes after COL Chamberlain repositioned his force, the Confederate infantry, moving up what they thought was an open flank, were thrown back by the redeployed left wing of the 20th Maine. Surprised and angry, they nonetheless attacked again. The Maine men rallied and held; the Confederates regrouped and attacked. "The Alabamians drove the Maine men from their positions five times. Five times they fought their way back again. At some places, the muzzles of the opposing guns almost touched." After these assaults, the Maine men were down to one or two rounds per man, and the determined Confederates were regrouping for another try. COL Chamberlain saw that he could not stay where he was and could not withdraw. So he decided to counterattack. His men would have the advantage of attacking down the steep hill, he reasoned, and the Confederates would not be expecting it. Clearly he was risking his entire unit, but the fate of the Union Army depended on his men.

The decision left COL Chamberlain with another problem: There was nothing in the tactics book about how to get his unit from their L-shaped position into a line of advance. Under tremendous fire and in the midst of the battle, COL Chamberlain again called his commanders together. He explained that the regiment's left wing would swing around "like a barn door on a hinge" until it was even with the right wing. Then the entire regiment, bayonets fixed, would charge downhill, staying anchored to the 83d Pennsylvania on its right. The explanation was clear and the situation clearly desperate.

When COL Chamberlain gave the order, 1LT Holman Melcher of F Company leaped forward and led the left wing downhill toward the surprised Confederates. COL Chamberlain had positioned himself at the boulder at the center of the L. When the left wing was abreast of the right wing, he jumped off the rock and led the right wing down the hill. The entire regiment was now charging on line, swinging like a great barn door—just as its commander had intended.

The Alabama Soldiers, stunned at the sight of the charging Union troops, fell back on the positions behind them. There the 20th Maine's charge might have failed if not for a surprise resulting from COL Chamberlain's foresight. Just then CPT Morrill's B Company and the sharpshooters opened fire on the Confederate flank and rear. The exhausted and shattered Alabama regiments thought they were surrounded. They broke and ran, not realizing that one more attack would have carried the hill.

The slopes of Little Round Top were littered with bodies. Saplings halfway up the hill had been sawed in half by weapons fire. A third of the 20th Maine had fallen, 130 men out of 386. Nonetheless, the farmers, woodsmen, and fishermen from Maine—under the command of a brave and creative leader who had anticipated enemy actions, improvised under fire, and applied disciplined initiative in the heat of battle—had fought through to victory.

COL Chamberlain's actions on 2 July 1863 earned him the Medal of Honor.

Critical Thinking

Can you identify the steps in the troop leading procedures COL Chamberlain used during the remarkable engagement at Little Round Top?

The Eight Steps of the Troop Leading Procedures

Troop leading procedures are the process by which you prepare your unit to accomplish a tactical (combat) mission. It begins when you receive the alert for a new mission. It starts again when you receive a change or a new mission.

The troop leading procedures include the eight steps detailed below in Figure 5.1. Steps 3 through 8 may not follow a rigid sequence. You can implement many of the steps at the same time. The amount of time you have available dictates the depth of detail in which you can analyze and implement each step. In combat, you will rarely have enough time to go through each step in detail. Even so, you should use the procedure as outlined, if only in abbreviated form, to ensure that you leave nothing out of your planning and preparations—and that your Soldiers understand the platoon's and squads' missions and prepare adequately.

Figure 5.1 illustrates the relationship between troop leading procedures and other analytical processes, tactics, techniques, and procedures. Collectively, they form a tactician's toolkit that you can use to plan and prepare for tactical missions. Training and experience help you as a tactical leader understand how the systems work together. Experience can mean knowing both a) when not to use a tool or step, given the time available; and b) whether you have enough information at hand to implement command guidance and accomplish your assigned mission.

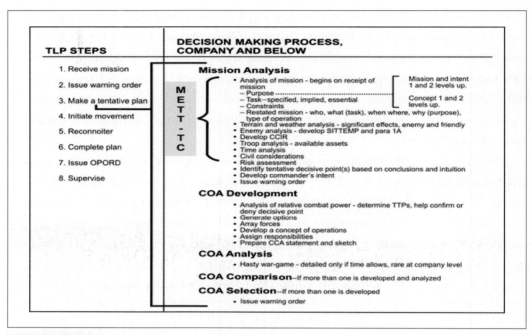

Figure 5.1 Tools of the Tactician Relationship

STEP 1—Receive the Mission

Troop leading procedures (TLP) begin when you receive an initial **warning order (WARNO)** from the company. They also may begin when you receive the commander's **operation order (OPORD),** or they may result from a change in the overall situation. When you receive the mission, you initiate the planning and preparation process so you can prepare an initial WARNO as quickly as possible. At this stage of the TLP, your mission analysis focuses on determining the unit's mission and the amount of available time. Your mission analysis is essentially the analysis of the factors of METT-TC, but you must not become involved in a detailed METT-TC analysis. This will occur after you issue your initial WARNO. Use METT-TC from the enemy's perspective to develop the details of possible enemy courses of action (COA). The following can assist in this process:

- Understand the enemy's mission
- Will the enemy's likely mission be based on his doctrine?
- Where does the enemy get logistical support and fire support?
- What cultural or religious factors are involved?
- What are the enemy's goals and are they tied to specific events or times?
- What are the enemy's capabilities?
- Does the weather aid or hinder the enemy?

Perhaps the most critical aspect of mission analysis is determining your force's combat power potential. Realistically and unemotionally determine which tasks your Soldiers are capable of performing. This analysis includes the troops attached to, or in direct support of, your platoon. Know the status of your Soldiers' experience and training level, and the strengths and weaknesses of your subordinate leaders. Your assessment includes knowing the status of your Soldiers and their equipment, and it includes understanding the full array of assets that support your platoon, such as additional antitank (AT) weapons, snipers, and engineers. For example, how much indirect fire is available and when is it available?

As addressed in the "receive the mission" TLP, time analysis is a critical aspect to your planning, preparation, and execution. Not only should you appreciate how much time is available, you must be able to appreciate the time-space aspects of preparing, moving, fighting, and sustaining. You must be able to see your own tasks and enemy actions in relation to time. Conduct backward planning and observe the **"one-third, two-thirds rule"** to allow your subordinates their own planning time. Examples of time analysis are as follows.

- Assess the impact of limited visibility conditions on the TLP
- How long does it take to prepare orders, conduct rehearsals, back-briefs, etc.?
- How long does it take to deploy a support by fire (SBF) element?
- How long does it take to assemble a bangalore torpedo and to breach a wire obstacle?
- Update timelines for your subordinates, listing all events that affect the platoon.

> **one-third, two-thirds rule**
>
> *an informal rule under which the leader should use no more than one third of the available time for planning and issuing an operation order—the remaining two thirds is for subordinates to plan and prepare for the operation*

Your commander will provide you with civil considerations that may affect the company and platoon missions. You must also identify any civil considerations that may affect only your platoon's mission. Platoons are likely to conduct missions in areas where there are numerous noncombatants and civilians on the battlefield. Some considerations may include refugee movement, humanitarian assistance requirements, or specific requirements related to the rules of engagement (ROE) or rules of interaction (ROI).

STEP 2—Issue a Warning Order

After you determine your platoon's mission and gauge the time available for planning, preparation, and execution, immediately issue an oral WARNO to your subordinates. In addition to telling your subordinates of the platoon's new mission, the WARNO also gives them your planning timeline. Relay all other instructions or information that you think will assist the platoon in preparing for the new mission. Such information includes information about the enemy, the nature of the overall plan, and specific instructions for preparation. Most importantly, by issuing the initial WARNO as quickly as possible, you enable your subordinates to begin their own planning and preparation while you start developing the platoon operation order. An example may include the squads rehearsing designated battle drills. This is called parallel planning.

STEP 3—Make a Tentative Plan

After receiving the company OPORD or **fragmentary order (FRAGO),** develop a tentative plan. The process of developing this plan when time is limited usually involves six steps:

1. receipt of the mission
2. mission analysis
3. COA development
4. COA analysis
5. COA selection
6. issue the order.

> **fragmentary order (FRAGO)**
>
> *an abbreviated form of an operation order (verbal, written, or digital), usually issued on a day-to-day basis.*

You rely heavily on the company commander's METT-TC analysis. This saves you time by focusing your analysis on areas that affect your plan. Typically, you will develop one COA. If more time is available, you may develop more than one—in which case you will need to compare these COAs and select the best one.

Mission analysis continues throughout the operation. It requires you to analyze all the factors of METT-TC in as much depth as time and quality of information will allow.

You don't always analyze the factors of METT-TC sequentially. How and when you analyze each factor depends on when you receive information. One technique for the analysis is based on the sequence of products that the company commander receives and produces: mission, enemy, terrain and weather, troops, time, civil considerations. You must develop significant conclusions about how each element will affect your mission accomplishment and then account for it in your plan.

You and your subordinates must have a clear understanding of the mission, intent, and concept of the operation of the commanders one and two levels higher. Without this understanding, it would be difficult to exercise disciplined initiative. One technique to quickly understand the operation is to draw a simple sketch of the battalion and company's concepts of the operation (if the commander doesn't provide one). In this way you can understand how the platoon mission relates to the missions of other units and how your mission fits into the overall plan. You can then capture this understanding of the purpose (why) in your restated mission statement. Write a restated mission statement using your analysis of these areas:

- the battalion mission, intent, and concept
- the company mission, intent, and concept
- identification of specified, implied, and essential tasks
- identification of risks
- any constraints.

You use the military aspects of terrain observation to analyze the ground. The sequence you use to analyze the military aspects of terrain can vary. You may prefer to determine obstacles first, avenues of approach second, key terrain third, observation and fields of fire fourth, and cover and concealment last. For each aspect of terrain, determine its effect on both friendly and enemy forces. Figure 5.2 lists the OAKOC aspects of terrain.

STEP 4—Initiate Movement

Initiate any movement that is necessary to continue preparations or to posture the unit for the operations. This may include moving to an assembly area (AA), battle position perimeter

OAKOC

OBSERVATION AND FIELDS OF FIRE.
AVENUES OF APPROACH.
KEY AND DECISIVE TERRAIN.
OBSTACLES.
COVER AND CONCEALMENT.

Figure 5.2 Military Aspects of Terrain

defense, or attack position; moving reconnaissance elements; or moving to compute time-distance factors for the unit's mission.

STEP 5—Conduct Reconnaissance

Even if you have made a leader's reconnaissance with the company commander at some point during TLP, you should still conduct a reconnaissance after developing your plan. The focus of the reconnaissance is to confirm the priority intelligence requirements (PIRs) that support the tentative plan.

- These PIRs are critical requirements needed to confirm or deny some aspect of the enemy (location, strength, movement). The PIRs also include assumptions about the terrain (you'll want to verify, for example, that a tentative SBF position actually will allow for suppression of the enemy, or to verify the utility of an avenue of approach).
- You may include a subordinate leader in the reconnaissance (or instruct a squad to conduct a reconnaissance patrol with specific objectives). This allows you to see as much of the terrain and enemy as possible. It also helps you visualize the plan more clearly.
- Your reconnaissance may include movement to or beyond a line of departure (LD) or from the forward edge of the battle area (FEBA) back to and through the engagement area along likely enemy routes. If possible, you should select a vantage point that provides the group with the best possible view of the decisive point.
- You may also conduct a leader's reconnaissance through other means. Examples of this type of reconnaissance include surveillance of an area by subordinate elements, patrols by infantry squads to determine where the enemy is (and is not) located, and establishment of observation posts (OPs) to gain additional information. If available, you may use video from unmanned aircraft systems (UAS) or video footage provided from helicopter gun cameras and digital downloads of 2D terrain products. The nature of the reconnaissance, including what it covers and how long it lasts, depends on the tactical situation and time available. You should use the results from the COA development process to identify information and security requirements for your platoon's reconnaissance operations.

Note: *You must evaluate the following discussion on reconnaissance and the amount or type of reconnaissance conducted by*

- *the amount of information needed*
- *the risk to leaders conducting the reconnaissance*
- *time available.*

The reconnaissance must be a coordinated effort with higher

STEP 6—Complete the Plan

Completing the plan includes several actions that transform the commander's intent and concept and your concept into a fully developed platoon OPORD. These actions include:

- preparing overlays
- refining the indirect-fire list
- completing sustainment and command and control (C2) requirements
- updating the tentative plan as a result of the reconnaissance.

Completing the plan also allows you to prepare the briefing site, briefing medium, and briefing material you will need to present the OPORD to your subordinates. Completing the plan also allows you to make final coordination with other units or the commander before issuing the OPORD to your subordinates.

STEP 7—Issue the Operation Order

The OPORD precisely and concisely explains the mission, the commander's intent, and the concept of how you want your squads to accomplish the mission. The OPORD must not contain unnecessary information that could obscure what is essential. Ensure that your squads know exactly what must be done, when it must be done, and how the platoon must work together to accomplish the mission and stay consistent with the commander's intentions.

- Issue the order in person, looking into the eyes of all your Soldiers to ensure each leader and Soldier understands the mission and what his or her element must achieve. Use visual aids, such as sand tables and concept sketches, to depict actions on the objective or movement.
- The format of the five-paragraph OPORD helps you paint a complete picture of all aspects of the operation: terrain, enemy, higher and adjacent friendly units, platoon mission, execution, support, and command. The format also helps address all relevant details of the operation. Finally, it provides your subordinates with a predictable, smooth flow of information from beginning to end.

STEP 8—Supervise and Refine

Supervise the unit's preparation for combat by conducting confirmation briefs, rehearsals, and inspections. Conduct a confirmation brief after issuing the oral OPORD to ensure that your subordinates know the mission, the commander's intent, the concept of the operation, and their assigned tasks. You can conduct confirmation briefs face to face or by radio, depending on the situation. Face to face is the desired method, because all section and squad leaders are together to resolve questions, and it ensures that each leader knows what the adjacent squad is doing.

Rehearsals

Your platoon then conducts rehearsals. During the rehearsals, leaders practice sending tactical reports IAW the unit's SOPs. You rehearse in detail reporting before, during, and after contact with the enemy, starting with actions on the objective. Rehearsals are not intended to analyze a COA.

Use rehearsals to:

- Improve performance by practicing essential tasks such as actions on the objective or the use of special weapons or demolitions
- Reveal weaknesses or problems in your plan
- Coordinate the actions of subordinate elements
- Improve Soldiers' understanding of the operation's concept.

Inspections

Conduct initial inspections shortly after you receive a WARNO. Then conduct spot checks throughout the unit's preparation for combat. You should inspect:

- Weapons and ammunition
- Uniforms and equipment
- Mission-essential equipment
- Solders' understanding of the mission and their specific responsibilities
- Communications
- Rations and water
- Camouflage
- Deficiencies you noted during earlier inspections.

Potential Challenges Associated With the Troop Leading Procedures

You should anticipate and overcome the following challenges while conducting troop leading procedures. With practice and experience, you will become comfortable in handling these challenges.

- *Determining specified, implied, and essential tasks.* You may have to act without all the information you would prefer.
- *Managing available time.* You should expect that you will not have all the time you would like for planning.
- *Delegating during planning and preparation.* Time constraints will probably dictate that you delegate many tasks to subordinate leaders.
- *Analyzing courses of action and making decisions.* Insufficient time and the lack of "perfect" information will make decision making a challenge.
- *Briefing on WARNO and FRAGO.* You must be clear, concise, and complete when briefing your subordinate leaders and Soldiers.
- *Conducting rehearsals and inspections.* Again, lack of time will challenge your ability to complete these important tasks.

Critical Thinking

Explain troop leading procedures as a specific example of the Army Problem Solving Process.

Critical Thinking

Explain how incomplete information affects the troop leading procedures.

CONCLUSION

You use troop leading procedures to prepare your unit to accomplish a tactical mission. The eight steps of the TLP begin when you receive the alert for a new mission. The amount of time you have available dictates the depth of detail in which you can analyze and implement each step. You can accomplish many of the steps at the same time.

In combat, you will rarely have enough time to go through each step in detail. Even so, you must use the procedure as outlined, if only in abbreviated form, to ensure that you leave nothing out of your planning and preparations—and that your Soldiers understand the platoon's and squads' mission and prepare adequately.

The time available to you may be the most critical factor in the process. Many of the challenges Army leaders face when using the troop leading procedures result from a lack of time. You should use no more than one-third of the time available for your own planning and for issuing your OPORD. You should leave the remaining two-thirds for your subordinates to plan and prepare. This is the one-third, two-thirds rule of time management.

Learning Assessment

1. List the eight steps of the troop leading procedures.
2. Explain the one-third, two-thirds rule of time management.
3. Explain how METT-TC and OAKOC relate to the troop leading procedures.
4. Identify common challenges you will face when implementing the troop leading procedures.

Key Words

warning order (WARNO)
operation order (OPORD)
one-third, two-thirds rule
fragmentary order (FRAGO)

References

Field Manual 3-21.8, *The Infantry Rifle Platoon and Squad.* 1 March 2007.

Field Manual 3-25.26, *Map Reading and Land Navigation.* Change 1. 30 August 2006.

Field Manual 5-0, *Army Planning and Orders Production.* 20 January 2005.

Field Manual 6-22, *Army Leadership: Competent, Confident, and Agile.* 10 December 2006.

Field Manual 34-130, *Intelligence Preparation of the Battlefield.* 8 July 1994.

SH21-76, *Ranger Handbook.* July 2006.

COMBAT ORDERS

Key Points

1 Characteristics of Good Operation Orders

2 Types of Orders

Introduction

Plans and orders are the means by which commanders express their mental picture of the battlefield (visualization), commander's intent, and decisions. They focus on what the commander expects to achieve. Commanders use plans and orders to synchronize military operations. They encourage initiative by providing the "what" and "why" of a mission, and leave the details on how to accomplish it to subordinates. They give subordinates the operational and tactical freedom to accomplish the mission by providing as few restrictions as possible and the details necessary for subordinates to synchronize and coordinate. Plans and orders:

- Permit subordinate commanders to prepare supporting plans and orders
- Implement instructions from a higher commander's plan or order
- Focus subordinates' activities
- Provide tasks and activities, constraints, and coordinating instructions necessary for mission accomplishment
- Encourage agility, speed, and initiative during execution
- Convey instructions in a standard, recognizable, clear, and simple format.

Von Moltke and *Auftragstaktik*

Helmuth von Moltke (1800–1891) was appointed chief of the Prussian (later German) General Staff in 1857. One of the important concepts he promulgated was *Auftragstaktik* (literally, "mission tactics"), a command method stressing decentralized initiative within an overall strategic design. Von Moltke understood that, as war progressed, its uncertainties diminished the value of any detailed planning that might have been done beforehand. He believed that, beyond calculating the initial mobilization and concentration of forces, no plan of operations extends with any degree of certainty beyond the first encounter with the main enemy force. He believed that, throughout a campaign, commanders had to make decisions based on a fluid, constantly evolving situation. For Von Moltke, each major encounter had consequences that created a new situation, which became the basis for new measures. Auftragstaktik encouraged commanders to be flexible and react immediately to changes in the situation as they developed. It replaced detailed planning with delegation of decision making authority to subordinate commanders within the context of the higher commander's intent. Von Moltke realized that tactical decisions had to be made on the spot; therefore, great care was taken to encourage initiative by commanders at all levels.

Von Moltke believed that commanders should issue only the most essential orders. These would provide only general instructions outlining the principal objective and specific missions. Tactical details were left to subordinates. For Von Moltke, "The advantage which a commander thinks he can attain through continued personal intervention is largely illusory. By engaging in it he assumes a task that really belongs to others, whose effectiveness he thus destroys. He also multiplies his own tasks to a point where he can no longer fulfill the whole of them." Von Moltke's thought, summarized in these statements, lies at the heart of mission command.

Critical Thinking

Do you think the concepts expressed by Von Moltke are still valid?
If so, are these concepts consistent with the Army Problem Solving Process, combat orders, and the troop leading procedures as you understand them?

Characteristics of Good Operation Orders

Good operation orders contain several distinguishing characteristics:

- *Inclusion of Critical Facts.* The commander and staff evaluate all facts and assumptions related to the operation. They retain for future reassessment only those facts and assumptions that directly affect an operation's success or failure. Operational plans include assumptions; operation orders (OPORDs) do not.

- *Authoritative Expression.* The plan or order reflects the commander's intention and will. Therefore, its language is direct. It states plainly what the commander wants subordinate commands to do.

- *Positive Expression.* The plans or orders state instructions affirmatively: for example, "The trains will remain in the assembly area," instead of, "The trains will not accompany the unit." As an exception, they state some restrictions in the negative: for example, "Do not cross Phase Line Blue before H+2."

- *Avoidance of Qualified Directives.* They do not use meaningless expressions such as, "as soon as possible (ASAP)." Indecisive, vague, and ambiguous language leads to uncertainty and lack of confidence. For example, do not use "try to retain"; instead say "retain until." Good plans and orders avoid using unnecessary modifiers and redundant expressions, such as "violently attack" instead of "attack," or "delay while maintaining enemy contact" instead of "delay." Army doctrine already requires attacking violently and maintaining enemy contact during delays.

- *Balance.* Good plans and orders balance centralized and decentralized control. The commander determines the appropriate balance for a given operation based on METT-TC. During the chaos of battle, it is essential to decentralize decision authority to the lowest practical level. Overcentralization slows action and inhibits initiative. Decentralized control, on the other hand, can cause loss of precision. The commander constantly balances competing risks while recognizing that loss of precision is usually preferable to inaction.

- *Simplicity*. Good plans and orders reduce all elements to their simplest form. Simple plans are easier to understand.

- *Brevity*. They are clear, concise, and include only necessary details. They use short words, sentences, and paragraphs. They do not include material covered in SOPs (standing operating procedures), but refer to those SOPs instead.

- *Clarity*. Everyone using the plan or order must readily understand it. Good plans and orders do not use jargon. They eliminate every opportunity for misunderstanding the commander's exact meaning. They use acronyms unless the acronyms hinder clarity. They are simple and use only doctrinal terms and graphics.

- *Completeness*. They provide all the information required for executing the plan or order. They use doctrinal control measures that are understandable and allow subordinates to exercise initiative. They provide adequate control means (headquarters and communications). They clearly establish command and support relationships and fix responsibility for all tasks.

- *Coordination*. Good plans and orders provide for direct contact among subordinates. They fit together all battlefield operating systems (BOS) for synchronized, decisive action. They identify the need for and provide mutual support while minimizing the chance of fratricide.

- *Flexibility*. They leave room for adjustments to counter the unexpected. The best plans provide for the most flexibility.

- *Timeliness*. Subordinates receive them in time enough to plan and prepare their own actions. In the interest of timeliness, commanders send imperfect products only when time is short.

Critical Thinking

Reflect on what you've learned in previous sections, such as those on leadership and on effective writing for officers. Are there additional distinguishing characteristics for good operation orders that you can derive from these and other earlier readings and discussions?

Types of Orders

An **order** is a written, oral, or electronic communication that conveys instructions from a superior to a subordinate. In a broad sense, the terms "order" and "command" are synonymous. An order, however, implies discretion in the details of execution, while a command does not. Combat orders pertain to operations and their service support. The different types of combat orders include:

- OPORDs
- Service support orders
- Movement orders
- Warning orders (WARNOs)
- Fragmentary orders (FRAGOs)

This section will examine the three most common combat orders—OPORD, WARNO, and FRAGO.

Operation Orders

An operation order is a directive a commander issues to subordinate commanders to coordinate the execution of an operation. Traditionally called the *five-paragraph field order,* an OPORD must always specify an execution date and time. The OPORD's five paragraphs are:

- Situation
- Mission
- Execution
- Service support
- Command and signal for the specified operation

The information that is needed in each sub-paragraph is contained in Table 6-1.

TABLE 6.1	Operation Order (OPORD)

OPORD [number] [code name]—[issuing headquarters] (Place the classification and short title of the OPORD at the top of the second and any subsequent pages.)

Task Organization: Describe the allocation of forces to support the concept of operations.

1. SITUATION.

Enemy forces. Express information in terms of two enemy echelons below yours. Describe the enemy's most likely and most dangerous COAs. When possible, provide a sketch of the enemy COA with the written description. Include an assessment of terrorist activities in the area of operation (AO).

Friendly forces. List the mission, commander's intent, and concept of operations for headquarters one and two levels up. Subparagraphs state the missions of flank and other units.

Environment.
- List all critical **terrain** and **weather** aspects that can impact operations
- List all critical **civil considerations** that can impact operations.

Attachments and detachments. Do not repeat information already listed under Task Organization. List units that are attached or detached to the headquarters that issues the order. State when the attachment or detachment is effective, if different from the effective time of the operation plan (such as, on-order, or on commitment of the reserve).

2. MISSION. Provide a clear, concise statement of the task and describe the purpose for doing it. Ensure who, what, when, where, and why are covered. A mission statement contains no subparagraphs. The mission statement covers on-order missions.

3. EXECUTION INTENT. State the commander's intent.

Concept of operations. The concept of operations describes how the commander sees the actions of subordinate units fitting together to accomplish the mission. At a minimum, the concept of operations includes the scheme of maneuver and concept of fires. Where the commander's intent focuses on the end state, the concept of operations focuses on the method used for the operation and synchronizes battlefield operating systems to translate vision and end state into action.

The concept of operations addresses the decisive and shaping operations. It describes the overall form of maneuver, designates the main effort for each phase of the operation, and includes any be-prepared missions. The concept of operations is concise, understandable and describes—

- The employment of major maneuver elements in a scheme of maneuver
- A plan of fire support or "scheme of fires" supporting the maneuver with fires
- The integration of other major elements or systems within the operation—these include ISR, intelligence, engineer, and air defense assets
- Any other details the commander considers appropriate to clarify the concept of operations and ensure unity of effort.

When an operation involves two or more clearly distinct and separate phases, the concept of operations may be prepared in subparagraphs describing each phase.

If the operation overlay is the only annex referenced, show it after "a. Concept of Operations." Place the commander's intent and concept of operations statement on the overlay if the overlay does not accompany the OPORD.

The number of subparagraphs, if any, is based on what the commander considers appropriate, the level of command, and the complexity of the operation. The following subparagraphs are examples of what may be required within the concept of operations.

Maneuver. State the scheme of maneuver. Be sure this paragraph is consistent with the operation overlay. It must address the decisive and shaping operations, including security operations and the use of reserves, and specify the purpose of each. This paragraph and the operation overlay are complementary, each adding clarity to, rather than duplicating, the other. Do not duplicate information in unit subparagraphs and the coordinating instructions.

TABLE 6.1	Operation Order (OPORD), Continued

Fires. Describe the scheme of fires. State which unit has priority of fires. Include the purpose of, priorities for, allocation of, and restrictions for fire support. A technique for writing the fires paragraph is to list essential fire support tasks using the task, purpose, method, and effect format.

    a) **Air support.** State allocation of close air support (CAS) sorties, if any.

    b) **Field artillery support.** Cover priorities such as counterfires or interdiction. State organization for combat. Include command and support relationships only if they are not clear in the task organization. Ensure that allocation of fires supports the concept of operations.

    c) **Additional combat support assets (engineers, air defense, artillery).** State the concept of employment of any combat support attachment or who gets priority of their use, how they are used, and how they will be controlled and by whom.

Tasks to maneuver units. State the missions or tasks assigned to each maneuver unit. Every task must include a purpose that links it to the concept of operations. Use a separate subparagraph for each unit. List units in task organization sequence. Include reserves. State only tasks that are necessary for comprehension, clarity, and emphasis. Place tasks that affect two or more units in paragraph 3d, Coordinating Instructions.

Tasks to other combat and combat support units. State the missions or tasks assigned to nonmaneuver combat units and CS units. List units in task organization sequence. List only those tasks that are not specified or implied elsewhere.

Coordinating instructions. List only instructions applicable to two or more units and not covered in unit SOPs.

    a) **Commander's critical information requirements.** List CCIR here.

    b) **Risk reduction control measures.** These are measures unique to this operation and not included in unit SOPs. They may include mission-oriented protective posture, operational exposure guidance, vehicle recognition signals, and fratricide prevention measures.

    c) **Rules of engagement (ROE).** Refer to annex E (ROE) if required.

4. SERVICE SUPPORT. Address service support in the areas shown below as needed to clarify the service support concept.

Support concept. State the concept of logistics support to provide a visualization of how the operation will be logistically supported. This could include:

- The location—current and proposed—of the unit support location
- Support command headquarters or support area locations, including locations of the next higher logistic bases if not clearly conveyed in the CSS overlay
- The next higher level's support priorities and where the unit fits into those priorities
- The commander's priorities of support
- The use of host-nation support
- Significant or unusual CSS issues and sustainment risks that might impact the overall operation.

Materiel and services.

    a) **Supply.** Information on all classes of supply of interest to the unit.

    b) **Transportation.** Constraints and limitations.

    c) **Services.** Information on the type of services available, designation, and location of the facility and schedule for service.

    d) **Maintenance.** Information that differs from the established SOP on maintenance of weapons and equipment.

    e) **Medical Evacuation.** Procedures for evacuation of wounded if different from SOP.

5. COMMAND AND SIGNAL.

    a) **Command.**
- Location of higher unit command and CP/unit leader or CP/alternate CP
- Succession of command if different from SOP.

    b) **Signal.**
- Listening silence, if applicable
- Methods of communication in priority/Emergency signals, visual signals/Code words.

Warning Orders

The warning order is a preliminary notice of an order or action that is to follow (see Figure 6.1a and 6.1b). WARNOs help subordinate units and staffs prepare for new missions. The WARNO uses the same five-paragraph format as the OPORD. They increase subordinates' planning time, provide details of the impending operation, and detail events that accompany preparation and execution. The amount of detail a WARNO includes depends on the information and time available when the commander issues it and on the information subordinates need to plan and prepare. The words "warning order" precede the message text. With the commander's (or chief of staff's or executive officer's) approval, a coordinating or special staff officer may issue a WARNO.

A WARNO informs recipients of tasks they must do now or notifies them of possible future tasks. A WARNO does not authorize execution other than planning, however, unless it specifically says so. A WARNO follows the OPORD format. It may include some or all of the following information:

- Series numbers, sheet numbers and names, editions, and scales of maps required (if changed from the current OPORD)
- The enemy situation and significant intelligence events
- The higher headquarters' mission
- The issuing headquarters' mission or tasks
- The commander's intent statement
- Orders for preliminary actions, including intelligence, surveillance, and reconnaissance (ISR) operations
- Coordinating instructions (estimated timelines, orders group meetings, and the time to issue the OPORD)
- Service support instructions, any special equipment needed, regrouping of transport, or preliminary unit movements.

Fragmentary Orders

A fragmentary order is an abbreviated form of an operation order (verbal, written, or digital) usually issued on a day-to-day basis. A FRAGO eliminates the need for restating information contained in a basic operation order. It may be issued in sections. It is issued after an operation order to change or modify that order or to execute a branch or sequel to that order. FRAGOs include all five OPORD paragraph headings (see Figure 6.2). After each heading, state either new information or "no change." This ensures recipients that they have received the entire FRAGO. Commanders may authorize members of their staff to issue FRAGOs in their name.

FRAGOs differ from OPORDs only in the degree of detail provided. They address only those parts of the original OPORD that have changed. FRAGOs refer to previous orders and provide brief and specific instructions. The higher headquarters issues a new OPORD when there is a complete change of the tactical situation or when the number of changes make the current order ineffective.

The five-paragraph order format applies to the OPORD, WARNO, and FRAGO. The notes below will assist you in constructing an order that provides the essential information needed for an operation.

[Classification]
(Change from verbal orders, if any) (Optional)
[Heading data is the same as for OPLAN/OPORD]

WARNING ORDER [number]

References: Refer to higher headquarters OPLAN/OPORD, and identify map sheets for operation (Optional).

Time Zone Used Throughout the Order: (Optional)

Task Organization: (Optional) (See paragraph 1c.)

> A warning order does not authorize execution unless specifically stated.

1. SITUATION.

    a. Enemy forces. Include significant changes in enemy composition, dispositions, and COAs. Information not available can be included in subsequent WARNOs.

    b. Friendly forces. (Optional) Address only if essential to the WARNO.

        (1) Higher commander's mission.

        (2) Higher commander's intent.

    c. Environment. (Optional) Address only if essential to the WARNO.

        (1) Terrain.

        (2) Weather.

        (3) Civil considerations.

Attachments and detachments. Initial task organization. Address only major unit changes.

2. MISSION. Issuing headquarters' mission. This may be the higher headquarters' restated mission or commander's decisions during the MDMP.

3. EXECUTION.

Intent:

    a. Concept of operations. This may be "to be determined" for the initial WARNO.

    b. Tasks to maneuver units. Any information on tasks to units for execution, movement to initiate, reconnaissance to initiate, or security to emplace.

    c. Tasks to other combat and combat support units. See paragraph 3b.

    d. Coordinating instructions. Include any information available at the time of the issuance of the WARNO. It may include the following:

- CCIR
- Risk guidance
- Time line
- Deception guidance
- Orders group meeting information
- Specific priorities, in order of completion
- Earliest movement time and degree of notice
- Guidance on orders and rehearsals

4. SERVICE SUPPORT. (Optional) Include any known logistics preparations.

    a. Special equipment. Identify requirements and coordinate transfer to using units.

    b. Transportation. Identify requirements, and coordinate for pre-position of assets.

Figure 6.1a Warning Order Format

5. COMMAND AND SIGNAL. (Optional)

    a. Command. State the chain of command if different from unit SOP.

    b. Signal. Identify the current SOI. Pre-position signal assets to support operation.

ACKNOWLEDGE:

[Authentication data is the same as for OPLAN/OPORD]

ANNEXES:

DISTRIBUTION:

[Classification]

Figure 6.1b Warning Order Format, *continued*

[Classification]

(Change from verbal orders, if any)

Copy ## of ## copies
Issuing headquarters
Place of issue
Date-time group of signature
Message reference number

FRAGMENTARY ORDER [number]

References: Refer to the order being modified.

Time Zone Used Throughout the Order:

1. SITUATION. Include any changes to the existing order or state, "No change"; for example, "No change to OPORD 02-XX."

2. MISSION. List the new mission or state, "No change."

3. EXECUTION. Include any changes or state, "No change."
Intent:

    a. Concept of operations.

    b. Tasks to subordinate units.

    c. Coordinating instructions. Include statement, "Current overlay remains in effect" or "See change 1 to annex C, Operations Overlay." Mark changes to control measures on the overlay or issue a new overlay.

4. SERVICE SUPPORT. Include any changes to existing order or state, "No change."

5. COMMAND AND SIGNAL. Include any changes to existing order or state, "No change."

ACKNOWLEDGE:

[Commander's last name]
[Commander's rank]

OFFICIAL:

[Authenticator's Name]
[Authenticator's Position]

ANNEXES:

DISTRIBUTION:

[Classification]

Figure 6.2 Fragmentary Order Format

CONCLUSION

The focus of this lesson was on the intent and function of combat orders (OPORD, WARNO, FRAGO) and how these orders direct the execution of tactical operations. These specific combat orders serve as the basis of small-unit management and are central to the TLP. Small-unit leaders will receive their mission in the form of a WARNO, OPORD, or FRAGO, and in turn, can use these combat orders to direct the execution of tactical operations for their own and subordinate units.

Learning Assessment

1. Briefly describe the format and content of the WARNO, OPORD, and FRAGO.
2. Explain the characteristics of a good OPORD.

Key Words

order

References

Field Manual 1-02, *Operational Terms and Graphics*. September 2004.

Field Manual 5-0, *Army Planning and Order Production*. 20 January 2005.

SH 21-76, *Ranger Handbook*. July 2006.

Von Moltke, H. (1911). *Moltke's Military Works*. Vol. 4, *War Lessons,* Part I. Operative Preparations for Battle. Berlin: Mittler. Quoted in: Delbrück, H. (1985). *History of the Art of War Within the Framework of Political History.* Vol. 4, *The Modern Era.* W. J. Renfroe, Jr., Trans. Westport, CT: Greenwood Press.

SQUAD TACTICS: TACTICAL MOVEMENT

Key Points

1 The Importance of Individual Movement

2 Movement Formations and Movement Techniques

Maneuvering with an army is advantageous; with
an undisciplined multitude, most dangerous.

Sun Tzu, *The Art of War*

Introduction

In Sections 1 and 2, you learned how to get from Point A to Point B. This section will discuss how you and the Soldiers in your small unit get there as safely as possible while maintaining control and combat effectiveness. Tactical movement is about getting your unit to the right place, at the right time, prepared to fight and win at any point along the way.

National Guardsmen Repel Insurgent Ambush

Shared combat experiences forge bonds between Soldiers, whose safety and lives depend on one another. 1st Lt. David Tiedeman and Sgt. Robert Betterton of the Tennessee Army National Guard found themselves depending on each other as they confronted a determined, dangerous enemy in Iraq. "He did save my life, there is no doubt about that," Betterton told a reporter. Betterton was referring to the actions of his fellow Soldier, Tiedeman. If not for the actions of both of these soldiers, the casualties sustained by their U.S. and Iraqi comrades would have been significantly greater.

Securing munitions has been a major task for Coalition forces since the fall of Saddam Hussein. In April 2005, Tiedeman and Betterton's 12-soldier team, along with two Iraqi companies, was conducting a search for weapons stolen from an Iraqi base. As the two Iraqi companies were searching a bunker complex, Tiedeman's team and one Iraqi gun truck headed further south to search another area. As they moved south of Balad Ruz, an area northeast of Baghdad, insurgents ambushed the Americans and Iraqi gun truck with mortars, machine guns, RPGs, and small arms fire. The enemy fire immediately disabled two trucks carrying Iraqi forces. Tiedeman stepped out of his vehicle and directed return fire against the enemy, with Betterton unleashing fire on the RPG gunners. Due to the force of the enemy's assault, Tiedeman guided his team out of the line of fire to an area where it could plan a more organized counterattack. Reacting quickly, Tiedeman then directed the counterassault, as well as air cover, which took out the enemy's heavy weaponry. The team then dismounted to clear the remaining insurgents from the surrounding canals. After enemy fire hit two fellow Soldiers, Tiedeman ran across the kill zone to administer aid. While treating his comrades, Tiedeman stopped twice to shoot back at the enemy that was targeting him and the wounded Soldiers.

Betterton saw insurgents targeting Tiedeman and the wounded Soldiers. The sergeant then placed himself in harm's way to distract the enemy. After jumping into a ditch to better target the insurgents, Betterton killed the RPG gunner that was taking aim at Tiedeman and two other Guardsmen who were providing medical attention to a fallen soldier. Betterton's intervention allowed for the evacuation of the Soldiers. Betterton exposed himself to great danger; he had been shot eight times in the hand, stomach, and leg. Incredibly, Betterton kept firing at a sniper who continued targeting him, even though he was alone and could not move.

Tiedeman observed Betterton's situation and, once again, ran across the battlefield, braving a barrage of bullets to reach him. Tiedeman had left behind his primary weapon to make himself more mobile. Betterton repeatedly told Tiedeman to leave him, but the lieutenant refused. Tiedeman blocked the enemy's line of fire with the body of a dead insurgent, and helped neutralize the threat to Betterton with a grenade. Seeing the break in the action he was looking for, Tiedeman carried Betterton to safety.

Tiedeman and Betterton's heroism resulted in the deaths of 17 insurgents. In addition, their actions led to the elimination of what Tiedeman had described to WREG-TV as "basically an insurgent training camp" that had been wreaking havoc across central Iraq. On Aug. 25, 2007, in a ceremony at Naval Air Station Mid-South, the Tennessee National Guard awarded Tiedeman the Silver Star, while Betterton received the Bronze Star with Valor.

The Importance of Individual Movement

In thinking about the importance of individual movement on the battlefield, consider a sports analogy. Think about the effect that an individual player's movement has on the team. The way each player moves on the field or court influences how the whole team moves. Picture a defensive basketball player operating in a zone defense. Imagine what would happen if that player did not understand what zone he or she was supposed to cover. Imagine if basketball players looked only in one direction and did not know what was going on around them. How effective is a football player who always lags behind the action, or a soccer player who stays too close to his or her teammate? Would you want these players on your team?

As with sports teams, the individual members of a fire team or rifle squad greatly affect how well that unit moves. And as with sports teams, individual members of a fire team have specific responsibilities. They must:

- Maintain visual contact with the team leader and fellow team members
- Maintain the appropriate space between fellow team members
- Maintain **situational awareness**
- Maintain security for an individual area of responsibility
- Receive and pass on hand-and-arm signals
- Maintain discipline over the noise and light they produce.

situational awareness

knowledge and understanding of the current situation that promotes timely, relevant, and accurate assessment of friendly, enemy, and other operations within the battlespace in order to facilitate decision making

Note:

The Buddy Team, the smallest unit in the Army, has two Soldiers. Consider the benefits of a buddy team versus an individual:

1. A buddy team can offer greater security—it can see more and has more firepower.
2. The buddy team members can keep each other alert.
3. The buddy team members can cover each other's movement under fire.
4. The buddy team members can monitor each other's status (e.g., health, stamina, equipment, etc.).

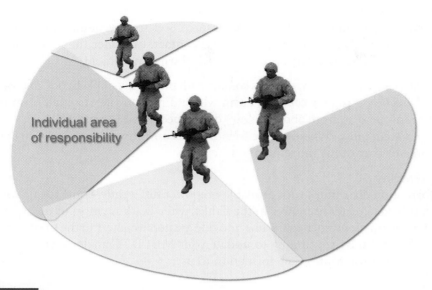

Figure 7.1 Individual Area of Responsibility

Movement Formations and Movement Techniques

Movement formations and **movement techniques** are related concepts. It's important that you understand the difference between them.

Note:

Squads use formations for control, flexibility, fire capability, and security. Leaders choose formations based on their analysis of METT-TC (mission, enemy, terrain and weather, time, troops available, civilians).

Note:

Like formations, movement techniques provide varying degrees of control, security, fire capability, and flexibility.

Formations are how Soldiers or elements are arranged. Movement techniques are how you move those arrayed formations across terrain. When you select a formation or movement technique, you must consider the need for *control, security, fire capability, and flexibility.*

Control

As a leader, you must always be able to command your unit's actions. During tactical movement, *control* means you can maintain the movement's speed and direction. It means maintaining situational awareness. It means maintaining accountability of your Soldiers and equipment. When determining the level of control a particular situation requires, consider the following:

- *The terrain you are moving on.* Ask yourself: Is the vegetation so thick that my Soldiers can't see each other? How easily can the enemy see me? How fast can my unit move across this terrain?
- *Your Soldiers' condition.* Are they alert? Are they loaded down with a lot of equipment? Are they well disciplined? What is your unit's training level?
- *Light and weather.* What will we be able to see during movement? How easily will the enemy be able to see us? How loud will our movement be, given the weather conditions?

Operation Iraqi Freedom has produced many reports of enemy insurgents killing or capturing individual Soldiers moving alone on the battlefield. Individual Soldiers make for easy targets in unconventional warfare.

movement formation

an ordered arrangement of troops and/or vehicles for a specific purpose

movement technique

the position of maneuver elements in relation to each other during movement

Security

When moving, you must always protect your force. Seek to prevent unwanted enemy contact and remain as ready as possible for surprise contact. Consider the following when you determine how much security your unit needs during movement:

- *Likelihood of enemy contact.* Is contact with the enemy unlikely, possible, or expected?
- *Direction of enemy contact.* From which direction (i.e., frontal, from the flanks, from the rear, from above/below) do I expect enemy contact?
- *Adjacent units.* Where are the friendly units operating in my area? Can they support me or part of my movement?

Fire Capability

Each formation distributes your available firepower differently. Some formations, such as the file, provide greater firepower to the flanks, while masking most of the squad's frontal fires. Other formations, such as the line, provide greater firepower to the front, while limiting fires to the flanks. By continuing to update your METT-TC analysis, you will be able to determine the most appropriate formation to use.

Flexibility

Flexibility refers to the ease with which you can change your unit's formation or movement technique. How quickly and easily will you and your unit be able to react to contact with the enemy or changing conditions? Will your smallest unit make contact with the enemy, or will your entire unit be committed upon initial contact? Consider the factors for control and security when you determine how much flexibility your unit needs during movement.

Other Considerations

In planning tactical movement, you should also consider the requirements for:

- *Dispersion.* Also known as **interval,** dispersion is the distance between individual Soldiers and units. Dispersion will vary throughout a movement, often dictated by terrain, visibility, or one of the other factors described above. Greater dispersion limits the effects of enemy fire on a unit by reducing the number of Soldiers in a blast radius, kill zone, or enemy engagement area. Generally speaking, however, the greater the dispersion, the more difficult it is for a leader to control the unit's movement and concentrate friendly fires.

- *Cover and concealment.* Cover is shelter or protection that reduces the effects of enemy fire. Concealment is what hides you from observation or surveillance. Cover may provide concealment, but concealment will not provide cover. During movement, leaders as well as individual Soldiers must continually identify places that offer cover and/or concealment. Your ability to quickly occupy such locations in the event of enemy contact is critical if you are to survive.

- *Speed.* You must consider the operational schedule and time available when you select movement formations. Though some formations inherently move faster than others, speedier movement often reduces control, flexibility, and security.

Movement Formations

Again, movement formations refer to how Soldiers or elements are arranged. The options available depend on the size of the unit.

The term *fire team formation* refers to the Soldiers' relative positions within the fire team. Fire team formations include the fire team wedge and the fire team file (Table 7-1). Both formations have advantages and disadvantages. Regardless of which formation the team employs, each Soldier must know his or her location in the formation relative to the other members of the fire team and the team leader. Each Soldier covers a set sector of

interval

the distance between individual Soldiers and units as set and maintained by the leader

Military convoys during Operation Iraqi Freedom have limited the number of friendly casualties from roadside IEDs (Improvised Explosive Devices) by maintaining adequate distance between vehicles.

Sometimes greater speed can translate to greater security. Speed and "violence of action" can help a unit seize the initiative and keep an enemy force off guard.

responsibility for observation and direct fire as the team is moving. To provide the unit with all-round protection, these sectors must interlock. Team leaders must be constantly aware of their team's sectors and correct them as required.

The team leader adjusts the team's formation as necessary while the team is moving. The mission, the nature of the threat, the closeness of the terrain, and the visibility determine the distance between Soldiers. As a general rule, the unit should be dispersed up to the limit of control. This allows for it to cover a wide area, makes the team's movement difficult to detect, and makes it less vulnerable to enemy ground and air attack. Fire teams rarely act independently. In the event that they do, however, when halted they use a perimeter defense to ensure all-around security.

Fire Team Wedge

The **wedge** (Figure 7.2) is the basic formation for the fire team. The interval between Soldiers in the wedge formation is normally 10 meters. The wedge expands and contracts depending on the terrain. Fire teams modify the wedge when rough terrain, poor visibility, or other factors make control of the wedge difficult. The normal interval is reduced so all team members can still see their team leader and all team leaders can still see their squad leader. The sides of the wedge can contract to the point where the wedge resembles a single file. Soldiers expand or resume their original positions when moving in less rugged terrain where control is easier.

In this formation the fire team leader is in the lead position with the Soldiers echeloned to the right and left behind the leader. The positions for all but the leader may vary. This simple formation permits the fire team leader to lead by example. The leader's standing order to the Soldiers is: "Follow me and do as I do." When the leader moves to the right, the Soldiers should also move to the right. When the leader fires, the Soldiers also fire. When using the lead-by-example technique, it is essential for all Soldiers to keep the leader in sight.

wedge

the basic formation for the fire team

Critical Thinking

Consider the two fire team wedge examples below (Figure 7.2). Under what METT-TC situations would you use the wedge formation on the left when conducting tactical movement? Under what situations would you use the one on the right?

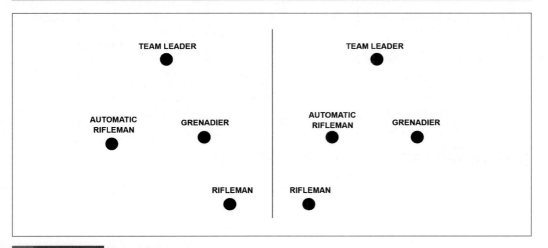

Figure 7.2 Examples of Fire Team Wedges

file

formation used when you can't use the wedge because of the terrain or other METT-TC factors

Fire Team File

Team leaders use the **file** when employing the wedge is impractical. This formation is most often used in severely restrictive terrain, such as inside a building, dense vegetation, limited visibility, and so forth. The distance between Soldiers in the column changes due to constraints of the situation, particularly when in urban operations (Figure 7.3).

Squad Formations

The term *squad formation* refers to the relative locations of the fire teams. Squad formations include the squad column, the squad line, and the squad file. Table 7.2 compares squad formations.

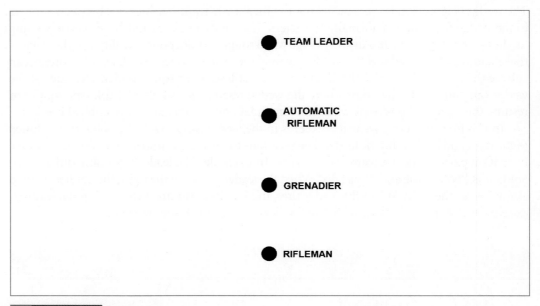

Figure 7.3 Fire Team File

MOVEMENT FORMATION	WHEN NORMALLY USED	CHARACTERISTICS			
		CONTROL	FLEXIBILITY	FIRE CAPABILITIES/ RESTRICTIONS	SECURITY
FIRE TEAM WEDGE	BASIC FIRE TEAM FORMATION	EASY	GOOD	ALLOWS IMMEDIATE FIRES IN ALL DIRECTIONS	GOOD
FIRE TEAM FILE	CLOSE TERRAIN DENSE VEGETA-TION, LIMITED VISIBILITY CONDITIONS	EASIEST	LESS FLEXIBLE THAN THE WEDGE	ALLOWS IMMEDIATE FIRES TO THE FLANKS, MASKS MOST FIRES TO THE REAR	LEAST

Table 7.1 Comparison of Fire Team Formations

The squad leader adjusts the squad's formation as necessary while moving, primarily through the three movement techniques. The squad leader exercises command and control primarily through the two team leaders and moves in the formation where he or she can best achieve this. The squad leader is responsible for 360-degree security, for ensuring that the team's sectors of fire are mutually supporting, and for rapidly transitioning the squad upon enemy contact.

The squad leader designates one of the fire teams as the base fire team. The squad leader controls the squad's speed and direction of movement through the base fire team while the other team and any attachments get their movement cues from the base fire team. This concept applies when not in contact and when in contact with the enemy.

Weapons from the weapons squad (a machine gun or a Javelin) may be attached to the squad for the movement or throughout the operation. The leader must position these high-value assets so they are protected and can be quickly brought into the engagement when required. Ideally, the leader should position these weapons so they are between the two fire teams.

Squad Column

The squad **column** is the squad's main formation for movement unless preparing for an assault (Figure 7.4). It provides good dispersion both laterally and in depth without sacrificing control. It also facilitates maneuver. The lead fire team is the base fire team. Squads can move in either a column wedge or a modified column wedge. Rough terrain, poor visibility, and other factors can require the squad to modify the wedge into a file for control purposes. As the terrain becomes less rugged and control becomes easier, the Soldiers assume their original positions.

> **column**
>
> *a squad's most common formation, in which each fire team travels behind the fire team in front of it*

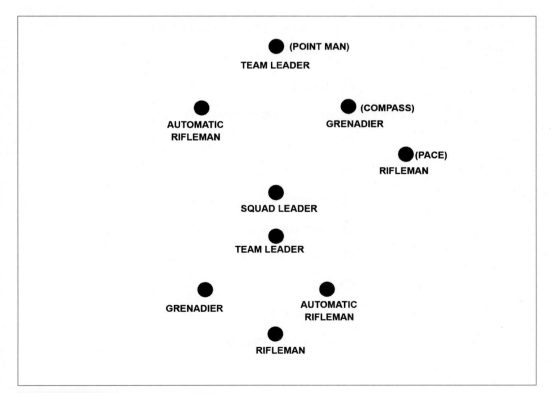

Figure 7.4 Squad Column With Fire Teams in Column

Squad Line

The squad **line** provides maximum firepower to the front and is used to assault or as a pre-assault formation (Figure 7.5). To execute the squad line, the squad leader designates one of the teams as the base team. The other team gets its movement cues from the base team. This applies when the squad is in close combat as well. From this formation, the squad leader can employ any of the three movement techniques or conduct fire and movement.

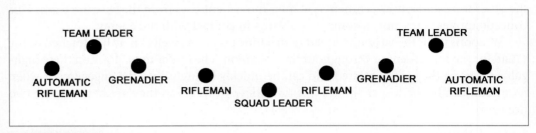

| Figure 7.5 | Squad Line |

Where's the leader? Squad and platoon leaders must position themselves where they can best control their units. This could mean changing their position several times during the movement.

Squad File

The squad file has the same characteristics as the fire team file (Figure 7.6). In the event that the terrain is severely restrictive or extremely close, teams within the squad file may also be in file. This disposition is not the best for enemy contact, but does provide the squad leader with the most control. If the squad leader wishes to increase control over the formation, he or she moves forward to the first or second position. Moving forward also enables the leader to exert greater morale presence by leading from the front, and to be immediately available to make key decisions. Moving a team leader to the last position can provide additional control over the rear of the formation.

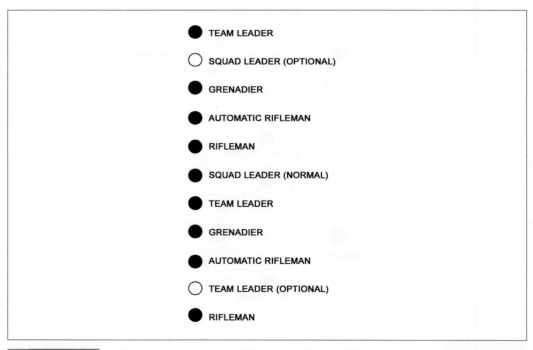

| Figure 7.6 | Squad File |

MOVEMENT FORMATION	WHEN NORMALLY USED	CHARACTERISTICS			
		CONTROL	FLEXIBILITY	FIRE CAPABILITIES/ RESTRICTIONS	SECURITY
SQUAD COLUMN	SQUAD PRIMARY FORMATION.	GOOD	FACILITATES MANEUVER. GOOD DISPERSION LATERALLY AND IN DEPTH	ALLOWS LARGE VOLUME OF FIRE TO THE FLANK --- LIMITED VOLUME TO THE FRONT.	ALL-ROUND
SQUAD LINE	WHEN MAXIMUM FIRE POWER IS REQUIRED TO THE FRONT.	NOT AS GOOD AS SQUAD COLUMN.	LIMITED MANEUVER CAPABILITY (BOTH FIRE TEAMS COMMITTED).	ALLOWS MAXIMUM IMMEDIATE FIRE TO THE FRONT.	GOOD TO THE FRONT, LITTLE TO THE FLANKS AND REAR.
SQUAD FILE	CLOSE TERRAIN VEGETATION VISIBILITY CONDITIONS.	EASIEST	MOST DIFFICULT FORMATION FROM WHICH TO MANEUVER.	ALLOWS IMMEDIATE FIRE TO THE FLANK MASKS MOST FIRE TO THE FRONT AND REAR.	LEAST

Table 7.2 Comparison of Squad Formations

Weapons Squad Movement Formations

The weapons squad is not a rifle squad and as a platoon leader, you should not treat it as such. During tactical movement you have one of two options when it comes to positioning the weapons squad. The weapons squad can either travel together as a separate entity, or you can break it up and distribute it throughout the formation. The advantage of keeping the weapons squad together is its ability to quickly generate support by fire and gain fire superiority under the direction of the weapons squad leader. The disadvantage of this approach is the lack of redundancy throughout the formation. The advantage of distributing the weapons squad throughout the rifle squads is the coverage that gives the entire formation. The disadvantage is that you lose the weapons squad leader as a single command and control element, and the time required to reassemble the weapons squad if you need to.

When the weapons squad travels dispersed, you can either attach it to squads or to the key leaders like the platoon sergeant, the weapons squad leader, or you as the platoon leader. There is no standard method for its employment. Rather, you should place the weapons using two criteria: ability to quickly generate fire superiority, and protection of these high-value assets.

Like the rifle squad, the weapons squad, when traveling as a squad, uses either a column or line formation. Within these formations, the two sections can also be in column or line formation.

Movement Techniques

Movement techniques are not fixed formations. They refer to the distances between Soldiers, teams, and squads that vary based on mission, enemy, terrain, visibility, and other factors that affect control. There are three movement techniques: *traveling, traveling overwatch,* and *bounding overwatch.* You select a movement technique based on the likelihood of enemy contact and the need for speed. Factors you should consider for each technique are control, dispersion, speed, and security. Individual movement techniques include the high and low crawl, and three-to-five-second rushes from one covered position to another.

From these movement techniques, you can conduct actions on contact, making natural transitions to fire and movement as well as to conducting tactical mission tasks. When you analyze the situation, you will know some enemy positions. However, most of the time enemy positions will only be likely (called **templated positions**). Templated positions are your "best guess" based on analyzing the terrain and your knowledge of the enemy. Throughout the operation, leaders are continuously trying to confirm or deny both the known positions as well as the likely positions.

Methods of Maneuvering Subordinates

There are two methods of bounding the squads: successive and alternate bounds. In **successive bounds** the lead element is always the same; in **alternate bounds** (called leapfrogging), the lead element changes each time (see Figure 7.10).

Successive Bounds

If the platoon uses successive bounds, the lead squad, covered by the trail squad, advances and occupies a support-by-fire position. The trail squad advances to a support-by-fire position abreast of the lead squad and halts. The lead squad moves to the next position and the move continues. Only one squad moves at a time, and the trail squad avoids advancing beyond the lead squad.

Alternate Bounds

Covered by the rear squad, the lead squad moves forward, halts, and assumes overwatch positions. The rear squad advances past the lead squad and takes up overwatch positions. The initial lead squad then advances past the initial rear squad and takes up overwatch positions. Only one squad moves at a time. This method is usually more rapid than successive bounds.

Squad Movement Techniques

As platoon leader, you determine and direct which movement technique the squad will use. Table 7.3 provides a quick reference for comparing the three techniques.

templated positions

a leader's best guess as to where the enemy positions are located

successive bound

the lead element, covered by the rear element, advances and takes up overwatch positions; the rear element then advances to an overwatch position roughly abreast of the lead element and halts; the lead element then moves to the next position, and so on; only one element moves at a time, and the rear element avoids advancing beyond the lead element; this method is easier to control and more secure than alternate bounding, but it is slower

alternate bound

covered by the rear element, the lead element moves forward, halts, and assumes overwatch positions; the rear element advances past the lead element and takes up overwatch positions; this sequence continues as necessary, with only one element moving at a time

MOVEMENT TECHNIQUES	WHEN NORMALLY USED	CHARACTERISTICS			
		CONTROL	DISPERSION	SPEED	SECURITY
TRAVELING	CONTACT NOT LIKELY	MORE	LESS	FASTEST	LEAST
TRAVELING OVERWATCH	CONTACT POSSIBLE	LESS	MORE	SLOWER	MORE
BOUNDING OVERWATCH	CONTACT EXPECTED	MOST	MOST	SLOWEST	MOST

Table 7.3 Movement Techniques and Characteristics

Squad Traveling

Use **traveling** when contact with the enemy is not likely and speed is needed (Figure 7.7).

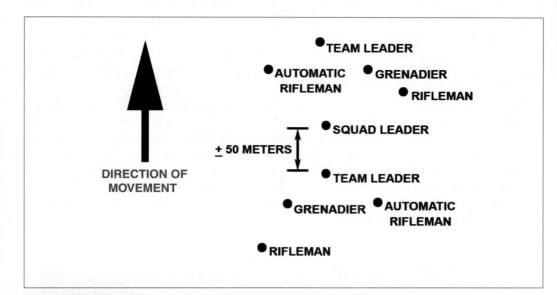

Figure 7.7 Squad Traveling

Squad Traveling Overwatch

Use **traveling overwatch** when contact is possible. Attached weapons move near the squad leader and under the leader's control so he or she can employ them quickly. Rifle squads normally move in column or wedge formation. Ideally, the lead team moves at least 50 meters in front of the rest of the element.

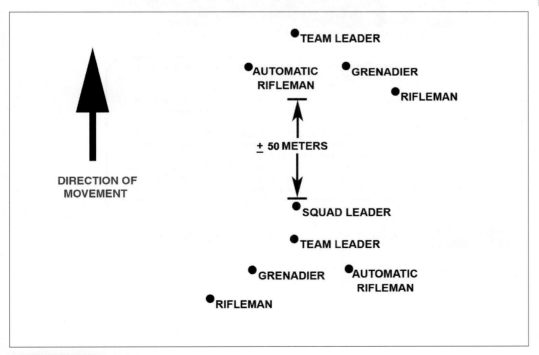

Figure 7.8 Squad Traveling Overwatch

Squad Bounding Overwatch

Use **bounding overwatch** when you expect contact with the enemy, when the squad leader feels the enemy is near (based on movement, noise, reflection, trash, fresh tracks, or even a hunch), or when the squad must cross a large open danger area. The lead fire team overwatches first. Soldiers in the overwatch team scan for enemy positions. The squad leader usually stays with the overwatch team. The trail fire team bounds and signals the squad leader when it completes its bound and is prepared to overwatch the movement of the other team.

Both team leaders must know which team the squad leader will be with. Overwatching team leaders must know the route and destination of the bounding team. Bounding team leaders must know their team's destination and route, possible enemy locations, and actions to take when the team arrives there. Bounding team leaders must also know where the overwatching team will be and how they will receive their instructions. The cover and concealment on the bounding team's route dictates how its Soldiers move.

Teams can bound successively or alternately. Successive bounds are easier to control; alternate bounds can be faster.

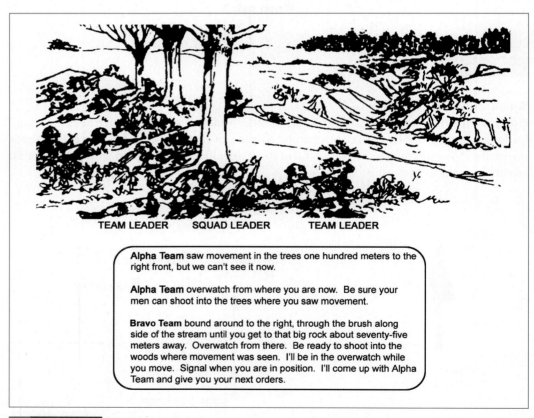

TEAM LEADER   SQUAD LEADER   TEAM LEADER

Alpha Team saw movement in the trees one hundred meters to the right front, but we can't see it now.

Alpha Team overwatch from where you are now. Be sure your men can shoot into the trees where you saw movement.

Bravo Team bound around to the right, through the brush along side of the stream until you get to that big rock about seventy-five meters away. Overwatch from there. Be ready to shoot into the woods where movement was seen. I'll be in the overwatch while you move. Signal when you are in position. I'll come up with Alpha Team and give you your next orders.

Figure 7.9 Example of a Squad Leader's Order to Bound

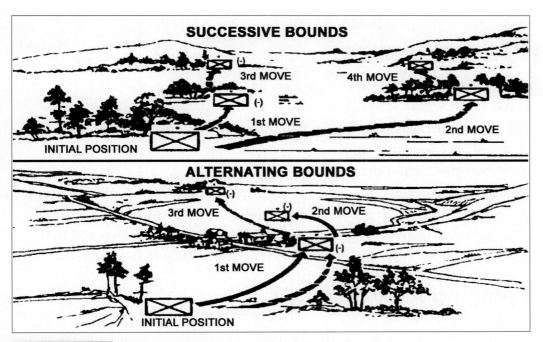

Figure 7.10 Squad Successive and Alternate Bounds

CONCLUSION

The movement *to* the objective, in many cases, will set the conditions for success or failure once you arrive at the objective. You must take care not to dismiss movement planning in any operation.

Remember, tactical movement is subject to the leader's constant assessment and METT-TC analysis. It is critical to your mission's success to maintain combat effectiveness throughout the movement. In the end, it's about making it to the right place, at the right time, with all your Soldiers, ready to fight and win.

Learning Assessment

1. Explain the relationship between control, security, fire capability, and flexibility when considering movement formations and techniques. Give an example of a tradeoff between two or more of these factors.

2. What movement formation might you use if you are moving as a squad independent of the platoon? What if you are running behind schedule and do not expect enemy contact?

3. How do the factors of METT-TC influence your movement formation and technique?

Key Words

situational awareness
movement formation
movement technique
interval
wedge
file
column
line
templated positions
alternate bound
successive bound
traveling
traveling overwatch
bounding overwatch

References

Field Manual 3-21.8, *The Infantry Rifle Platoon and Squad*. 28 March 2007.

Tennessee Army National Guard 1st Lt. David Tiedeman and Sgt. Robert Betterton. (29 August 2007). *Heroes*, Vol. 2, Issue 31. Defense Link. Retrieved 12 April 2008 from http://www.defenselink.mil/heroes/profiles/files/bettertonTiedeman_20070829.pdf

SH 21-76, *Ranger Handbook*. July 2006.

SQUAD TACTICS: PATROLLING

Key Points

1 Patrols

2 Departing from Friendly Lines

3 Patrol Base Operations

4 Reentering Friendly Lines

The art of war is simple enough. Find out where your enemy is. Get at him as soon as you can. Strike him as hard as you can and keep moving on.

GEN Ulysses S. Grant

Introduction

Patrolling. Does this word conjure up memories of stories told by earlier generations of family members, teachers, or neighbors who have talked about "patrolling the 'Nam'" during the Vietnam War, "patrolling the border" during the Cold War, or "patrolling the DMZ" in Korea? Perhaps you are current on US and world events and have watched or read about US Soldiers conducting patrols in Afghanistan and Iraq. The Army still practices the art of patrolling, but it continuously adjusts its tactics, techniques, and procedures (TTPs) to adapt to the enemy's TTPs and to the terrain in the contemporary operating environment (COE). Before the Vietnam War, the Army conducted patrols on the relatively defined, linear battlefields of Western Europe. They targeted a Cold War enemy who had rigid and predictable doctrinal procedures. During the Vietnam War, the Army faced an enemy that was unpredictable, chose when and where to fight, and avoided decisive engagements against superior US numbers and weapons. After Vietnam, the Army faced a modern, armor-heavy Soviet Union with a well-defined and predictable war-fighting doctrine. The pendulum has swung again, and US Soldiers currently face an adaptive and agile enemy in today's 21st century terrorist and insurgent forces. Although doctrine has changed over the years, the Army will always require competent, adaptive small-unit leaders to lead decentralized combat patrols to find, fix, and destroy the enemy on the ever-changing battlefield.

On September 28, 1994, I received the mission to conduct security patrols to protect the Haitian Parliament from FRAPH (Revolutionary Front for the Advancement and Progress of Haiti) and attachés intervening in Parliamentary procedures. To accomplish this mission, each squad carried the following equipment: one M60 Machine Gun, two Squad Automatic Weapons (SAW), and two M203 Grenade Launchers. For navigation each squad carried an AN/PSN-11 Global Positioning System (PLUGGER). For communications, each squad and the Platoon Leader and Platoon Sergeant carried an AP/PRC 126 Squad Radio. The headquarters element had 2 AN/PRC 119 (SINCGARS).

At 1300, I issued a hasty OPORD. My plan was to have squads negotiate the route using traveling overwatch, and one squad remain in reserve at the Parliament building with the company commander. We were to travel along a designated route and report "suspicious" activity. I exited the wire at 1400. At Checkpoint 2, I lost communications with the trail squad. The distance from my location to the Parliament building was less than 300 meters. I halted the patrol, and after several failed attempts on the squad radio, I contacted the company RTO via SINCGARS. I relayed the message to move to the trail squad. Apparently, the squad leader had left his PLUGGER in his ruck and had returned to retrieve it. After about five minutes he returned and moved. Eventually, the trail squad was in sight. I instructed the squad leader on the radio to follow us along the route at the current interval. As I reached Checkpoint 3, the platoon was executing the mission smoothly. I proceeded north to Checkpoint 4, but the trail squads continued east off the designated route. Just beyond Checkpoint 4, the lead quad encountered an MP platoon conducting a cordon and search of a suspected FRAPH house only 100 meters from our defense. I relayed this information, and neither the company commander nor the battalion commander was aware of the operation. . . .

CPT Michael Dane Acord, Bravo Company, 3rd Battalion, 14th Infantry

(Department of the Army, 1997)

Patrols

A patrol is a detachment sent out by a larger unit to conduct a specific combat, reconnaissance, or security mission. Patrols operate semi-independently and return to the main body upon completion of their mission. Patrolling fulfills the infantry's primary function of finding the enemy to either engage him or report his disposition, location, and actions. Patrols act as both the eyes and ears of the larger unit and as a fist to deliver a sharp devastating jab—and then withdraw before the enemy can recover.

A patrol's organization is temporary and specifically matched to the immediate task. Because a patrol is an organization, not a mission, it is not correct to speak of giving a unit a mission to "patrol." A commander sends a patrol out from the main body to conduct a specific tactical task with an associated purpose. Upon completion of that task, the patrol leader returns to the main body, reports to the commander, and describes the events that took place, the status of the patrol's members and equipment, and any observations.

A patrol can consist of a unit as small as a fire team. Squad- and platoon-size patrols are normal, however. Sometimes, for combat tasks such as a raid, the patrol can consist of most of the combat elements of a rifle company. Unlike operations in which the infantry platoon or squad is integrated into a larger organization, the patrol is semi-independent and relies on itself for security.

Planning a Patrol

The patrol planning process begins when you, the platoon leader, receive the mission. The first thing you do is to ascertain what type of patrol your platoon will conduct (the "M" in METT-TC). The *reconnaissance patrol* and *combat patrol* each have their own unique planning, coordinating, and execution requirements. After you know the type of mission, you consider the enemy you may encounter, the area of operation you must cover, and the friendly troops available, (the "E", "T", and "T" in METT-TC), to determine how you must task organize your platoon to conduct the patrol assigned to you.

Task Organization

A patrol is organized to perform specific tasks. It must be prepared to secure itself, navigate accurately, identify and cross danger areas, and reconnoiter the patrol objective. If it is a combat patrol, it must be prepared to breach obstacles, assault the objective, and support those assaults by fire. Additionally, a patrol must be able to conduct detailed searches as well as deal with casualties and prisoners or detainees.

The patrol leader (PL) identifies those tasks the patrol must perform and decides which elements will implement them. Where possible, the PL should keep squads and fire teams together.

Squads and fire teams may perform more than one task during the time a patrol is away from the main body, or they may be responsible for only one task. The PL must plan carefully to ensure that he or she has identified and assigned all required tasks in the most efficient way.

Elements and teams for platoons conducting patrols include the common and specific elements for each type of patrol. The following elements are common to all patrols.

Headquarters Element
The headquarters element normally consists of the PL and a radio operator. The platoon sergeant may be designated as the assistant patrol leader (APL). Combat patrols may include a forward observer and perhaps a radio operator. Any attachments that you as platoon leader decide that you or the platoon sergeant must control directly are also part of the headquarters element.

Aid and Litter Team(s)
Aid and litter teams are responsible for locating, treating, and evacuating casualties.

Enemy Prisoner of War (EPW)/Detainee Team(s)
EPW teams are responsible for controlling enemy prisoners in accord with the five S's (see the nearby note) and the leader's guidance. These teams may also be responsible for accounting for and controlling detainees or recovered personnel.

Surveillance Team(s)
Patrols use surveillance teams to establish and maintain covert observation of an objective for as long as it takes to complete the patrol's mission.

En Route Recorder
The PL can designate an en route recorder to record all information collected during the mission.

Compass and Pace Man
If the patrol does not have access to Global Positioning Systems (GPS), or if it is operating in a location where there is no satellite reception, it may be necessary to navigate by dead reckoning. The PL appoints a compass man and a pace man to do this.

Assault Team(s)
Combat patrols designate assault teams to close with the enemy on the objective or to clear the ambush kill zone.

Support Team(s)
Combat patrols designate teams to provide direct fire in support of the breach and assault teams.

Breach Team(s) and Search Team(s)
Combat patrols have breach teams to assist the assault team in getting to the objective. Search teams conduct a cursory or detailed search of the objective area.

Elements Common to Combat Patrols

A combat patrol has three essential elements: security, support, and assault. Assault elements accomplish the mission during actions on the objective. Support elements suppress or destroy the enemy on the objective in support of the assault element. Security elements assist in isolating the objective by preventing the enemy from entering and leaving the objective area. It also ensures the patrol's withdrawal route remains open. The size of each element is based on the situation and PL's analysis of METT-TC.

Assault Element
The assault element is the combat patrol's decisive effort. Its task is to conduct actions on the objective. The assault element is responsible for accomplishing the unit's task and purpose. This element must be able (through inherent capabilities or positioning relative to the enemy) to destroy or seize the combat patrol's target. Tasks typically associated with the assault element include:

The Five S's

Search—*thoroughly* check each prisoner for weapons and information.

Silence—do not allow any prisoner to speak with fellow prisoners or to give your position away.

Segregate—separate prisoners from their leaders. This will prevent them from planning and executing an escape.

Safeguard—protect prisoners from harm and treat them in accordance with the Geneva Convention and the Law of Land Warfare.

Speed to the rear—quickly pass prisoners off for interrogation. This will provide friendly forces with timely intelligence and allow your patrol to continue its mission.

- Conduct of assault across the objective to destroy enemy equipment, capture or kill enemy, and clearing of key terrain and enemy positions
- Deployment close enough to the objective to conduct an immediate assault if detected
- Being prepared to support itself if the support element cannot suppress the enemy
- Providing support to a breach element in reducing obstacles (if required)
- Planning detailed fire control and distribution
- Conducting controlled withdrawal from the objective.

Your analysis of METT-TC, particularly for a raid, may result in your organizing a separate breach force. At times this may include breaching an obstacle. Additional tasks/special purpose teams may include:

- *Search teams* – to find and collect documents, equipment, and information that can be used as intelligence
- *Demolition teams* – to plan and execute the destruction of obstacles and enemy equipment
- *Breach team* – to create small-scale breaches in protective obstacles to facilitate the completion of the patrol's primary task.

Support Element

The support element suppresses the enemy on the objective using direct and indirect fires. The support element is a shaping effort that sets conditions for the mission's decisive effort. This element must be able, through inherent means or positioning relative to the enemy, to support the assault element. You can divide up the support force into two or more elements if required.

The support element addresses a secondary threat of enemy interference with the assault element(s). The support force suppresses, fixes, or destroys elements on the objective. The support force's primary responsibility is to suppress the enemy to prevent reposition against decisive effort. The support force:

- Initiates fires and gains fire superiority with crew-served weapons and indirect fires
- Controls rates and distribution of fires
- Shifts/ceases fire on signal
- Supports the withdrawal of the assault element.

Security Element

The security element(s) is a shaping force that has three roles. The first is to isolate the objective from enemy personnel and vehicles attempting to enter the objective area. Its actions range from simply providing early warning, to blocking enemy movement. This element may require several different forces located in various positions. As patrol leader you must be careful to consider enemy reserves or response forces that, once the engagement begins, will be alerted. The second role of the security element is to prevent the enemy from escaping the objective area. The third role is to secure the patrol's withdrawal route.

There is a subtle yet important distinction for the security element. All elements of the patrol are responsible for their own local security. What distinguishes the security element is that it protects the entire patrol. Its positions must be such that it can, in accordance with its engagement criteria, provide early warning of approaching enemy.

The security element addresses the primary threat to the patrol—being discovered and defeated by enemy security forces before your patrol can execute actions on the objective. To facilitate the success of the assault element, the security element must fix or block (or at a minimum screen) all enemy security or response forces located on parts of the battlefield away from the raid.

Elements Common to Reconnaissance Patrols

Reconnaissance Elements

The task of the reconnaissance element is to obtain the information needed to facilitate tactical decision making. The primary means is reconnaissance (or surveillance) enabled by tactical movement and continuous, accurate reporting. The reconnaissance patrol leader decides how in-depth the reconnaissance will be. A thorough and accurate reconnaissance is important. However, avoiding detection is equally important.

Below are some of the additional tasks normally associated with a reconnaissance element:

- Reconnoiter all terrain within the assigned area, route, or zone
- Determine trafficability routes or potential avenues of approach (based on the personnel or vehicles you will use on the route)
- Determine the time it takes to traverse the route
- Reconnoiter to the limit of direct-fire range
- Within capabilities, reconnoiter natural and man-made obstacles to ensure mobility along the route
- Locate a bypass or reduce/breach, clear, and mark key areas
- Determine the size, location, and composition of society/human demographics
- Identify key infrastructure that could influence military operations, including the following:
  - Political, government, and religious organizations and agencies
  - Physical facilities and utilities (such as power generation, transportation, and communications networks)
- Find all threat forces that influence movement along the area, route, or zone
- Report information.

Security Element

The security element has two tasks: provide early warning of approaching enemy; and provide support by fire to the reconnaissance elements if they come in contact with the enemy. The security element's purpose is to protect the reconnaissance element, thereby allowing it to obtain the required information. Security elements tasked to provide early warning must be able to observe avenues of approach into and out of the objective area. If the reconnaissance element is compromised, the security element must be able to quickly support it. It does this by occupying positions that enable Soldiers to observe the objective as well as cover the reconnaissance element. Soldiers in these positions must be able to engage the enemy with direct and indirect fire. They must also be able to facilitate communication with higher command as well as with any supporting assets. You must think out and rehearse well this worst-case scenario.

Initial Planning and Coordination for Patrols

You plan and prepare for patrols using the troop leading procedures and an estimate of the situation. You must identify required actions on the objective, **plan backward** to the departure from friendly lines, then forward to the reentry of friendly lines.

As patrol leader, you will normally receive the OPORD in the battalion or company command post (CP) where communications are good and key personnel are available for coordination. Because patrols act semi-independently, move beyond the direct-fire support of the parent unit, and often operate forward of friendly units, coordination must be thorough and detailed.

You may routinely coordinate with elements of the battalion staff directly. You and subordinate leaders should develop tactical SOPs with detailed checklists to preclude omitting any items vital to accomplishing the mission.

backward planning

planning the operation's timeline starting with the time stated in Paragraph II of the OPORD – the leader then includes all key events in reverse order of occurrence, ending with the time the warning order (WARNO) was given

You must coordinate with higher command's staff, normally at the battalion level, before conducting a patrol forward of friendly lines. You must receive the most current update on the enemy situation (including terrain, weather, and light data), and ensure you have the most current maps from the intelligence officer (S-2). You must meet with the battalion signal officer to receive the most current communications security and signal operation instructions (SOI). (The last thing you need is to be out of range of mutual support, in contact with the enemy, and unable to communicate with higher command. Worse, the patrol cannot reenter friendly lines if it does not know the updated signals, codes, or passwords for reentry.)

Items you coordinate with the battalion staff or company commander include:

rally point

an easily identifiable point on the ground at which a patrol can reassemble and reorganize if they become dispersed

- Changes or updates in the enemy situation
- Best use of terrain for routes, **rally points,** and patrol bases
- Light and weather data
- Changes in the friendly situation
- The attachment of Soldiers with special skills or equipment
- Use and location of landing or pickup zones
- Departure and reentry of friendly lines
- Fire support on the objective and along the planned routes, including alternate routes
- Rehearsal areas and times
- Special equipment and ammunition requirements
- Transportation support, including transportation to and from the rehearsal site
- Signal plan—call signs, frequencies, code words, pyrotechnics, and challenge and password.

You coordinate with the unit through which your platoon or squad will conduct its forward and rearward passage of lines. As platoon leader, you also coordinate patrol activities with the leaders of other units that will be patrolling in adjacent areas at the same time.

Critical Thinking

Recall what you learned about the "one-third, two-thirds" rule of planning from troop leading procedures. Explain why this practice would be especially critical in patrol planning and preparation.

Completing the Patrol Plan

As you complete your patrol plan, you consider the following elements:

Essential and Supporting Tasks

As PL, you ensure that you have assigned all essential tasks to be performed on the objective, at rally points, at danger areas, at security or surveillance locations, along the route(s), and at **passage lanes.**

passage lane

a lane through an enemy or friendly obstacle that provides a safe passage for a passing force

Key Travel and Execution Times

You estimate time requirements for movement to the objective, leader's reconnaissance of the objective, establishment of security and surveillance, compaction of all assigned tasks on the objective, movement to an objective rally point to debrief the platoon, and return through friendly lines.

Primary and Alternate Routes

You select primary and alternate routes to and from the objective (Figure 8.1). Return routes should differ from routes to the objective. You may delegate route selection to a subordinate but are ultimately responsible for the routes selected. You may handrail terrain—moving between terrain features—or use dead reckoning with azimuths and distances when planning routes.

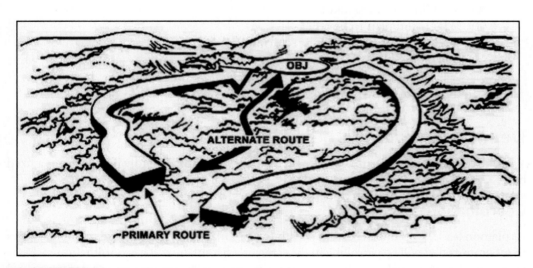

Figure 8.1   Primary and Alternate Routes

Signals

As patrol leader, you should consider the use of special signals. These include arm-and-hand signals, flares, voice, whistles, radios, and visible and nonvisible lasers. Rehearse all signals to ensure that all Soldiers know what they mean.

Challenge and Password Outside Friendly Lines

Do not use the challenge and password from the signal operating instructions (SOI) when your patrol is outside friendly lines. The unit's tactical SOP should state the procedure for establishing a patrol challenge and password as well as other combat identification features and patrol markings.

Locations of Leaders

You should consider where you, the platoon sergeant, and other key leaders should be located for each phase of the patrol mission. The platoon sergeant is normally with the following elements for each type of patrol:

- On a raid or ambush, the platoon sergeant normally controls the support element
- On an area reconnaissance, the platoon sergeant normally supervises security at the **objective rally point (ORP)**
- On a zone reconnaissance, the platoon sergeant normally moves with the reconnaissance element that sets up the link-up point.

Actions on Enemy Contact

Your plan must address actions on chance contact with the enemy at each phase of the patrol mission.

- The plan must address how to handle seriously wounded and killed in action (KIAs)
- The plan must address how to handle prisoners captured as a result of chance contact and not as part of the planned mission.

Contingency Plans

Whenever you leave the ORP, patrol base, or the patrol main body for any reason, you leave the APL a **five-point contingency plan**. The contingency plan is described by the acronym GOTWA, and includes:

- **G:** Where you are GOING
- **O:** OTHERS you are taking along
- **T:** TIME you plan to be gone
- **W:** WHAT to do if you do not return in time
- **A:** ACTIONS that the main body takes on chance contact with the enemy while you are gone, and actions you will take if chance contact with the enemy is made while you're away from the main body.

Departing From Friendly Lines

You must thoroughly plan and coordinate the departure from friendly lines or from a fixed base.

Coordination

As platoon leader, you must coordinate with the commander of the forward unit and leaders of other units that will be patrolling in the same or adjacent areas. The coordination includes SOI information, signal plan, fire plan, running passwords, procedures for departure and reentry of lines, planned dismount points, initial rally points, actions at departure and reentry points, and information about the enemy.

---

objective rally point (ORP)

a point beyond lines but out of sight, sound, and small-arms range of the objective, normally located in the direction the patrol will move after completing its mission—the patrol reconnoiters the objective from this point before moving on the objective

---

five-point contingency plan

method for issuing instructions to subordinate leaders that describe the actions to be taken in the event of contact with the enemy or mission delay

You provide the forward unit leader with your unit identification, size of the patrol, departure and return times, and area of operation.

The forward unit leader provides you with the following:

- Additional information on terrain just outside the friendly unit lines
- Known or suspected enemy positions in the near vicinity
- Likely enemy ambush sites
- Latest enemy activity
- Detailed information on friendly positions, obstacles, and OPs
- Friendly unit fire plan
- Support the unit can provide (fire support, litter teams, guides, communications, and reaction force).

Planning

In your plan for the departure of friendly lines, you should consider the following sequence of actions:

- Making contact with friendly guides at the contact point
- Moving to a coordinated initial rally point just inside friendly lines
- Completing final coordination
- Moving to and through the **passage point**
- Establishing a security-listening halt beyond the friendly unit's **final protective fires**

Rally Points

You must also consider the use and locations of rally points. A rally point is a place you designate where the platoon moves to reassemble and reorganize if it becomes dispersed. Rally points must:

- be easy to find
- have no recent signs of enemy activity
- provide cover and concealment
- be located away from natural lines of drift and avenues of approach
- be defendable for short periods of time.

Selection of Rally Points

You physically reconnoiter routes to select rally points whenever possible. If you can only conduct a map reconnaissance, you select tentative points. You confirm routes through actual inspection as the platoon moves through them. Rally points must:

- be easy to recognize on the ground
- have cover and concealment
- be away from natural lines of drift
- be defendable for short periods.

Types of Rally Points

The most common types of rally points are *initial, objective, reentry, near- and far-side* and *en route.* Soldiers must know which rally point to move to at each phase of the patrol mission. They should know which actions are required there and how long they are to wait at each rally point before moving to another. Following are descriptions of these five rally points:

passage point (PP)

a specifically designated place where the passing units will pass through the stationary unit

final protective fires (FPF)

an immediately available prearranged barrier of fire designed to impede enemy movement across defensive lines or areas

The best way to make a rally point easy to find is to associate it with an obvious feature on the ground (e.g., a large boulder, fallen tree, or unique terrain feature). Remember, Soldiers must be able to recognize the terrain feature when returning from the opposite direction of your travel if they have just broken contact with an enemy force or when visibility is different than when you designated the RP.

1. **Initial rally point.** An initial rally point is a place inside friendly lines where a unit may assemble and reorganize if it makes enemy contact while departing friendly lines or before reaching the first en route rally point. The commander of the friendly unit normally selects it.

2. **Objective rally point.** The objective rally point (ORP) is a point out of sight, sound, and small-arms range of the objective area. It is normally located in the direction that the platoon plans to move after completing its actions on the objective. The ORP is tentative until the objective is pinpointed. Actions at or from the ORP include:

   • issuing a final FRAGO
   • disseminating information from reconnaissance if contact was not made
   • making final preparations before continuing operations
   • accounting for Soldiers and equipment after actions at the objective are complete
   • reestablishing the chain of command after actions at the objective are complete.

3. **Reentry rally point.** The reentry rally point (RRP) is located out of sight, sound, and small-arms weapons range of the friendly unit through which the platoon will return. This also means that the RRP should be outside the final protective fires of the friendly unit. Your platoon occupies the RRP as a security perimeter.

4. **Near- and far-side rally points.** These rally points are on the near and far side of danger areas. If your platoon makes contact while crossing the danger area and you lose control, Soldiers on either side move to the rally point nearest them. They establish security, reestablish the chain of command, determine their personnel and equipment status, continue the patrol mission, and link up at the ORP.

5. **En Route Rally Point.** During movement, you designate en route rally points every 100 to 400 meters based on the terrain, vegetation, and visibility. When you designate a new rally point, the previously designated rally point is the rally point that the patrol will reorganize at if the patrol makes contact with the enemy. This is necessary to ensure the patrol can break contact and move a safe distance away in order to have time to consolidate and reorganize. In other words, if you gave the rally point arm signal 200 meters ago, and the patrol makes contact with the enemy, 200 meters may not be a great enough distance to fall back to. This method also precludes uncertainty over which rally point Soldiers should move to if contact is made immediately after the leader designates a new rally point. There are three ways to designate a rally point:

   1. Physically occupy it for a short period. This is the preferred method, as it allows Soldiers to become familiar with the terrain and vegetation that makes the rally point easily identifiable.

   2. Pass near the rally point and designate it using hand-and-arm signals.

   3. Walk through the rally point and designate using hand-and-arm signals.

   Most unit SOPs will require Soldiers in the patrol to look back at the ORP several times as they move farther beyond the ORP. This will allow Soldiers to see what the terrain will actually look like if the Soldier has to move back to the ORP from the direction of enemy contact.

Patrol Base Operations

As PL, you must plan primary and alternate patrol bases and the routes to them. You consider the mission and select locations that allow the patrol to accomplish its patrol within the time constraints placed on it. You consider active and passive security measures when selecting the location of patrol bases, such as terrain that the enemy would probably

Critical Thinking

Planning for EPWs. How will EPWs or detainees affect your patrol? When is the best time to plan for EPWs and detainees?

consider of little tactical value; is off main lines of drift; is difficult enough to impede foot movement (such as an area of dense vegetation that is close to the ground, or swampy or marshy areas); is near a clean water source; can be defended for a short period of time and offers good cover and concealment. You avoid known or suspected enemy positions, built-up areas, ridges and hilltops, (except as needed for maintaining communication), roads and trails, and small valleys. When planning a patrol base, the plan includes listening posts/observation posts (LP/OPs); methods for communication with the LP/OPs; a patrol base defense plan; a withdrawal plan if enemy contact is made (including routes, rally points, and alternate patrol bases); a security and sleep plan to ensure the appropriate level of security is maintained at all times; and a plan to conduct and enforce noise and light discipline.

Patrol Base Occupation

You reconnoiter and establish the patrol base the same as you do an ORP or RRP, except that the platoon enters at a 90-degree turn (Figure 8.2). Apply common sense to METT TC and if there is nothing to be gained by entering at a 90-degree turn (on flat desert terrain, for example), then you need not.

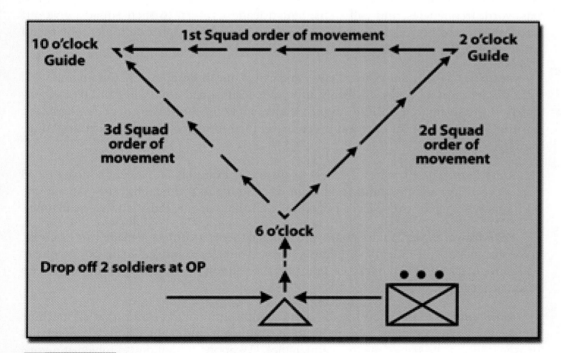

Figure 8.2 Occupation of the Patrol Base

You leave a two-man OP at the turn. The APL and the last fire team will cover any tracks from the turn into the patrol base. The platoon moves into the patrol base as depicted in Figure 8.2. (Squads occupy a cigar-shaped perimeter at their designated leg of the triangle.) All squad leaders move to the left flank of their squad leg. The PL and support element or weapons squad leader start at 6 o'clock and move in a clockwise manner adjusting the perimeter (meeting each squad leader at his or her squad's left flank). If you or the support element leader find a better location for one of the machine guns, you reposition it.

After you have checked each squad's sector, the squad leaders and one squad member from each squad report to the command post (CP) as an R&S team. You issue the three R&S teams a contingency plan and remind them that they are looking for the enemy, water, built-up areas or human habitat, roads and trails, and any possible rally points. (Squads occupying a patrol base on their own do not send out R&S teams at night.) The R&S team members depart from the left flank of their squad's sector and move out a given distance, as stated in your instructions. The team moves in a clockwise direction and reenters the patrol base at the right flank of the squad's sector. The R&S team will prepare a sketch of the squad's front and turn it in to the PL at the conclusion of their R&S patrol.

The distance the R&S team moves away from the squad's sector will vary depending on the terrain and vegetation (anywhere from 200 to 400 meters). All members of the platoon are on 100 percent alert during this time. The R&S team is of little value at night without the use of night vision devices. The PL ensures that each R&S team has a radio.

If you feel that the platoon may have been tracked, you may elect to maintain 100 percent security and wait awhile in total silence before sending out the R&S teams. Once all squad leaders (R&S teams) have completed their reconnaissance, they report back to you at the CP. You gather the information from your three R&S teams and determine if the platoon will be able to use the location as a patrol base.

Patrol Base Activities

If you determine that you will be able to use the location as a patrol base, you inform the APL and squad leaders. You also disseminate other information such as daily challenge and password, frequencies, and call signs. Squad leaders return to their squads, give out information, and begin the priorities of work as stated by the platoon leader. The patrol must sterilize the patrol base upon departure.

Security. Use only one point of entry and exit at one of the apexes. Maintain noise and light discipline at all times. Challenge everyone. Each squad establishes an OP and may quietly dig hasty fighting positions. Squad leaders supervise the placement of aiming stakes, ensure Claymores are set out, and prepare and turn in sector sketches, including range cards.

Alert Plan. The PL states the alert posture (for example, 50 percent security or 33 percent security) and the stand-to time for day and night. You establish the plan and the APL supervises it. OPs are relieved periodically, and at least one leader is awake at all times.

Withdrawal Plan. You designate which signal to use if contact is made (for example, color star cluster), the order of withdrawal if forced out (for example, squads not in contact will move first), and the rendezvous point for the platoon (if the platoon is not to link up at an alternate patrol base).

Maintenance Plan. The PL redistributes ammunition and ensures that all machine guns, other weapon systems, communication equipment, and night vision devices are not broken down at the same time for maintenance. (Weapons are not disassembled at night.)

Sanitation and Personal Hygiene Plan. The APL ensures the platoon slit trench is dug and marked at night with a chemical light inside the trench. Squad leaders designate squad urine areas. All Soldiers accomplish the following daily: shave; brush teeth; wash face, hands, armpits, groin, and feet; and change socks. Soldiers ensure that no trash is left behind.

Mess Plan. No more than half of the patrol base eats at one time.

Water Resupply. The APL organizes a watering party, including Soldiers to perform security. Canteens and squad-issued water-filtering devices are loaded into an empty - rucksack. Soldiers fill up each canteen using the filter and return to the patrol base (if there are no water-filtering devices, Soldiers must chemically treat each canteen of water).

Reentering Friendly Lines

At the conclusion of the combat, recon, or tracking patrol, the PL plans to reenter during daylight if at all possible to reduce the chance of fratricide. The patrol halts at the RRP and establishes security. From the RRP, you make radio contact with the friendly forward unit (FFU) to advise them that you are in the RRP and wish to make contact at the RP with the guide. (If operating on a nonsecure radio net, you must use the pre-established codeword, or the SOI codeword for the patrol in the RRP, or the codeword for attempting link-up.) The friendly unit must acknowledge the message and confirm a time when the guide will be at the reentry point.

If radio communications are not possible, you, the radio operator (RTO), and a buddy team security element move forward and attempt to contact an OP using the challenge and password. The OP notifies the friendly unit that the platoon is ready to return and requests a guide. If you cannot find an OP, you go with the RTO and security element to locate the coordinated reentry point. You must move straight toward (and away from) friendly lines, never parallel to them. All lateral movement should be outside of small-arms weapons range. (If reentering at night, use other backup signals to make contact with friendly units. The preferred method is to wait until daylight.)

Once the friendly unit acknowledges your patrol's intent to return, you issue a five-point contingency plan to your patrol at the RRP and move with your RTO and security element on a determined azimuth and pace to the reentry point. You use far and near recognition signals to establish contact with the guide. You signal the platoon forward (radio) or return and lead it to the reentry point. You may post the security element with the guide at the enemy side of the reentry point. The APL counts and identifies each Soldier as he or she passes through the reentry point. The guide leads the patrol to the assembly area on the friendly side of the passage point (this may be the IRP the patrol used prior to departing on the patrol). You report to the friendly unit's command post to conduct a back brief. You then rejoin the patrol in the assembly area and lead it to a secure area for debriefing, which typically includes size, composition and mission of the patrol, departure and return times, routes, detailed description of terrain and enemy positions that you identified, time, location and results of any contact with the enemy, personnel status at the conclusion of the patrol, disposition and location of wounded in action (WIA) and killed in action (KIA), and conclusions or recommendations.

CONCLUSION

Conducting a successful patrol involves planning and considering many aspects of METT-TC. The type, purpose, composition, number, frequency, and area of operation of the patrol missions that you will plan, coordinate, and execute as an Army officer will vary depending on your duty position, the unit you are assigned to, and the theater of operation you will operate in. As you have learned, patrols share many common characteristics, but each patrol also has unique characteristics as well. With this section as your patrolling foundation, you can look forward to learning more about patrolling, having the opportunity to conduct realistic training patrols, and perhaps one day leading your own Soldiers on a patrol.

Learning Assessment

1. Which elements are common to all patrols?
2. What is the sequence of actions in a departure from friendly lines?
3. What is the sequence of actions in a reentry of friendly lines?
4. When do you use a patrol base?

Key Words

backward planning
rally point (RP)
passage lane
objective rally point (ORP)
five-point contingency plan (GOTWA)
passage point
final protective fires (FPF)

References

Acord, M. D. (1997). *Operations Other Than War.* "*Patrolling During Operation Uphold Democracy.*" Fort Benning, GA: USA Infantry School Library. Retrieved 30 June 2008 from https://www.infantry.army.mil/monographs/content/other/STUP5/AcordMichael%20D%20CPT.

Field Manual 1-02, *Operational Terms and Graphics.* September 2004.

Field Manual 3-21.8, *Infantry Rifle Platoon and Squad.* 1 March 2007.

SH 21-76, *US Army Ranger Handbook.* July 2006.

BATTLE DRILLS

Key Points

1 **Battle Drills**

In the absence of orders, go find something and kill it.

German Field Marshal Erwin Rommel

Introduction

battle drill

a collective action, rapidly executed without applying a deliberate decision making process, in which a unit applies fire and maneuver to common situations of enemy combat

A **battle drill** is a collective action, rapidly executed without applying a deliberate decision making process. Battle drills describe how platoons and squads apply fire and maneuver to commonly encountered situations. They require leaders to make decisions rapidly and to issue brief oral orders quickly. Battle drills are the foundation of all combat operations. *Drills* are actions that you and your unit will practice again and again, until they become second nature. At that point, you can count on your Soldiers to execute the drill, even if the circumstances differ completely from those during training. Likewise, your commander will count on you and your platoon to execute any of a number of battle drills rapidly and effectively.

Due to the nature of today's nonlinear battlefield, it is becoming more common for branches besides the Infantry to make contact with enemy forces and rely on battle drills to survive. While similar in many ways, a battle drill is not the same thing as a unit standing operating procedure (SOP). Both require minimal leader orders to accomplish, require sequential actions for success, and generally apply to platoon-sized or smaller units. But a battle drill differs from an SOP in an important way: A battle drill is an immediate response to enemy contact that requires fire and maneuver in order to succeed. SOPs do not necessarily demand an immediate response to enemy contact and do not require fire or maneuver to succeed.

Artillery Specialist Earns Bronze Star

Spc. Raymond Loftis, a wire systems installation specialist, earned a Bronze Star for protecting a Soldier and manning the weapons station of an ammunition supply vehicle during a June 1 terrorist attack in Baghdad.

Loftis, 28, was serving with the 1st Armored Division, 2nd Battalion, 3rd Field Artillery regiment. Responding to an explosion, Loftis' patrol found a tracked ammunition carrier that was hit with an improvised explosive device. It was sitting disabled at the corner of a four-way intersection.

After removing a seriously wounded Soldier from the vehicle, and realizing that the patrol was receiving fire from buildings on the other three corners of the intersection, Loftis acted as a human shield for the wounded Soldier as he provided suppressive fire with his squad automatic weapon.

"I could feel the bullets going by my head and hitting the wall (behind me), and the concrete falling down my shirt," he said.

"I was just doing my job," he said. "All of the first aid and combat training I received from my (noncommissioned officers) fell into place; I just reacted."

(Bronze Star, 2004)

Battle Drills

The various battle drills share many common steps and principles. Learn these key points and you and your unit will enjoy more success in executing any battle drill.

1. All contacts will require you and your unit to perform some form of immediate "react to contact."

2. Upon contact, you and your Soldiers will first immediately return fire, hit the ground (except in a near ambush), and then seek to occupy a covered and concealed position.

3. Success in all your battle drills will depend on your unit's ability to gain and maintain **suppressive fires**.

4. Getting out of or avoiding the enemy's kill zone will maintain your combat power.

5. Maintaining communication up and down the chain of command, throughout the contact, is essential.

6. To maintain your unit's combat effectiveness, you must **consolidate and reorganize** after each direct-fire contact.

Note:

Gaining and maintaining suppressive fire over an enemy force is essential before beginning your assault. Suppressive fires will enable your unit to maneuver without sustaining serious casualties. Otherwise, you may not be able to successfully execute the battle drill on your own. You will have to call for reinforcements.

---

suppressive fires

a condition achieved when a unit's volume and accuracy of fires against an enemy force permits greater freedom to maneuver

consolidate and reorganize

actions taken immediately at the conclusion of enemy contact to prepare to defend against a counterattack, resume a unit's mission, or prepare for follow-on missions

Critical Thinking

Explain how the overall process of battle drills reinforces the Army leadership qualities of Be-Know-Do.

Critical Thinking

Relate the concept of a well-rehearsed collective action to areas outside the military. Consider sports teams, emergency responders such as firefighters and paramedics, and even families who have home fire evacuation plans. How are they similar to battle drills? How are they different?

Battle Drill—React to Contact

Situation: A squad or platoon receives fires from enemy individual or crew-served weapons.

Required Actions:

1. Soldiers immediately return fire and take up the nearest covered positions, continuing to return fire in the direction of contact.

2. Team/squad leaders locate and engage known or *suspected* enemy positions with well-aimed fire, and pass information to the squad/platoon leader.

Note:

Suspected enemy positions. It is critical that your Soldiers be trained and encouraged to quickly return fire upon contact; however, rules of engagement (ROE) may prevent you from returning fire indiscriminately without first identifying the enemy. Identify these positions, and upon contact you will be able to quickly return fire and engage enemy positions.

Note:

The leader must determine if the unit is in an enemy kill zone or engagement area. If so, the leader must risk what little cover or concealment the unit has to move out of the kill zone. If the unit remains in the kill zone, it will be destroyed—by design.

Determining the direction of enemy contact is often difficult, given certain conditions. Consider the case of a roadside IED detonating in the middle of your wheeled convoy. What was the direction of contact? Where is the enemy combatant who detonated it? Is he or she on the other side of the levee? Or is "he" the woman you just passed, dressed in civilian clothes?

3. Fire team leaders control fire using standard fire commands (initial and supplemental) containing the following elements:
   - Alert
   - Direction
   - Description of target
   - Range
   - Method of fire (manipulation and rate of fire)
   - Command to commence firing.

   Example: "Enemy bunker, 1 o'clock, 200 meters, suppressive fire!"
   or "Enemy truck, 11 o'clock, 100 meters, AT4 engage!"

4. Soldiers maintain contact with the Soldiers on their left and right.

5. Soldiers maintain contact with their team leaders and report the location of enemy positions.

Note:

When a Soldier, buddy team, or fire team moves too far forward, becoming isolated, separated, or cut off from other squad members, the results can be disastrous.

---

6. Leaders check the status of their personnel.

7. The team/squad leaders maintain contact with the squad/platoon leader.

Note:

The squad leader decides to fight through, fire and maneuver, or break contact with the enemy based partly on information in ACE and SALUTE reports from team leaders. (LACE gives liquid, ammunition, casualty, and equipment status; SALUTE gives size, activity, location, unit, time, and equipment information about the enemy.)

Following the end of major combat operations in Iraq (2003), enemy fires (direct and indirect) were largely inaccurate. Fear of American fire superiority and lethality, coupled with a lack of training, compelled enemy insurgents to quickly retreat after the initial volley, instead of placing well-aimed fires on their target.

8. The squad/platoon leader:

    a. Moves up to the fire team/squad in contact and links up with its leader. (As platoon leader, you should bring a radio telephone operator (RTO), platoon forward observer (FO), the squad leader of the nearest squad, and one machine gun team. The squad leader of the trail squad moves to the front of its lead fire team. The platoon sergeant also moves forward with the second machine gun team and links up with the platoon leader, ready to assume control of the base-of-fire element.)

    b. Determines whether or not the squad/platoon must move out of an engagement area.

    c. Determines whether or not the unit can gain and maintain suppressive fires with the element already in contact (based on the volume and accuracy of enemy fires against the element in contact).

Note:

Recall the discussion of suppressive fire. Note that the volume and accuracy of *enemy* fires are a good measure of the volume and accuracy of *your platoon's* fires.

    d. Makes an assessment of the situation identifying:
- The location of the enemy position and obstacles
- The size of the enemy force (The number of enemy automatic weapons, the presence of any vehicles, and the employment of indirect fires are indicators of the enemy strength)
- Vulnerable flanks
- Covered and concealed flanking routes to the enemy position.

    e. Determines the next course of action—for example, fire and movement, assault, breach, knock out bunker, enter, and clear a building or trench. (In many instances, executing *react to contact* will result in the need to execute another battle drill.)

    f. Reports the situation to the platoon leader/company commander and begins to maneuver.

    g. Calls for and adjusts indirect fire (mortars or artillery). (Squad leaders relay requests through the platoon leader.)

9. Team leaders lead their teams by example: for example, "Follow me, do as I do."

10. Leaders relay all commands and signals from the platoon chain of command.

Battle Drill—Break Contact

Situation: The squad/platoon is under enemy fire and must break contact.

Note:

The actions a leader/unit takes leading up to conducting a Break Contact battle drill are generally the same as those in the React to Contact drill. The unit reacts to the contact in the same manner, but takes the following additional steps to break contact.

Required Actions: (Figure 9.1)

1. The squad/platoon leader directs one fire team/squad in contact to support the disengagement of the remainder of the unit.

2. The squad/platoon leader orders the first fire team/squad to move in a distance and direction, to a terrain feature, or to the last objective rally point.

3. The base of fire (fire team/squad) continues to suppress the enemy.

4. The moving element uses fragmentation, concussion, and smoke grenades to mask its movement.

5. The moving element takes up the designated position and engages the enemy.

6. The platoon leader directs the base-of-fire element to move to its next location. (Based on the terrain and the volume and accuracy of the enemy's fire, the moving fire team/squad may need to use fire and movement techniques, as described in Section 7.)

7. While continuing to suppress the enemy as it breaks contact, the squad/platoon continues to bound away from the enemy until:
   - It breaks contact;
   - It passes through a higher-level support-by-fire position; or
   - Its fire teams/squads are in the assigned position to conduct the next mission.

8. The leader should consider changing the direction of movement once the squad/platoon breaks contact. This will reduce the ability of the enemy to place effective indirect fires on the unit.

9. If the squad or platoon becomes disrupted, Soldiers stay together and move to the last designated rally point.

10. Squad/platoon leaders account for Soldiers, report, reorganize as necessary, and continue the mission.

UNIT IS ENGAGING ENEMY
AND MUST BREAK CONTACT.

BOUNDING TEAM USES SMOKE
TO CONCEAL MOVEMENT TO
NEXT POSITION.

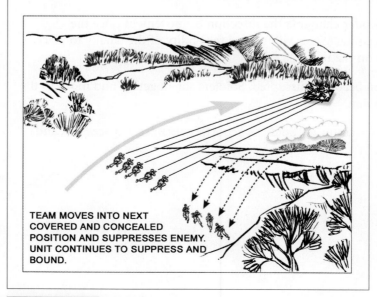

TEAM MOVES INTO NEXT
COVERED AND CONCEALED
POSITION AND SUPPRESSES ENEMY.
UNIT CONTINUES TO SUPPRESS AND
BOUND.

Figure 9.1 Break Contact

Battle Drill—React to Ambush

Situation: The squad/platoon enters a kill zone and the enemy initiates an ambush with a high volume of fire that produces casualties.

Required Actions: (Figures 9.2)

1. In a near ambush (within hand-grenade range), Soldiers receiving fire immediately return fire, take up covered positions, and throw fragmentation, concussion, and smoke grenades.

   a. Immediately after the grenades detonate, Soldiers in the kill zone assault through the ambush using fire and movement.

   b. Soldiers not in the kill zone immediately:
   - Identify enemy positions
   - Initiate immediate suppressive fires against the enemy
   - Take up covered position
   - Shift fires as the Soldiers in the kill zone assault through the ambush.

2. In a far ambush (beyond hand-grenade range), Soldiers receiving fire immediately return fire, take up covered positions, and suppress the enemy by:
   - Destroying or suppressing enemy crew-served weapons first
   - Obscuring the enemy position with smoke (M203)
   - Sustaining suppressive fires.

   a. Soldiers (teams/squads) not receiving fires move by a covered and concealed route to a vulnerable flank of the enemy position and assault using fire and movement techniques.

   b. Soldiers in the kill zone continue suppressive fires and shift fires as the assaulting team/squad fights through the enemy position.

3. The platoon FO calls for and adjusts indirect fires as you direct. On order, the FO lifts fires or shifts them to isolate the enemy position or to attack enemy fighters with indirect fires as they retreat.

4. You report, reorganize as necessary, and continue the mission.

Note:

The kill zone in an ambush is named appropriately—especially with near ambushes. The longer you stay in the kill zone, the greater your chances are of being killed. In near ambushes, you must, in the blink of an eye, weigh the risk of hitting the ground or seeking cover versus immediately returning fire onto the enemy and assaulting through his ambush position in order to remove yourself from the kill zone and survive the ambush.

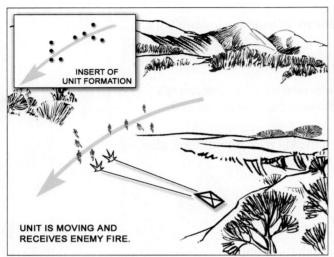

INSERT OF
UNIT FORMATION

UNIT IS MOVING AND
RECEIVES ENEMY FIRE.

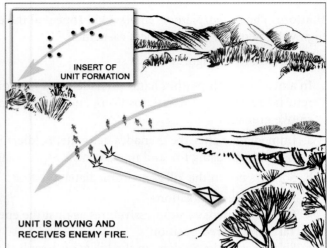

INSERT OF
UNIT FORMATION

UNIT IS MOVING AND
RECEIVES ENEMY FIRE.

SOLDIERS IN THE KILL ZONE
IMMEDIATELY RETURN FIRE.

SOLDIERS IN THE KILL ZONE
IMMEDIATELY RETURN FIRE.

SOLDIERS IN SUPPORT POSITION
SHIFT FIRES AS SOLDIERS IN KILL
ZONE ASSAULT ENEMY POSITION(S).

SOLDIERS IN SUPPORT POSITION
SHIFT FIRES AS SOLDIERS IN KILL
ZONE ASSAULT ENEMY POSITION(S).

Figure 9.2   React to Ambush

React to Indirect Fire (Dismounted)

Situation: Your squad is moving through open terrain (dismounted), when suddenly you hear incoming rounds and shells exploding in the vicinity of your position.

Required Actions:

1. Any Soldier announces, "Incoming!"

   a. Shout "incoming!" once you hear incoming rounds, shells exploding, or shells passing overhead.

   b. Your squad's safety depends on your ability to react to indirect fire quickly and safely.

   c. Yelling "incoming!" will alert everyone in your squad to the imminent danger posed by the incoming rounds.

Note:
Any Soldier may shout "incoming." The first Soldier who detects incoming rounds or indirect fire can alert the squad.

---

2. Soldiers immediately assume the prone position or move to immediate available cover during initial impacts.

3. The squad leader orders the squad to move to a rally point by giving a direction and distance.

   a. Analyze the situation.

   b. Your Soldiers will immediately look to you for additional instructions.

   c. This will create a single line of command and prevent mass confusion caused by too many people trying to determine the proper action.

   d. After the impacts, Soldiers move rapidly in the direction and distance to the designated rally point.

Note:
After the squad is alerted by one or all of the squad members shouting "incoming," the squad leader will direct the squad to move out of or away from the impact area. For example, the squad leader can shout, "3 o'clock, 200 meters." This directs all squad to move out rapidly in the 3 o'clock direction from their present location and to travel in that direction for 200 meters.

---

4. The unit leader reports the contact to higher headquarters.

   a. Issue a situation report (SITREP).

   b. Report the attack in the SALUTE format (i.e., Size, Activity, Location, Unit, Time and Equipment).

5. Continue the mission.

React to Indirect Fire (Mounted)

Situation: Your squad is moving through open terrain (mounted), when suddenly you hear incoming rounds and shells exploding in the vicinity of your position.

Required Actions:

1. Any Soldier announces, "Incoming!"

2. Vehicle commanders repeat the alert over the radio.

3. The leader gives the direction and link up location over the radio.

4. Soldiers close all hatches if applicable to the vehicle type; gunners stay below turret shields or get down into vehicle.

5. Drivers move rapidly out of the impact area in the direction ordered by the leader.

6. The unit leader reports the contact to higher headquarters.

7. Continue the mission.

React to a Chemical Attack

Situation: Your squad is moving through open terrain, when suddenly one of your Soldiers shouts "Gas, Gas, Gas!"

Required Actions:

1. Soldier(s) who recognize or are alerted to chemical attack don protective mask in accordance with published standards and give the alarm.

    a. Don your protective mask when:
        i. A chemical alarm sounds
        ii. A positive reading is obtained on detector paper
        iii. Individuals exhibit symptoms of chemical/biological (CB) agent poisoning
        iv. You observe a contamination marker
        v. You are directed to put on your mask
        vi. You see personnel wearing protective masks
        vii. You observe other signs of a possible CB attack.

Note:

You, or commanders at any level, may establish a modified policy when chemical weapons have been employed by designating additional events as automatic masking criteria.

2. Protect yourself from CB contamination using your protective mask without fastening the hood.

Note:

The mask gives immediate protection against inhalation of agent vapors. Do not fasten the hood. Go to the next step immediately. REMEMBER: STOP BREATHING FIRST!!!

3. Give the alarm

   a. Yell "GAS!"

   b. Give the appropriate hand-and-arm signal.

   c. Take cover to reduce exposure, using whatever means is readily available.

   d. Decontaminate exposed skin using the individual decontaminating kit, as necessary.

4. Assume mission-oriented protective posture (MOPP) 4. Cover all your skin (your head and shoulders are already protected by the mask and the overgarment).

   a. Put on the gloves with liners.

   b. Zip and fasten the overgarment jacket.

   c. Secure the hood, then secure the overgarment to increase protection.

   d. Put on the overboots.

Note:

Combat boots provide protection but should be covered because they absorb chemicals. It takes a long time to put on the overboots, so put them on last in an emergency.

---

5. Decontaminate personal equipment using the individual decontaminating kit as necessary. Notify others of any CB hazard markers or indicators. Continue the mission.

6. After assuming MOPP4 and performing all the tasks according to the unit SOP, perform the following actions:

   a. Use all means of CB detection to check your surrounding area for the presence of contamination.

   b. Contact higher headquarters (HQ) if no contamination is found or if you determine the attack was non-CB.

   c. Await further guidance. (Higher HQ contacts all adjacent/attached units to check the status of CB contamination in their areas. If all units report the absence of contamination, the information is reported up the chain of command.)

   d. Annotate the above actions on your duty log (DA Form 1594).

7. Report the incident to higher headquarters.

8. Continue the mission.

Dismount a Vehicle

Situations: The squad is moving mounted and conducting operations as part of a larger element. The squad is ordered to dismount and provide security.

Required Actions:

1. As platoon leader, you select a covered or concealed position as the dismount point.

Note:
Move to the best covered and concealed position available that provides protection for the dismounting personnel.

2. Give the order to dismount over the radio.

3. Vehicle commanders monitor radios and alert the Soldiers in the vehicle.

Note:
When the command "Dismount" is given, all Soldiers dismount in the order specified and clear the area per unit SOP.

4. The drivers move their vehicles to the designated dismount point seeking the best cover and concealment available.

5. The driver stops the vehicle and the vehicle commander dismounts and occupies a security position.

6. Soldiers dismount in the specified order, clear the area, and move to covered and concealed positions.

Note:
An example technique is the 5-25-200 meter search—each Soldier immediately scans 5 meters around the vehicle prior to dismounting and then moves out 25 meters, scans back towards the vehicle and depending on the duration of the halt will scan 200 meters out from lower to upper within his or her assigned sector of observation.

7. The vehicles occupy overwatch positions and designated Soldiers man crew-served weapons and scan for enemy activity.

   a. Soldiers occupy positions.

   b. Vehicle gunners scan for enemy activity.

8. Squad leaders reposition their Soldiers as needed in overwatch positions.

9. The unit leader reports to higher headquarters.

Evacuate Wounded Personnel from Vehicle

Situation: Your squad is stationary and one of your vehicles is disabled due to enemy contact. An occupant of the vehicle has been injured and must be evacuated.

Required Actions:

1. The squad suppresses the enemy and moves out of the engagement area, if possible.
2. Once out of the engagement area, or when the enemy is suppressed, establish security.
3. Designated Soldiers move to the vehicle to treat and evacuate the casualty.
4. The Soldiers remove the casualty from the vehicle so as not to cause further injury.
5. Soldiers administer first aid.
6. The unit leader requests medical evacuation (MEDEVAC) if necessary.
7. The unit leader reports the contact to higher headquarters.
8. Continue the mission.

Establish Security at the Halt

Situation: Your section is moving tactically, conducting operations. An unforeseen event causes the squad to halt (dismounted or mounted). Enemy contact is possible.

Required Actions: (Figure 9.3)

1. Dismounted –

   a. As platoon leader, you give the arm-and-hand signal to halt.

   b. Soldiers clear the area and establish local security.

   c. Solders occupy hasty fighting positions as you designate.

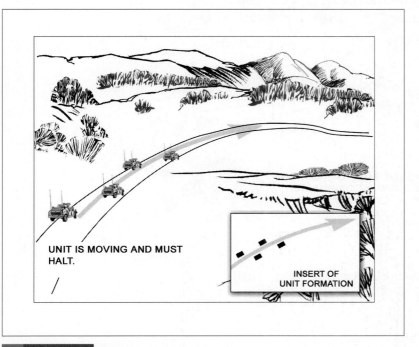

UNIT IS MOVING AND MUST HALT.

INSERT OF UNIT FORMATION

Figure 9.3   Secure at Halt (Mounted)

Figure 9.4 Secure at Halt (Mounted – Herringbone)

Figure 9.5 Secure at Halt (Mounted – Coil)

d. Squad/team leaders adjust positions as necessary.

e. You report the situation to higher headquarters.

2. Mounted –

a. You give the order over the radio to stop movement.

b. The platoon halts in the herringbone or coil formation according to the unit SOP (Figures 9.4 and 9.5).

c. Each vehicle commander ensures his or her vehicle is correctly positioned, using cover and concealment, and the crew-served weapon is manned and scanning.

d. Vehicle commanders order Soldiers to dismount, clear the area, and provide local security.

e. Soldiers dismount and occupy hasty fighting positions as designated by the leader.

f. Squad/team leaders adjust positions as necessary.

g. You report the situation to higher headquarters.

Checkpoint Entry Operations

Situation: Your platoon is conducting operations as part of a higher headquarters and has received an operation order (OPORD) or fragmentary order (FRAGO) to establish checkpoints at the locations specified. All necessary personnel and equipment are available.

Required Actions:

1. Gain and/or maintain situational understanding using information that is gathered from maps, intelligence summaries, SITREPs, and other sources.

2. Confirm friendly and enemy situations.

   a. Identify the location of forward and adjacent friendly elements, if applicable.

   b. Update enemy situation and increase force protection, if applicable.

   c. Clarify priority intelligence requirement (PIR).

   d. Confirm any changes to the higher headquarters and company task or purpose.

3. Issue an OPORD to your unit.

4. Plan checkpoint operations using troop leading procedures.

   a. Conduct a digital and/or conventional map reconnaissance.

      i. Identify general location of other checkpoints.

      ii. Identify likely avenues of approach.

      iii. Mark tentative dismount points.

   b. Confirm the purpose of the checkpoint.

   c. Confirm whether the checkpoint will be deliberate or hasty.

   d. Identify force requirements to execute the mission.

      i. Request civil police (as needed).

      ii. Request female military police support (as needed) if possible and/or practical.

    e. Request additional assets (as needed).

        i. Engineer support

        ii. Military working dog (MWD) team

        iii. Light sets, etc.

    f. Plan and coordinate indirect fire support (if available).

    g. Identify direct fire responsibilities (if applicable).

    h. Ensure checkpoint is covered by fire.

    i. Ensure unit is organized to accomplish the mission and/or compensate for combat losses.

        i. Include vehicle search teams.

        ii. Include personnel search teams.

            1. Use civil authorities or female Soldiers for female searches, if possible.

            2. Ensure Soldiers are aware of special search requirements.

            3. Conduct operations in accordance with unit SOP and local culture and customs.

5. Disseminate pertinent information to keep subordinates abreast of the situation.

6. Issue instructions to include rules of engagement (ROE) and rules of instruction (ROI). Issue clear and concise tasking to subordinates. Topics include:

    a. Use of lethal force to stop a vehicle or pedestrian.

    b. Vehicle and personnel searches.

    c. Questioning techniques.

    d. Inspection of documents.

        i. Required documents.

        ii. Documents are current and appropriate for the area of operations (AO).

        iii. Documents are not counterfeit.

    e. Apprehension and detention of civilian personnel in accordance with ROE and ROI.

    f. Processing contraband.

Note:

Drivers should not be able to see a checkpoint from more than a short distance away to prevent them from avoiding it. Ideal locations include tunnels, culverts, bridges, and sharp bends or dips in a road. Checkpoints should not present such a surprise that drivers cannot stop safely.

---

7. Execute checkpoint operations.

8. Supervise checkpoint and/or roadblock operations. Issue clear and concise tasking to subordinates. Topics include:

Note:

Ensure that your Soldiers show politeness and respectful treatment of individuals at all times. Respect is an Army Value that will help build trust between local people and US forces.

---

a. Establish shifts for 24-hour operations.

b. Review requirements for correct documentation to pass through the checkpoint.

c. Maintain communications with higher headquarters and reserve force.

d. Request reserve force, if required.

e. Employ the reserve force as part of the unit.

f. Report to higher headquarters as required.

g. Prepare for future operations.

9. Consolidate and reorganize as necessary.

10. Secure enemy prisoners of war (EPW) as required.

11. Evacuate casualties as required.

12. Process captured documents and/or equipment as required.

13. Continue operations as directed.

Vehicle Rollover Drill

Situation: A vehicle has rolled over.

Required Actions:

1. Execute Rollover Drill (not in water):

a. Driver

   i. Releases the accelerator, plants feet flat on the floor and attempts to maintain control of steering.

   ii. Yells "Rollover, Rollover, Rollover!"

   iii. Keeps hands on the steering wheel, tucks chin into chest, and braces for impact.

b. Vehicle Commander (VC) and Crew

   i. Yells "Rollover, Rollover, Rollover!"

   ii. Pulls gunner into cab.

   iii. Tucks chin into chest, plants feet firmly on the floor and braces for impact, while holding onto the gunner.

c. Gunner

   i. Yells "Rollover, Rollover, Rollover!"

   ii. Drops down into vehicle.

   iii. Tucks chin into chest, holds onto a stationary object, and braces for impact.

Note:
Never attempt to jump from a rolling vehicle. It may roll over you. Ensure that the vehicle has stopped rolling before exiting.

---

2. After the rollover has stopped:

a. Driver, VC, and rear crew:

   i. Driver turns off motor.

   ii. Braces one hand on ceiling.

   iii. Unbuckles seat belt with other hand and immediately puts both hands on ceiling.

   iv. Slides out of seat.

   v. Disconnects headset.

   vi. Orients self to nearest door.

  vii. Unlocks combat door locks.

 viii. Gets door open. If door does not open, tries a different door.

   ix. Exits with weapon.

   x. Assists crew to exit.

   xi. Establishes security.

  xii. Recovers sensitive items.

 xiii. Provides first aid.

 xiv. Assists in vehicle recovery.

 b. Gunner:

   i. Disconnects headset.

   ii. Orients self to nearest door.

  iii. Unlocks combat door locks.

  iv. Gets door open. If door does not open, tries different door.

   v. Exits with weapon.

   vi. Assists crew to exit.

  vii. Establishes security.

 viii. Recovers sensitive items.

   ix. Provides first aid.

   x. Assists in vehicle recovery.

3. If vehicle rolls onto side:

 a. Soldier in lower position, if able:

   i. Unbuckles seat belts.

   ii. Assists Soldiers in higher positions to release seat belts and lower carefully.

 b. Crew, if doors are jammed:

   i. Exits through hatch or cargo area if possible.

   ii. Works as a team to open jammed doors.

Critical Thinking

Consider the statement, "Battle drills prepare Soldiers for unknown situations for which they have no specific training." Do you agree? Why or why not?

CONCLUSION

In combat, rapid execution of battle drills saves lives. Only through repetition will performing these drills become second nature for you and your Soldiers. Training should not only be repetitive, but should incorporate a wide variety of scenarios and conditions—direction of contact, type of enemy element, terrain, levels of visibility, varying weather, non-combatants, etc. Chances are that the first time you and your platoon make contact with a live enemy force, there will be variables unique to the situation that you could not predict or rehearse. Yet your well-trained platoon will still be able to execute, thanks in part to its mastery of battle drills.

Learning Assessment

1. How do battle drills differ from other combat operations?
2. Describe the relationship between Battle Drill—React to Contact and the other battle drills discussed in this chapter.
3. Compare and contrast battle drills and SOPs.

Key Words

battle drill
suppressive fires
consolidate and reorganize

References

ARTEP 7-1-DRILL, *Warrior Battle Drills.* 20 July 2006.

Artillery Specialist Earns Bronze Star. (4 November 2003). *Soldier Stories.* Retrieved 8 April 2005 from http://www4.army.mil/ocpa/soldierstories/story.php?story_id_key=5375

SH 21-76, *Ranger Handbook.* July 2006.

Center of Army Lesson Learned (CALL), COIN Patrolling, No 08-11, April 2008.

SQUAD TACTICS: OFFENSIVE OPERATIONS

Key Points

1 Offensive Operations

2 Types of Attack

3 Movement to Contact

4 Tactical Road Marches and Infiltrations

In war the only sure defense is offense, and the efficiency of the offense depends on the war-like souls of those conducting it.

GEN George S. Patton

Introduction

Our modern military is characterized by its emphasis on the offense. For more than a century, the United States has operated on the premise that a strong national defense is best achieved by a powerful offense. Success in battle hinges on the actions of platoons and squads in close combat: on their ability to react to contact; employ suppressive fires; maneuver to a vulnerable flank; and fight through to defeat, destroy, or capture the enemy. The successful actions of small units rely on Soldiers' and leaders' ability to use terrain to their advantage—to operate their weapons with accuracy and deadly effect; to outthink, outmaneuver, and outfight the enemy. This section examines the characteristics of the offense as seen from the perspective of a squad or platoon member and explores the most basic offensive operation: *movement to contact.*

Surprise and Audacity at Chancellorsville

MG Joe Hooker began the Chancellorsville, Va., campaign on 27 April 1863. Within three days, some 40,000 Federals had splashed through the upriver fords, their presence detected by Confederate cavalry. On 29 April, a sizable Union force led by MG John Sedgwick's Sixth Corps erected pontoon bridges below Fredericksburg and also moved to Confederate GEN Robert E. Lee's side of the river.

With both wings of the enemy across the Rappahannock, Lee faced a serious dilemma. Conventional military wisdom dictated that the understrength Army of Northern Virginia retreat south and escape Hooker's trap. Lee opted instead to meet the Federal challenge head-on. Correctly deducing that Hooker's primary threat lay to the west, "Marse Robert" assigned 10,000 troops under MG Jubal A. Early to man the old Fredericksburg entrenchments. The balance of the Army would turn west toward the tangled Wilderness to confront Hooker's flanking column.

By mid-afternoon of 30 April, that column, now containing 50,000 men and 108 artillery pieces, rendezvoused at the most important road junction in the Wilderness. A large brick tavern named Chancellorsville dominated this intersection of the Orange Turnpike with the Orange Plank, Ely's Ford, and River Roads. . . .

The Federals had encountered virtually no opposition to this point. Moreover, they could now press eastward, break clear of the Wilderness, and uncover Banks' Ford downstream, thus significantly shortening the distance between their two wings. Hooker, however, decided to halt at Chancellorsville and await the arrival of additional Union troops. This fateful decision disheartened the Federal officers on the scene, who recognized the urgency of maintaining the momentum they had thus far sustained.

"Stonewall" Jackson, gladly seizing the initiative that Hooker needlessly surrendered, left the Fredericksburg lines at 3:00 a.m. on 1 May and arrived at Zoan Church five hours later. There he found two divisions of Confederate infantry, MG Richard H. Anderson's and MG Lafayette McLaws', fortifying a prominent ridge covering the Turnpike and Plank Road. Although his corps had not yet appeared, Jackson ordered Anderson and McLaws to drop their shovels, pick up their rifles, and advance to the attack.

Jackson's audacity dictated the shape of the Battle of Chancellorsville. When Hooker at last authorized an eastward movement late in the morning of 1 May, his troops on the Turnpike and Plank Road ran flush against "Stonewall's" outgunned but aggressive brigades. Union front-line commanders had not expected this kind of resistance. They sent anxious messages to Hooker, who quickly ordered his generals to fall back to the Wilderness and assume a defensive posture. The Federal columns on the River Road marched almost to Bank's Ford without seeing a rebel. They returned to Chancellorsville fuming, fully realizing the opportunity that had slipped through their fingers. . . .

Hooker's confidence had faded to caution, but whether he was "whipped" depended upon Lee and Jackson. Those two officers reined up along the Plank Road at its intersection with a byway called the Furnace Road on the evening of 1 May. Transforming discarded Federal cracker boxes into camp stools, the generals examined their options. . . .

About midnight, Lee's cavalry chief, "Jeb" Stuart, galloped up to the little campfire. The flamboyant Virginian carried thrilling intelligence. The Union right flank was "in the air"—that is, resting on no natural or artificial obstacle! From that moment on, the generals thought of nothing but how to gain access to Hooker's vulnerable flank. . . .

Before dawn, Lee and Jackson studied a hastily drawn map and decided to undertake one of the biggest gambles in American military history. Jackson's corps, about 30,000 troops, would follow a series of country roads and woods paths to reach the Union right. Lee, with the remaining 14,000 infantry, would occupy a position more than three miles long and divert Hooker's attention during Jackson's dangerous trek. Once in position, "Stonewall" would smash the Federals with his full strength while Lee cooperated as best he could. The Army of Northern Virginia would thus be fractured into three pieces, counting Early's contingent at Fredericksburg, any one of which might be subject to rout or annihilation if the Yankees resumed the offensive.

Jackson led his column past the bivouac early on the morning of 2 May. He conferred briefly with Lee, then trotted down the Furnace Road with the fire of battle kindled in his eyes. . . .

Meanwhile the bulk of Jackson's column snaked its way along uncharted trails barely wide enough to accommodate four men abreast. "Stonewall" contributed to Hooker's faith in a Confederate retreat by twice turning away from the Union line—first at Catharine Furnace, then again at the Brock Road. After making the desired impression, Jackson ducked under the Wilderness canopy and continued his march toward Howard's insensible Soldiers.

Acting upon a personal reconnaissance recommended by Cavalry GEN Fitzhugh Lee, Jackson kept his column northbound on the Brock Road to the Orange Turnpike where the Confederates would at last be beyond the Union right. The exhausting march, which altogether traversed more than 12 miles, ended at about 1500 when "Old Jack's" warriors began deploying into battle lines astride the Turnpike. Jackson, however, did not authorize an attack for some two hours, providing 11 of his 15 brigades time to take position in the silent forest. The awe-inspiring Confederate front measured nearly two miles across. . . .

Suddenly, a bugle rang out in the afternoon shadows. Bugles everywhere echoed the notes up and down the line. As waves of sweat-soaked Soldiers rolled forward, the high defiance of the rebel yell pierced the gloomy woods. Jackson's Corps erupted from the trees and sent the astonished Unionists reeling. "Along the road it was pandemonium," recalled a Massachusetts Soldier, "and on the side of the road it was chaos."

Most of Howard's men fought bravely, drawing three additional battle lines across Jackson's path. But the overmatched Federals occupied an untenable position. The screaming gray legions overwhelmed each Union stand and eventually drove the Eleventh Corps completely from the field (Green, n.d.).

Offensive Operations

Units undertake offensive operations to destroy enemy forces and their will to fight; to seize key terrain; to learn enemy strength and disposition; or to deceive, divert, or fix the enemy. Platoon and squad leaders must understand these principles, tactics, techniques, and procedures associated with the offense. They must comprehend their role when operating within a larger organization's operations, and when operating independently. They must recognize how the complementary and reinforcing effects of other maneuver and supporting elements relate to their own capabilities. They must also understand the impact of terrain, open or restrictive, on their operations.

Key Terrain and Decisive Terrain. *Key terrain* is any locality, or area, the occupation of which affords a marked advantage to whoever holds it. *Decisive terrain* is key terrain that has an extraordinary impact on the mission. Decisive terrain is relatively rare. To designate terrain as decisive is to recognize that the successful accomplishment of the mission, whether offensive or defensive, depends on seizing or securing it. (To *seize* is to employ combat forces to occupy physically and to control a designated area. To *secure* is to gain possession of a position or terrain feature, with or without force, and to prevent its destruction or loss by enemy action.) The commander designates decisive terrain to communicate its importance in his or her concept of operations.

Characteristics of Offensive Operations

Effective squad and platoon offensive operations make the most of accurate intelligence and other relevant information regarding enemy forces, weather, and terrain. Commanders maneuver their forces to advantageous positions before making contact with the enemy. Force protection hinders the enemy from acquiring accurate information about friendly forces. The enemy only sees what the friendly commander wants him to see. The commander limits contact with enemy forces before the decisive operation to the smallest element possible. Contact with the enemy is then deliberate, designed to shape the tactical situation. The decisive operation is a sudden, shattering action that takes advantage of Soldiers' initiative—in this case squads and platoons—and a common operational picture (COP) to expand throughout the area. When directed by their commanders, squads and platoons execute violently without hesitation to break enemy forces' will or destroy them. **Surprise**, **concentration**, **tempo**, and **audacity** characterize the offense.

Surprise

To achieve surprise at the operational level of war—at which campaigns and major operations are planned and conducted to accomplish strategic objectives—commanders must estimate the enemy forces' intent and deny them the ability to gain thorough and timely understanding of the situation. Unpredictability and boldness help gain surprise. The direction, timing, and force of the attack also help achieve surprise. Surprise is crucial because it delays enemy reactions, overloads and confuses their command and control (C2) systems, induces psychological shock in enemy soldiers and leaders, and reduces the coherence of the enemy's defense. By diminishing enemy combat power, surprise enables attackers to exploit enemy paralysis and hesitancy.

At the *tactical* level of war—at which battles and engagements are planned and executed to accomplish military objectives—squads and platoons can also achieve surprise. While operational surprise creates the conditions for successful tactical operations, tactical surprise is fleeting. Tactical surprise can cause the enemy to hesitate or misjudge a situation. So commanders must exploit it before the enemy realizes what is happening.

Outright surprise is difficult to achieve at squad, platoon, or higher levels. Modern surveillance and warning systems, the availability of commercial imagery products, and global news networks make surprise more difficult. Commanders must achieve surprise by operating in a way the enemy does not expect. They deceive the enemy as to the nature, timing, objective, and force of an attack. They can use bad weather, seemingly impassable terrain, feints, demonstrations, and false communications to lead the enemy into inaccurate perceptions. Sudden, violent, and unanticipated attacks have a paralyzing effect. Airborne, air assault, and special operations forces (SOF) attacks—combined with strikes by Army and joint fires against objectives the enemy regards as secure—create disconcerting psychological effects on the enemy.

Concentration

Concentration is the massing of overwhelming combat power to achieve a single purpose. Commanders balance the necessity for concentrating forces to mass effects with the need to disperse them to avoid creating lucrative targets. Advances in ground and air mobility, target acquisition, and long-range precision fires enable attackers to rapidly concentrate effects. Squads and platoons on a smaller scale can also mass their weapons and forces to achieve concentration. Squad leaders can concentrate their *organic firepower*—the weapons normally assigned to their unit—to destroy or suppress the enemy in support of larger units' operations. Platoon leaders, on the other hand, can also concentrate organic firepower and mass squads to overwhelm or hold the enemy in place in support of a mission.

---

surprise

a key element in combat tactics that allows offensive operations to proceed under cover and concealment to prevent detection by the enemy

concentration

a degree of force in which firepower, personnel, or other combat resources are massed against an enemy at one point or in a narrow area to multiply the power of an offensive operation

tempo

the rate of military action

audacity

intrepid boldness marked by originality and verve with a disregard for normal restraints

Attacking commanders manipulate their own and the enemy's force concentration by combining dispersion, concentration, military deception, and attacks. By dispersing, attackers stretch enemy defenses and deny lucrative targets to enemy fires. By massing forces rapidly along converging axes (squads, platoons, companies, etc.), attackers overwhelm enemy forces at decisive points with concentrated combat power. After a successful attack, commanders keep their forces concentrated to take advantage of their momentum. Should enemy forces threaten them, they may disperse again. Commanders at all levels adopt the posture that best suits the situation, protects the force, and sustains the attack's momentum.

Tempo

Controlling or altering tempo is necessary to retain the initiative. At the tactical level, a faster tempo allows attackers to quickly penetrate barriers and defenses and destroy enemy forces in depth before they can react. Squads and platoons support increased tempo by rapidly executing missions and sustaining the force.

Commanders at all levels adjust tempo as tactical situations, logistics requirements, or opportunities allow to ensure proper coordination. Rapid tempo demands quick decisions even at the squad level—especially in today's contemporary operating environment. It denies the enemy the chance to rest, regroup, reorganize, or refocus, and continually creates new opportunities.

By increasing tempo, commanders also maintain momentum. They identify the best avenues for attack, plan the action in depth with the right mix of squads and platoons, provide for quick transitions to other operations, and concentrate and combine forces effectively. Once combat begins, attackers execute violently. They follow reconnaissance units or successful probes and quickly move through gaps before defenders recover. Attackers shift combat power quickly to widen penetrations, roll up exposed flanks, and reinforce successes. Friendly forces attack in depth and maneuver to shatter the enemy's coherence and overwhelm his C2. While maintaining a tempo faster than the enemy's, attackers balance the tempo with the ability to exercise their own C2. Commanders never permit the enemy to recover from the shock of the initial assault. They prevent defenders from massing against the friendly decisive operation.

Audacity

Audacity is a plan of action boldly executed. Commanders display audacity by developing bold, inventive plans that produce decisive results. Squads and platoons demonstrate audacity by violently applying combat power as the commander directs. Commanders understand when and where to take risks and do not hesitate to execute their plan. Commanders dispel uncertainty through decisive action. They compensate for lack of information by seizing the initiative and pressing the fight. Audacity inspires Soldiers in squads and platoons to overcome adversity and danger.

Critical Thinking

In what ways did the Confederate forces develop and use the characteristics of the offense in the Chancellorsville vignette at the beginning of this section?

Types of Offensive Operations

The four types of offensive operations are **movement to contact**, **attack**, **exploitation**, and **pursuit.** Squads and platoons conduct these missions normally as part of a larger force. Commanders direct these offensive operations one after another and in combination to generate as much combat power as possible to destroy the enemy. For instance, a successful attack may lead to an exploitation, which can lead to a pursuit. A deliberate attack to complete the enemy's destruction can follow a pursuit. In other cases, commanders may direct an attack against enemy forces during a pursuit to slow their withdrawal.

movement to contact

a form of the offense designed to develop the situation and to establish or regain contact with the enemy

attack

an offensive operation that destroys or defeats enemy forces, seizes and secures terrain, or both

exploitation

an offensive operation that usually follows a successful attack and is designed to disorganize the enemy in depth

pursuit

an offensive operation designed to catch or cut off a hostile force attempting to escape, with the aim of destroying it

Types of Attack

Platoons and squads attack as part of a larger force. Attacks involve coordinated movement supported by direct and indirect fires. They may be either decisive or shaping operations. They may be hasty or deliberate, depending on the time available for assessing the situation, planning, and preparing. Commanders execute *hasty attacks* when the situation calls for immediate action with available forces and minimal preparation. They conduct *deliberate attacks* when they have time to develop plans and coordinate preparations. The same fundamentals of the offense apply to each type of attack. Success depends on skillfully massing combat power while maintaining the momentum and initiative.

- *Hasty attack*—Commanders direct hasty attacks to seize opportunities to destroy the enemy or seize the initiative. These opportunities are fleeting. They usually occur during movements to contact and defensive operations to take advantage of agility and surprise.

- *Deliberate attack*—In contrast to hasty attacks, deliberate attacks are highly synchronized operations characterized by detailed planning and preparation. Commanders take the time necessary to position forces and develop sufficient intelligence to strike the enemy with bold maneuvers and accurate, annihilating fires. Commanders direct deliberate attacks only when the enemy cannot be bypassed or overcome with a hasty attack.

- *Special-purpose attacks*—Commanders direct special-purpose attacks to achieve objectives different from those of other attacks.
- *Spoiling attack*—An attack that preempts or seriously impairs an enemy attack while the enemy is planning or preparing to attack.
- *Counterattack*—An attack by part or all of a defending force against an enemy attacking force to deny enemy forces their goal in attacking.
- *Raid*—A normally small-scale attack involving swift entry into hostile territory to secure information, confuse the enemy, or destroy installations.
- *Ambush*—An attack by fire or other means from concealed positions on a moving or temporarily halted enemy.
- *Feint*—An attack used to deceive the enemy about the location or time of the actual decisive operation.
- *Demonstration*—An attack designed to deceive the enemy about the location or time of the decisive operation using a display of force.

Movement to Contact

Movement to contact (MTC) is a type of offensive operation designed to develop the situation and establish or regain contact with the enemy. Commanders normally conduct MTCs at the battalion level or higher, but in some cases company-sized elements may do so. Platoons and squads conduct MTCs as part of these larger units. Commanders order MTCs when the enemy situation is vague or not specific enough to conduct an attack.

Infantry units use two techniques for conducting a movement to contact—*search and attack* or *approach march.* Leaders select the technique based on the enemy situation they expect to find. They use *search and attack* when enemy forces are dispersed; when they expect enemy forces to avoid contact or quickly disengage and withdraw; or to deny them movement in an area. They choose the *approach march* when they expect the enemy to deploy using relatively fixed offensive or defensive formations.

Critical Thinking

The United States is waging the Global War on Terrorism primarily against insurgents who use guerrilla tactics to strike at US forces. As you continue reading about the two types of movement to contact, consider which technique is more applicable in military operations against this type of enemy force.

Search-and-Attack Technique

A commander conducts a search and attack for one or more of the following purposes:

- *Destroy the enemy:* render enemy units in the AO ineffective in combat
- *Deny the area:* prevent the enemy from operating unhindered in a given area
- *Protect the force:* prevent the enemy from massing to disrupt or destroy friendly military or civilian operations, equipment, property, and key facilities
- *Collect information:* gain information about the enemy and the terrain to confirm the enemy course of action predicted as a result of the intelligence preparation of the battlefield

A commander employs this type of MTC, conducted primarily by light forces and often supported by heavy forces, when the enemy is operating as small, dispersed elements, or when the task is to deny the enemy the ability to move within a given area. The search-and-attack technique involves multiple squads and fire teams coordinating their actions to make contact with the enemy. Platoons attempt to *find* enemy forces, then *fix* and *finish* them. They combine patrolling techniques with the need for hasty or deliberate attacks once they have found the enemy. Planning considerations for this type of attack include:

- The factors of METT-TC
- The requirement for decentralized execution (the platoon leader coordinates the actions of squads)
- The requirement for mutual support (the platoon leader must be able to reinforce the squad in contact using squads that are not in contact)
- The length of operations (the plan may need to address continuous operations)
- The Soldier's load (search and attack requires stealth.)
- Resupply and MEDEVAC
- The positioning of key leaders and personnel
- The employment of key weapons
- The requirement for patrol bases
- The concept for entering the zone of action
- The concept for linkups (all squad and team leaders must know how they will link up once contact is made)

Task Organization of Forces

The goal of the commander during a MTC is to find, fix and finish the enemy. The commander uses reconnaissance to find the enemy, uses the advance guard to fix the enemy, and uses the main body (and sometimes a reserve) to destroy the enemy. Normally, the task of reconnaissance (find the enemy) is left to the battalion scouts; however, this mission can be given to a maneuver element other than scouts. Economy of force is considered when tasking the mission of fixing the enemy. The maneuver commander wants to fix the enemy with the smallest force possible in order to mass the combat power of the finishing force onto the enemy to finish him off. The fixing force may initiate contact with and maintain contact with the enemy, or maneuver to block his attempts to break contact. The finishing force maneuvers around the fixing force in order to attack and destroy the enemy. During a Search-and-Attack, there may be multiple platoons tasked to maneuver through the AO to fix the enemy until the main body can close with and finish the enemy. During the approach march technique, one company or platoon is designated the advance guard and moves forward of the main body to fix the enemy. The main body of the approach march then maneuvers to finish the enemy. When task organizing for the MTC, you must also consider if METT-TC dictates the requirement for a reserve. A reserve is a maneuver element not assigned a primary task to find, fix or finish the enemy. The maneuver

The concept of movement to contact is best characterized by its three fundamental steps: Find, Fix, Finish.

fix

a tactical task in which a unit undertakes actions to prevent the enemy from moving any part of his forces either from a specific location or for a specific period of time by holding or surrounding them to prevent their withdrawal for use elsewhere commander can commit the reserve at the decisive point of the battle to ensure a victory. The reserve is normally committed to reinforce the finishing force, but can also be committed to reinforce the fixing element to prevent the enemy from escaping from the finishing force, or the reserve can be committed to prevent the enemy from successfully counterattacking.

Planning a Search and Attack

A commander conducting a search and attack will assign subordinate units—in this case platoons—specific missions (i.e., reconnaissance, fixing, or finishing force) to accomplish for the MTC. Platoon leaders then implement the eight-step troop leading procedures (TLP) to prepare their forces for the mission. Depending upon the mission, the platoon leader will then assign each squad specific responsibilities in executing the plan. For example, when the commander assigns the platoon the reconnaissance mission, the platoon leader plans to conduct the appropriate type of recon mission (area, zone, or route, depending upon METT-TC). Once the reconnaissance force locates the enemy forces, the fixing and finishing forces can fix and destroy them using overwhelming firepower and supporting fires. The commander also develops a contingency plan (assigns other platoons within the company secondary missions in support of the reconnaissance force) in case the reconnaissance force is compromised.

Executing a Search and Attack

Once the reconnaissance force finds the enemy force, the fixing force develops the situation, and then executes one of two options based on the commander's guidance and METT-TC. The first option is to block identified routes that the enemy can use to escape or to rush in reinforcements. The fixing platoon maintains contact with enemy forces and positions its squads to isolate and fix the enemy before the finishing platoon attacks. In the second option, the platoon attacks to fix the enemy in their current positions until the finishing force arrives. The fixing force attacks if that action meets the commander's intent and it can generate sufficient combat power against the enemy (in this example, an enemy platoon-sized element).

Brigades may establish fire-support bases in support of their subordinate unit's fixing force to provide fire-support coverage throughout the area of operations during search-and-attack operations in restricted terrain. Battalion and company indirect fire assets (usually mortars) are also available to provide direct support to units in contact.

If conditions are not favorable for the finishing force to attack the enemy, the reconnaissance or the fixing force can continue to conduct reconnaissance and surveillance activities to further develop the situation. Whenever this occurs, the force maintaining surveillance must be careful to avoid detection and possible enemy ambushes.

The finishing force may move behind the reconnaissance and fixing forces, or it may position itself at a pickup zone (PZ) and launch an air assault into a landing zone (LZ) near the enemy force once the other platoons locate it. The finishing force must be responsive enough to engage the enemy before they can break contact with the reconnaissance force or the fixing force.

The commander uses the finishing force to destroy the fixed enemy by conducting hasty or deliberate attacks; maneuvering to block enemy escape routes while another unit conducts the attack; or employing indirect fire or close air support to destroy the enemy. The commander may have the finishing force establish an area ambush and use the reconnaissance and fixing forces to drive the enemy into the ambushes.

Approach March Technique

march objective

the end of an approach march; used as a control measure to end a movement-to-contact operation or transition to an attack

An *approach march* is the advance of a combat unit when it intends to come into direct contact with the enemy. It emphasizes speed over tactical deployment. Both heavy and light forces conduct tactical road marches and approach marches.

The concept behind the approach march is to make contact with the smallest element, allowing the commander the flexibility to maneuver or bypass the enemy force. As part of a larger unit using the approach-march technique, platoons may act as the advance, flank, or rear guard. They may also receive on-order missions as part of the main body. The commander employs an approach march when the enemy's approximate location is known, since it allows the force to move with greater speed and less physical security or dispersion. The approach march terminates in a **march objective,** such as an attack position, assembly area, or assault position. The commander can use it to transition to an attack.

Advance Guard

As the *advance guard,* the platoon finds the enemy forces and locates gaps, flanks, and weaknesses in their defense. The advance guard attempts to make contact on ground of its own choosing, to gain the advantage of surprise, and to develop the situation (either fight through or support the main body's assault). The advance guard operates within the range of the main body's indirect fire support and deploys as follows:

- One rifle squad leads the advance guard
- The platoon uses appropriate formations and movement techniques
- The platoon leader rotates the lead squad as necessary to keep Soldiers fresh.

Flank or Rear Guard

The entire platoon may act as the *flank* or *rear guard* for a battalion conducting a movement to contact using this technique. In this situation, the platoon:

- Moves using the appropriate formation and movement technique
- Provides early warning
- Destroys enemy reconnaissance units
- Prevents direct fires upon or observation of the main body.

Main Body

Commanders may task platoons moving as part of the main body to assault, bypass, or fix an enemy force; or to seize, secure, or clear an assigned area. The commander may also detail the platoon to provide squads as flank guards, stay-behind ambushes, rear security, or additional security to the front. These squads may come under the company commander's direct control. Platoons and squads use appropriate formations and movement techniques, assault techniques, and ambush techniques.

Critical Thinking

Explain how the characteristics of offensive operations reinforce what you've just read about *search-and-attack* and *approach-march* movements to contact.

Tactical Road Marches and Infiltrations

In addition to participating in a movement to contact, *tactical road marches* and *infiltrations* are other methods of movement squads and platoons conduct as part of a larger force when contact with the enemy is possible or anticipated. Tactical road marches emphasize considerations such as security and de-emphasize efficiency and ease of movement. The commander organizes the unit to conduct combat operations in a tactical movement. A unit generally maintains unit integrity throughout its movement. It plans for enemy interference either en route to or shortly after arrival at its destination. Units conducting tactical road marches use formations and techniques consistent with the factors of METT-TC. The unit may conduct them over unsecured routes if there are no friendly forces between the foremost elements of the moving force and the enemy.

An *infiltration,* on the other hand, is a maneuver in which an attacking force moves undetected through or into an area occupied by enemy forces to take up a position of advantage in the enemy rear while exposing only small elements to enemy defensive fires. The need to avoid detection and contact may limit infiltrating forces' size and strength. Infiltration rarely defeats an enemy defense by itself. Commanders direct squads and platoons to conduct infiltrations to attack lightly defended enemy positions or stronger positions from the flank and rear; to secure key terrain to support the decisive operation; or to disrupt enemy sustaining operations. Typically, forces infiltrate in small groups and reassemble to continue their mission.

CONCLUSION

Offensive operations are intended to destroy or defeat an enemy. Their purpose is to impose US will on the enemy and achieve decisive victory. No matter what type of attack squads or platoons must execute, they seek to capitalize on the four characteristics of the offensive. When making the most of surprise and audacity, even small units like squads and platoons can overcome seemingly insurmountable odds. When small-unit situations are vague, the commander uses movement to contact to shape the battlefield and develop a better understanding of the enemy.

Learning Assessment

1. Why do you think the US military is offense oriented?
2. How do the characteristics of offensive operations apply to a movement to contact?
3. Consider the differences between the two movement-to-contact techniques. Describe the conditions for the appropriate application of each of the techniques.

To move swiftly, strike vigorously, and secure all the fruits of victory is the secret of successful war.

LTG Thomas J. "Stonewall" Jackson, 1863

Key Words

surprise

concentration

tempo

audacity

movement to contact (MTC)

attack

exploitation

pursuit

fix

march objective

References

ARTEP 7-8-Drill, *Battle Drills for the Infantry Rifle Platoon and Squad.* 20 July 2006.

Field Manual 3-0, *Operations.* 14 June 2001.

Green, A. Wilson. (n.d.) The Battle of Chancellorsville, 1863. National Park Service. Retrieved 12 April 2005 from http://www.nps.gov/frsp/chist.htm

SQUAD TACTICS: RECONNAISSANCE

Key Points

1 Reconnaissance Patrols

2 Fundamentals of Reconnaissance

Know your enemy as you know yourself, and you can fight 100 battles with no danger of defeat.

Sun Tzu, *The Art of War*

Introduction

Section 8 outlined the principles of patrolling. In this section, you will learn more about one function of patrols: reconnaissance. Reconnaissance, or *recon,* is the act of gathering information about an enemy. Recon *patrols* are one way to collect such information. Today's US military employs a wide array of intelligence collection assets—many of them extremely high-tech. Yet nothing can replace the thinking, breathing recon Soldier on the ground. These silent warriors may come face-to-face with the enemy and never exchange blows. In fact, more often than not, the enemy never even knows they were there.

Team Compromise—10 Feet Away

Despite all of the planning, not all insertions go as planned. SSG Peter D. Armstrong's team, Team 1-1, E-165th [Military Intelligence Battalion], was one of three teams inserted for the campaign. Bedouin dogs compromised the team soon after its insertion into central Iraq. After the dogs followed the team to its secondary site, the team quickly moved to its tertiary site and went to ground. As an example of how disciplined the Soldiers are and how effective their hide techniques are, Armstrong's team spent over 48 hours in an 18-inch-deep hole with a sheet covering six Soldiers. Iraqis, actively searching for them, came within 10 feet of the team's hide site. SSG Armstrong lay flat on his back, peering through a small hole in the camouflaged sheet with his weapon tracking the Iraqi leader who was looking for them. Once the Iraqis moved off, the team exfiltrated to an alternate extraction site and was picked up safely.

On Point: The United States Army in Operation Iraqi Freedom, 2004

Reconnaissance Patrols

Reconnaissance patrols provide timely and accurate information about the enemy and terrain. They confirm the soundness of the leader's plan before it is executed. Units on reconnaissance operations collect specific information (**priority intelligence requirements (PIR)**) or general information (**information requirements** (IR)) based on their higher commander's instructions. The commander informs the subordinate leader of the specific information requirements for each mission.

The three types of reconnaissance patrols are *area*, *zone*, and *route* reconnaissance.

Organization

In addition to the common elements found in every patrol (see Section 8), reconnaissance patrols have a *reconnaissance team* and a *reconnaissance and security team*.

1. *Reconnaissance Team.* Reconnaissance teams reconnoiter the objective area from various vantage points once the security teams are in position. Normally reconnaissance teams are two-Soldier teams (buddy teams), to reduce the possibility of detection.

2. *Reconnaissance and Security Team.* You normally use R&S teams in a zone reconnaissance, but they may be useful in any situation when it is impractical to separate reconnaissance and security.

3. *Security Element.* When the responsibilities for reconnaissance and security are separate, the security element provides security at danger areas, secures the objective rally point (ORP), isolates the objective, and supports the withdrawal of the rest of the platoon once the recon is complete. The security element may have separate security teams, each with an assigned task or sequence of tasks.

4. *Surveillance Team.* The surveillance team is a two-Soldier team that you place at a static vantage point. It observes the objective for an extended or determined period and gathers PIR or IR on the enemy or the objective. A surveillance team differs from a recon team in that the recon team maneuvers around the objective on multiple approaches in order to observe the objective from many vantage points.

Task to Subordinate Units

Normally, the platoon leader controls the platoon on a reconnaissance patrol mission.

1. As platoon leader, you must consider the requirements for reconnaissance and security in assigning tasks to your squads or fire teams. You may separate the tasks so that one or more squads conduct the reconnaissance while other squads or fire teams provide security at various locations. Or you may assign R&S tasks to each squad or team. When a fire team conducts a reconnaissance patrol, it operates as a single R&S team.

2. In assigning tasks, you must also consider the size and number of reconnaissance objectives, the requirement to secure the ORP and other points, and the time available to conduct the mission.

reconnaissance

an operation designed to obtain information on the enemy, potential enemy, or the characteristics of a particular area—reconnaissance may be accomplished through passive surveillance, technical means, or human interaction (human intelligence (HUMINT) or spies), or by making direct contact with the enemy

priority intelligence requirement

specific information a commander directs units to collect; the reconnaissance mission has not been accomplished until this information is obtained, distributed to all members in the reconnaissance patrol, and passed along to higher commands

information requirement

items of information regarding the enemy and their environment that units must collect and process to meet a commander's needs

Fundamentals of Reconnaissance

For a successful area reconnaissance, you must apply the fundamentals of reconnaissance to your plan during the operation.

1. *Gain All Required Information.* The parent unit tells the patrol leader what information it requires. It does so through the IR (information requirements) and PIR (priority intelligence requirements). You then tailor the platoon's mission to the required information. During the entire patrol, members must continuously exchange all information they gather. But you cannot consider the mission accomplished unless you have gathered all PIR, distributed it to all members in the reconnaissance patrol, and passed it along to higher commands.

> The following are examples of **priority intelligence requirements** for commanders of Operation Enduring Freedom upon entering a new town:
>
> 1. From where does the enemy receive resupply of weapons and ammunition?
>
> 2. Who are the tribal leaders of this village?
>
> 3. What is the status of the local infrastructure—sewer, water, electricity, hospital, etc.?

Note:

Do not confuse **information** with **intelligence**. Reconnaissance patrols collect *information* through direct observation. Recon Soldiers and leaders do not interpret the information collected. Commanders and their staffs analyze the information the patrols provide and turn the data into *intelligence*.

2. *Avoid Detection by the Enemy.* A patrol must not let the enemy know that it is in the objective area. If enemy forces know they are under observation, they may move, change their plans, or increase their security measures. You can avoid detection by:

   a. minimizing movement in the objective area (area recon).
   b. moving no closer to the enemy than necessary.
   c. using long-range surveillance devices or night-observation devices when possible.
   d. employing camouflage, stealth, noise, and light discipline.
   e. minimizing radio traffic.

3. *Employ Security.* A recon patrol must provide its own security. You organize an R&S team with enough Soldiers both to perform the recon mission and to provide the security needed to overwatch the recon mission. When a recon patrol requires separate or multiple security teams, you employ these individual security teams in a manner that allows the security teams to overwatch the recon element. Security teams watch for enemy activity on the objective and for enemy fighters near or approaching the recon element. The security and recon elements maintain radio contact: Security provides updates to the recon element and helps the recon element avoid detection by the enemy. Via radio, security advises where the recon element should move to remain undetected, or, if necessary, how best to maneuver to break contact.

4. *Task Organization.* After receiving the OPORD and conducting mission and terrain analysis, you must organize your platoon for the reconnaissance patrol. You first consider the type of reconnaissance patrol required to meet the higher command's mission statement and intent (area, zone, or route recon). You then decide how to organize your platoon around the required tasks to accomplish the type of recon you must conduct. If a zone recon is required, you as the platoon leader might appoint yourself the patrol leader and conduct the zone recon with your entire platoon, using the fan method. If an area or route recon is required, you might task each squad leader to be a patrol leader and conduct squad-level area or route recons. Depending on the mission, or if the platoon is conducting the company's main reconnaissance effort, you must also consider how to organize the tasks for elements attached to your platoon or under its operational control (OPCON) for the recon mission. If company mortars can reach the recon elements from the patrol base, then it is best to leave them at the patrol base to help you maintain stealth during the recon. You can also task the company mortars to secure the patrol base, freeing up your own Soldiers to add to the recon effort. You must also consider how to task organize any machine gun crews from the company weapons platoon. You can task machine gun crews to secure the patrol base, or you can use the machine gun crews to provide overwatch and security to a recon team. You must also consider how to task organize other elements that may be attached to your platoon or under your OPCON, such as forward observers (FOs), engineers, interpreters, or additional medics. FOs should be task organized to the element in which they will best be able to observe the objective or recon elements in the event they must call for indirect fire support. Engineers are especially useful in evaluating roads, bridges, and slopes, and in assessing how to defeat existing and reinforcing obstacles. If you receive additional medics, you may wish to attach them to individual recon elements or consider designating the patrol base as the casualty collection point (CCP), tasking the additional medics to remain there to run the CCP.

Area Reconnaissance

The purpose of an area recon is to obtain information about a specific location and the area around it. You may receive the location as a grid coordinate or as an objective identified on a map overlay. A commander may task you to conduct an area recon of key terrain such as a bridge, a road intersection, a fordable water crossing, high ground, or a likely ambush site along a route. How you conduct the area recon will depend on many of the factors you consider during your mission and terrain analysis. Steps common to most area recons include establishing and securing the ORP; placing security and/or surveillance teams to observe the objective; deploying teams to recon the objective; reassembling teams and elements back in the ORP; distributing information among all patrol members; reporting PIR and IR to higher command; and returning to the patrol base or friendly lines (Figure 11.2).

Critical Thinking

Consider the benefits of a squad-sized unit versus a platoon-sized unit in conducting a reconnaissance patrol.

1. ***Establishing the ORP.*** The recon patrol establishes the ORP at least one terrain feature away from the objective or at a distance that prevents the enemy from detecting the patrol. Ideally, the patrol leader task organizes the security elements, the surveillance teams, and the recon elements or teams when conducting troop leading procedures (TLPs) behind friendly lines or while in the patrol base. You leave a security team or element in the ORP while the recon patrol conducts the area recon. All patrol members must know the five-point contingency plan, the challenge and password, the running password, and the number combination so they may safely return to the ORP without a fratricide (friendly fire incident).

2. ***Security and Surveillance.*** Depending on the enemy situation and terrain, you may need to employ one or more security teams, one or more surveillance teams, or both. Generally, you place security teams between the enemy's likely avenues of approach and the recon team. This gives the recon team early warning of an approaching enemy so that the recon team can avoid contact or, if necessary, provide supporting fires to allow the recon element to break contact. In the example of an area recon to confirm an ambush site along a route, the patrol leader would place one security team on the left and right flanks of the objective to give early warning to the recon element while they attempt to pinpoint the kill zone. In the example of an area recon to confirm the disposition and strength of an enemy defensive position, you may choose to place one or more surveillance teams at vantage points that would also provide early warning and security for the recon element. In addition, you can leave the surveillance team in place to observe the objective if you need to distribute information in the ORP or adjust the current plan.

3. ***Recon Elements and Teams.*** Depending on the enemy situation and terrain, you may chose to deploy one or more R&S teams, a recon element (such as a leader's recon of the objective), or one or more recon teams. R&S teams provide their own security, and you may task them to recon certain portions of the objective. You must take care that the R&S teams know where other R&S teams are to prevent fratricide. During a leader's recon, you will take key leaders and the security and/or surveillance team. You will designate a release point (RP), and from the RP you will station the security and surveillance teams before taking your key leaders on the recon of the objective. When you complete the leader's recon, you will either retrieve your security and surveillance elements or you will radio them to return to the RP.

    You use recon teams when stealth is the priority. They consist of two or three Soldiers. You may task the recon teams to recon specific areas on or around the objective, or you may task them to recon the objective using the clock method. When using the clock method, both teams may start at 6 o'clock with one team working clockwise and the other team working counterclockwise. The two meet at 12 o'clock, disseminating PIR and IR and returning together to the ORP. Or, after disseminating information at the 12 o'clock location, both teams could continue reconnoitering back to the 6 o'clock position. In this way, the teams reconnoiter each area twice, each time with a different team.

Note:
You distribute information to every member of the patrol so that as long as at least one Soldier returns from the patrol, the information gathered from the mission can still be passed on to higher headquarters.

You record and relay information using the SALUTE report format:

S ize of enemy unit being observed.

A ctivity the enemy unit is participating in.

L ocation of enemy unit.

U niform or other distinguishing marks of the enemy unit you're observing.

T ime of the observation.

E quipment the enemy is using (vehicles, weapons, special tools, etc.).

4. ***Reassembling and Distributing PIR in the ORP.*** After the patrol has gathered all PIR and IR or the recon patrol reaches its designated no-later-than time (NLT), all elements return to the RP and move back to the ORP. The assistant patrol leader (APL) readjusts the perimeter as necessary and PIR and IR are immediately distributed to each patrol member. This is necessary in case the platoon is discovered and takes casualties; any surviving patrol member will still have the commander's PIR and IR. Once information is disseminated, the patrol leader prepares and sends a SALUTE report to higher command as soon as it is safe to do so (remember that radio silence may be required when conducting recon patrols). If the patrol is to await further orders, the patrol will move to and occupy a new patrol base. If operating from a forward operating base (FOB) or an assembly area (AA), the patrol reenters friendly lines and returns to the FOB or AA.

Note:
Rarely will you be able to obtain all PIR from one vantage point.

The cloverleaf method is a movement technique that is based on the fact that the human eye more easily notices lateral movements (movements parallel to the objective) than it does changes in distance (movements perpendicular the objective).

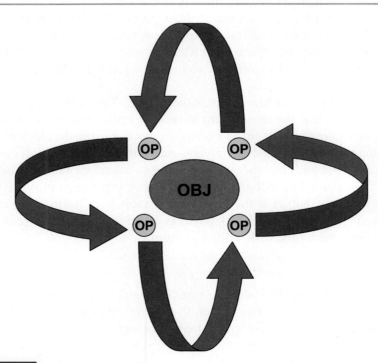

Figure 11.1 Cloverleaf Method

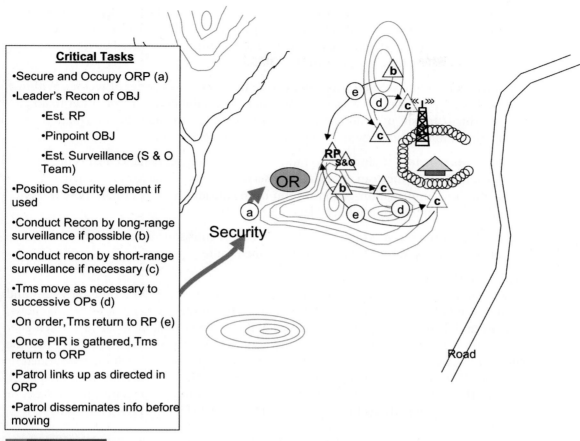

Critical Tasks

- Secure and Occupy ORP (a)
- Leader's Recon of OBJ
    - Est. RP
    - Pinpoint OBJ
    - Est. Surveillance (S & O Team)
- Position Security element if used
- Conduct Recon by long-range surveillance if possible (b)
- Conduct recon by short-range surveillance if necessary (c)
- Tms move as necessary to successive OPs (d)
- On order, Tms return to RP (e)
- Once PIR is gathered, Tms return to ORP
- Patrol links up as directed in ORP
- Patrol disseminates info before moving

Figure 11.2 Actions on the Objective—Area Recon

Zone Reconnaissance

You conduct a zone reconnaissance to obtain information about the enemy, terrain, and routes within a specified zone. Zone-reconnaissance techniques include using moving elements, stationary teams, or a series of area-reconnaissance actions.

Moving Elements. You plan the use of squads or fire teams moving along multiple routes to cover the entire zone. Methods for moving multiple elements through a zone include the *fan,* the *box, converging routes,* and *successive sectors.*

1. *Fan method.* You first select a series of ORPs throughout the zone. The platoon establishes security at the first ORP. Each R&S team moves away from the ORP along a different fan-shaped route that overlaps with others to ensure reconnaissance of the entire area. You maintain a reserve at the ORP. When all R&S teams have returned to the ORP, the platoon collects and disseminates all information to every Soldier before moving on to the next ORP.

2. *Box method.* You send your R&S teams from the ORP along routes that form a boxed-in area. You send other teams along routes through the area within the box. All teams meet at a link-up point at the far side of the box from the ORP.

3. ***Converging routes method.*** You select routes from the ORP through the zone to a link-up point at the far side of the zone from the ORP. Each R&S team moves along a specified route and uses the fan method to reconnoiter the area between routes. You designate a time for all teams to link up.

4. ***Successive sector method.*** You may divide the zone into a series of sectors. Within each sector, the platoon uses the converging routes method to reconnoiter to an intermediate link-up point, where it collects and disseminates the information gathered to that point before it reconnoiters the next sector.

5. ***Stationary teams.*** Using this technique, you position surveillance teams in locations where they can collectively observe the entire zone for long-term, continuous information-gathering You must consider how to sustain these teams when developing your Soldiers' load plan.

6. ***Multiple area reconnaissance.*** You task each of your squads to conduct a series of area-reconnaissance actions along a specified route.

Actions on the Objective—Zone Recon

When conducting a zone recon, you plan an ORP and issue an NLT time for teams and elements to link up and disseminate PIR and IR. If time and the enemy situation allows, prepare and distribute sketches as well (again, if only one patrol member survives, higher command will still receive the PIR, IR, and zone sketch). Some unit SOPs direct that the succession of command is responsible for retrieving IR and PIR from the wounded or killed leader rather than having multiple copies of IR, PIR, and sketches with the patrol. As with the area recon, the patrol will either move to and occupy a new patrol base, or conduct reentry operations to return to the FOB or AA (Figures 11.3, 11.4, and 11.5).

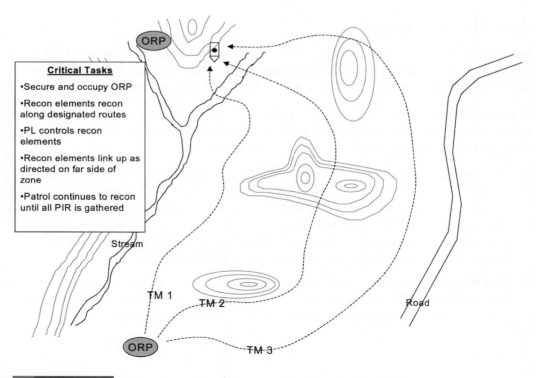

Critical Tasks

•Secure and occupy ORP

•Recon elements recon along designated routes

•PL controls recon elements

•Recon elements link up as directed on far side of zone

•Patrol continues to recon until all PIR is gathered

Figure 11.3 Actions on the Objective—Zone Recon, Box Method

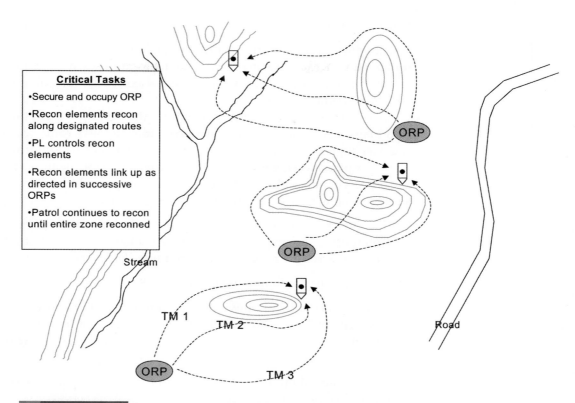

Figure 11.4 Actions on the Objective—Zone Recon, Converging Routes Method

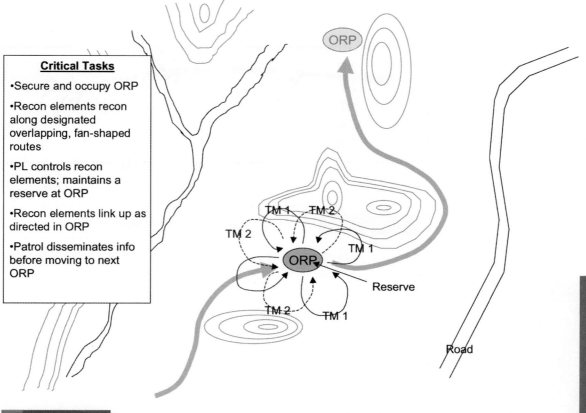

Figure 11.5 Actions on the Objective—Zone Recon, Fan Method

Route Reconnaissance

You conduct a route reconnaissance to obtain detailed information about one or more routes and all the adjacent terrain, or to locate sites for placing obstacles. A route reconnaissance is oriented on a road; a narrow axis, such as an infiltration lane; or a general direction of attack.

Normally, engineers are attached to the Infantry unit for a complete route reconnaissance. Infantry can, however, conduct a hasty route reconnaissance without engineer support. A route reconnaissance results in detailed information about whether routes are passable; enemy activity; nuclear, biological, or chemical (NBC) contamination; and aspects of adjacent terrain from both the enemy and friendly viewpoint. In planning a route reconnaissance, you should consider the following.

1. The preferred method for conducting a route reconnaissance is the fan method. You must ensure that the fans are wide enough to reconnoiter intersecting routes beyond direct-fire range of the main route (Figure 11.6).

2. The recon patrol should use a different return route.

3. If all or part of the proposed route is a road, you must treat the road as a danger area. The platoon moves parallel to the road, using a covered and concealed route. When required, reconnaissance and security teams move close to the road to reconnoiter key areas.

4. You should submit the patrol report in an overlay format in accordance with FM 5-34 or GTA 5-2-5 (Figure 11.7).

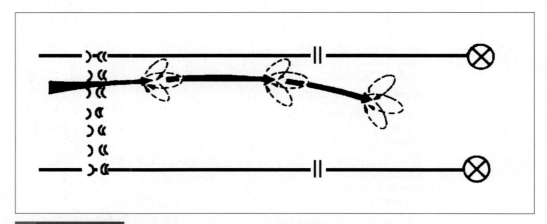

Figure 11.6   Route Reconnaissance Using Fans

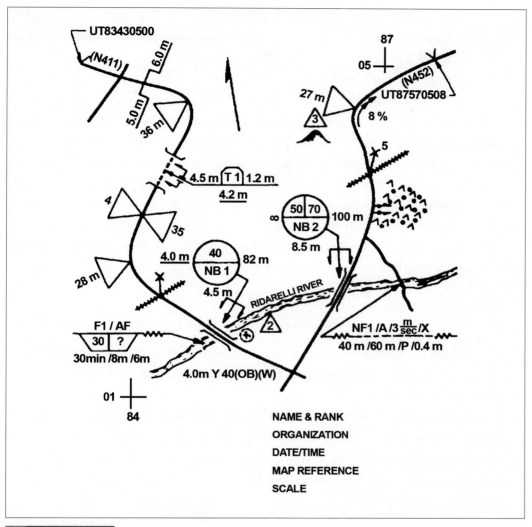

Figure 11.7   Route Reconnaissance Overlay

Critical Thinking

Explain how the various reconnaissance techniques help meet both information requirements and priority intelligence requirements for a headquarters.

Critical Thinking

Describe how the general process of reconnaissance translates into area, zone, and route reconnaissance.

CONCLUSION

Recon patrols are maneuver commanders' eyes and ears. They provide necessary and timely information for commanders to use in planning future operations. The success (or failure) of your recon patrol will determine the success (or failure) of future operations. Your commander will issue you specific tasks that you must complete when conducting a recon mission. The most important task, however, may be the implied task of remaining undetected. Remaining undetected will increase your chances of a successful mission. On the other hand, being detected will almost always result in a complete or partial mission failure.

Learning Assessment

1. Which kind of reconnaissance patrol might you conduct if your commander wanted to gain information about the activities at a suspected terrorist training facility?
2. What elements or characteristics distinguish a recon patrol from a combat patrol? (Recall the discussion of combat patrols in Section 8.)
3. Describe the fundamentals of reconnaissance. Why do you think they are so important for successful recon patrols?
4. Compare and contrast a zone and an area reconnaissance.

Key Words

reconnaissance
priority intelligence requirement (PIR)
information requirement (IR)
reconnaissance and security team

References

Department of the Army. (2004). *On Point: The United States Army in Operation Iraqi Freedom*. Retrieved 3 February 2005, from http://onpoint.leavenworth.army.mil

Field Manual 1-02, *Operational Terms and Graphics*. September 2004.

Field Manual 3-21.8, *The Infantry Rifle Platoon and Squad*. 28 March 2007.

Field Manual 5-34, *Engineer Field Data*. 10 April 2003.

Field Manual 7-92, *The Infantry Reconnaissance Platoon and Squad*. 13 December 2001.

SH 21-76, *Ranger Handbook*. April 2000.

SQUAD TACTICS: AMBUSH

Key Points

1 Planning

2 Ambush Categories

3 Ambush Types

4 Ambush Formations

5 Leader Actions in the Ambush

Any blow, to be successful, must be sudden and hard.

GEN Robert E. Lee

Introduction

An ambush is a surprise attack from a concealed position. Its purpose is to destroy or capture a moving or temporarily halted enemy and the enemy's equipment. An ambush is a useful tactic because it allows a small, well-trained, disciplined force, with limited weapons and equipment, to destroy much larger enemy forces. It reduces the enemy's overall combat effectiveness by destruction and harassment of forces. Enemy morale and effectiveness suffer heavily at little cost to the force executing the ambush. A successful ambush must be executed with precision, violence, speed, and audacity of execution. For success, ambush operations must emphasize surprise, coordinated firepower and shock effect, and control by the leader. Ambushes are classified by *category*—hasty or deliberate; *type*—point or area; and *formation*—linear or L-shaped. The leader uses a combination of category, type, and formation in developing an ambush plan, based on METT-TC and the commander's intent.

Ambush at Phu Loc

The mission of the 2d Platoon, Company C, 327th Infantry (Airmobile) was to conduct night ambushes to interdict Viet Cong/North Vietnamese Army movement into the village. One squad (reinforced) was deployed on the western edge of Cau Hai to conduct a night ambush to interdict enemy movement into the village.

A reconnaissance of the ambush position was conducted during the day prior to occupation of the site. Personnel conducting the reconnaissance included the platoon leader, platoon sergeant, squad leaders, radio operators, and one Soldier for each of the positions to be occupied during the ambush. The actual position sites were reconnoitered while moving through the area during a routine patrol. Each patrol member was briefed beforehand and made mental notes en route without stopping or otherwise drawing undue attention to his actions. The location of the ambush position was selected based on a calculation that the enemy would most likely travel along the main trail located to the south and southwest or from the west along the paddy dikes. The primary killing zone was oriented to the south and southwest.

Following a final briefing, SGT Robert L. Sprangenberg's patrol began its movement to the ambush position at approximately 1855 hours on 19 December 1969. Moving by a direct route, in file formation, the patrol was concealed by heavy overcast and vegetation, arriving at the pre-selected ambush site at approximately 1915 hours. The Soldiers occupied the site and were established in final positions within 10 minutes.

The ambush site was occupied by four separate team positions, the machine gun being located to cover the primary killing zone as well as a secondary route of approach from the west. Claymore anti-personnel (AP) mines were emplaced to cover the primary and secondary killing zones and were camouflaged with natural vegetation. Each team position was under the supervision of one designated trooper, and overall command and control was exercised by the patrol leader.

The exact tactical formation employed by the enemy could not be determined. It appeared that the point element, consisting of two or three men and restricted by a confining dike, was moving in file. Based on the rapid return of rocket-propelled grenade (RPG) fire, it was evident that a supporting element was set up in a firing position to cover the point element. The enemy force consisted of at least seven men.

The only identifiable weapons employed by the enemy were AK47s and RPGs. Enemy noise discipline was excellent; however, light discipline was extremely poor. The enemy's use of a flashlight (believed to be a signal device) confirmed the point element's presence and identified its location. The enemy's weakness lay in his selection of a route of movement. His strong points were dispersion, stealth, and accurate and responsive supporting fire.

The first sighting of the enemy occurred at 2130 hours, when one man from the rear security element observed movement on the dike to his right front. He quickly directed a trooper employing the night vision device to scan the suspected location and confirmed the presence of two enemy soldiers. At that time, the enemy personnel were stationary, apparently continuing their reconnaissance of the village to their front. The remainder of the US ambush patrol, already on 100 percent alert, began to scan the area for additional movement. Then, the lead enemy Soldier appeared to signal with a flashlight toward his rear (west). Suddenly, he moved forward, appearing to have detected a Claymore mine. As he approached for a closer examination, the Claymore was detonated, and the patrol members delivered an instantaneous volume of grazing fire within their assigned sectors. Within a few seconds, the enemy returned fire with one RPG round from the west, followed shortly afterward by two additional rounds. The enemy fire struck a house to the rear of the ambush site, injuring one Vietnamese woman. During the initial phase of the action, another enemy Soldier was observed to the west, and engaged by an M79 high-explosive grenade and M60 machine gun fire. Following a rapid estimate of the situation, the platoon leader requested 81-mm mortar, 155-mm howitzer, and helicopter flareship support. The first 81-mm mortar illumination was overhead in less than two minutes and the 155-mm howitzer illumination in approximately $3\frac{1}{2}$ minutes. Unfavorable weather conditions precluded the employment of flareships, and handheld flares were employed until 81-mm mortar illumination was received. Although the enemy returned small arms fire, it was totally ineffective, and artillery blocking fires were employed to seal off the suspected enemy routes of withdrawal. Following a quick check of personnel and redistribution of ammunition, the ambush patrol conducted an aggressive sweep to locate any remaining enemy forces. The sweep revealed the bodies of the two enemy Soldiers engaged by the first Claymore, one body approximately 50 meters to the west who appeared to have been hit by a Claymore, and further west, another body also killed by a Claymore. One RPG round was found near the last body.

When the patrol leader determined that no enemy remained in the area, he regrouped and relocated the patrol and had the slightly wounded civilian evacuated. At first light, another sweep was conducted with negative results. A combat tracker team was employed but was unable to discover the enemy's trail due to the high volume of civilian and animal traffic that had previously passed through the area. The patrol was subsequently debriefed and released for maintenance and rest.

Planning

Ambush planning begins well before the objective. Patrol leaders not only plan for actions during the ambush but also for those actions before and after: departing friendly forward lines, routes to and from the ambush site, setting up the patrol base and objective rally point (ORP), indirect fire support, and actions after the objective (withdrawal). In planning an ambush, you must plan for these key considerations:

- Covering the entire kill zone by fire
- Using existing or reinforcing obstacles (**Claymores** and other mines) to keep the enemy in the kill zone
- Protecting the assault and support elements with mines, Claymores, or explosives
- Using security elements or teams to **isolate** the kill zone
- Killing all enemy within the kill zone and, when the situation dictates, searching for dead and wounded, assembling prisoners, and collecting equipment (the assault element must be able to move quickly through its own protective obstacles)
- Timing the actions of all elements of the platoon to preclude loss of surprise
- Using only one squad to conduct the entire ambush and rotating squads over time from the ORP, this technique is useful when the ambush must be manned for a long time.

Ambush Categories

As noted above, the two categories of ambush are the *hasty* ambush and the *deliberate* ambush.

Hasty Ambush

You can conduct a hasty ambush when the enemy has not detected your patrol. If you have the time to apply METT-TC, you can decide whether to conduct the ambush, withdraw, or seek cover and concealment to allow the enemy to pass by. If you decide to conduct the ambush, you do so when your patrol makes visual contact with an enemy force and has time to establish the ambush without being detected. Your platoon's actions for a hasty ambush must be well rehearsed and part of its battle-drill training, so that Soldiers know what to do on signal from you or their squad leader. They must also know what action to take if the enemy detects them before they are ready to initiate the ambush.

Claymore

command-detonated USM18A1 anti-personnel mine weighing 3.5 lbs, containing explosives and ball bearings used to defend Soldiers from mass infantry attacks; it can also be used to produce mass casualties during ambushes

In their fight against US forces in Iraq, military insurgents used what were essentially homemade antipersonnel mines similar to Claymores, better known as improvised explosive devices (IEDs).

isolate

a tactical task given to a unit to seal off (both physically and psychologically) an enemy from sources of support, to deny an enemy freedom of movement, and prevent an enemy unit from having contact with other enemy forces—enemy fighters must not be allowed sanctuary within their present position

Critical Thinking

Think about the definition of a battle drill. The above description of a hasty ambush sounds very much like the definition of a battle drill. Can you explain why the hasty ambush is not a battle drill?

In planning and rehearsing a hasty ambush, you should consider the following sequence of actions:

Using visual signals, any Soldier alerts the platoon that an enemy force is in sight. The Soldier continues to monitor the location and activities of the enemy force until relieved by the team or squad leader. The platoon or squad halts and remains motionless. As the platoon leader, you determine the best nearby location for a hasty ambush. You use hand-and-arm signals to direct Soldiers to covered and concealed positions. You designate the location and extent of the kill zone. Security elements move out to cover each flank and the rear. You direct the security elements to move a given distance, set up, and rejoin the platoon on order or after the ambush (when the sound of firing ceases). At the squad level, the two outside buddy teams normally provide flank security as well as fires into the kill zone (Figure 12.1).

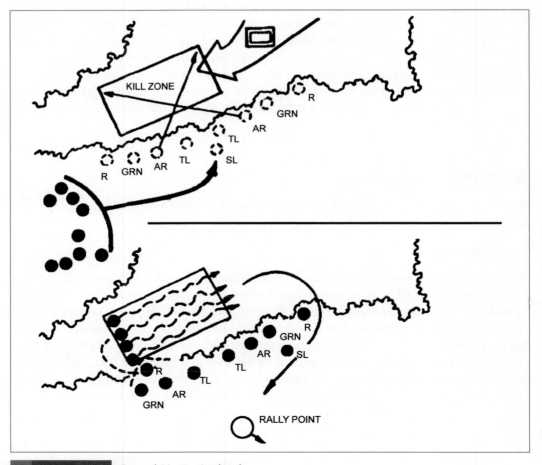

Figure 12.1 Squad Hasty Ambush

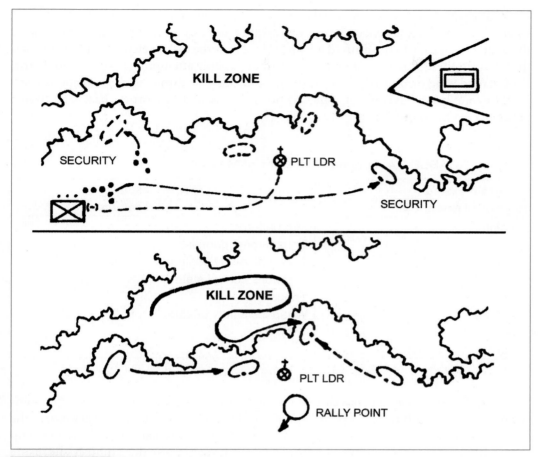

Figure 12.2 Platoon Hasty Ambush

At platoon level, fire teams make up the security elements (Figure 12.2).

Note:
Never discount the need for rear security—especially on the nonlinear battlefield of the contemporary operating environment. The enemy can be virtually anywhere.

Soldiers move quickly to covered and concealed positions, normally five to 10 meters apart. Soldiers ensure that they have good observation and fields of fire into the kill zone. You initiate the ambush with the weapon that produces the most casualties when the majority of the enemy force enters the kill zone. (If time and terrain permit, the squad or platoon should place out Claymores and use them to initiate the ambush as they are the preferred casualty producing weapon organic to a squad or platoon.) Your unit avoids becoming decisively engaged both during the ambush and by follow-on elements.

Note:
The most important element when considering a hasty ambush is the element of surprise. If the enemy detects the platoon, squad, or patrol before they enter the kill zone, then you are no longer conducting a hasty ambush. You and your Soldiers must now execute the React to Contact battle drill.

As the patrol leader, you control the rate and distribution of fires. You order "cease fire" when the enemy force is destroyed or stops resisting. You direct the assault element to move through the kill zone to the **limit of advance** (LOA). As the assault element moves through the kill zone, the assault team members destroy any enemy attempting to resist, and disarm any surrendering or injured enemy fighters by kicking or throwing their weapons away from them. When it has completed these actions, the assault team forms a hasty 360-degree perimeter on the objective.

TABLE 2.4 Common Fire Control Measures

Terrain-Based Fire Control Measures	Threat-Based Fire Control Measures
Target reference point	Fire patterns
Engagement area	Engagement priorities
Sector of fire	Weapons ready posture
Maximum engagement line	Weapons control status
Final protective line	Trigger
Principal direction of fire	Weapons safety posture
Final protective fire	
Restrictive firing line	

After the assault element has cleared through the kill zone, the support element rejoins the platoon. You position the support teams to seal the objective. You then call forward the aid and litter, enemy prisoner of war (EPW), and demolitions teams to quickly finish up their mission on the objective. The platoon withdraws from the ambush site using preplanned signals and a covered and concealed route. The platoon returns to the ORP, collects and disseminates all information among all members, reorganizes as necessary, and moves to an alternate or a new patrol base.

Deliberate Ambush

You conduct a deliberate ambush against a specific target at a predetermined location. In setting the stage for a deliberate ambush, you must conduct a thorough enemy analysis to determine:

- Size and composition of the targeted enemy unit
- Weapons and equipment available to the enemy
- The enemy's most probable course of action (route, direction of movement, and movement formation and technique)
- Times that the targeted unit will reach or pass specified points along the route
- The enemy's most dangerous course of action

The ambush is in place not later than the time specified in the OPORD or FRAGO. Your patrol surprises the enemy and engages the enemy main body. The patrol kills or captures all enemy in the kill zone and destroys equipment based on the commander's intent. The patrol then withdraws all personnel and equipment from the objective within the time specified in the order. You obtain all available priority information requirements (PIR) from the ambush and continue follow-on operations.

Ambush Types

Besides the two categories of ambush, there are also two different types: the *point* ambush and the *area* ambush.

Point Ambush

In a point ambush, Soldiers deploy to attack an enemy in a single kill zone. Consider the following sequence of actions when planning a deliberate point ambush:

Security Element

Position the security or surveillance team(s) first. The support element moves out of the release point before the assault element in order to be in place before the assault element occupies the assault position. The support element must overwatch the movement of the assault element into position.

Note:
Recall the principles of patrolling from Section 8. The order of emplacement and recovery of elements is important to avoid violating the principle of *security*.

Assault Element

You are the leader of the assault element. You must check each Soldier once the assault and rear element has established the assault position. If you use a surveillance team and flank security are in place, you signal the surveillance team to rejoin the assault element. The assault element identifies individual sectors of fire, sets up aiming stakes, emplaces Claymores and other protective devices (to include those necessary in any dead space inside the kill zone), camouflages its position, and takes its weapons off "safe"—taking care not to compromise the mission by the sound of the metallic click when moving the selection lever.

Note:
One weapon being taken off "safe" may not alert the enemy moving through the kill zone, but consider the "typewriter" sound effect as 30 Soldiers (a platoon-sized ambush) take their weapons off safe all at the same moment in time.

You use aiming stakes as part of your direct fire control measures. Aiming stakes ensure interlocking fires on the kill zone, but also protect against fratricide between members of the assault, support, and flank security elements.

Support Element

The support team identifies sectors of fire for all its weapons, especially machine guns. It sets up limiting stakes to prevent friendly fire from hitting the assault element, especially when conducting an L-shaped ambush. The team also emplaces Claymores and other protective devices.

Communication

Your instructions to security teams must include how to notify you of the enemy's approach into the kill zone. The security element must also keep you informed if any enemy forces are following the lead force.

Dead space is any area in the kill zone that your elements cannot cover with direct fire. Such an area will afford the enemy some measure of cover and concealment. Consider the use of mines, indirect fires (such as mortars or artillery), or M203 grenade launchers to cover the dead space.

Critical Thinking

Would you initiate an ambush if there is a follow-on enemy unit?
Why or why not?

Note:
Recall the lesson on patrolling. Your initial patrol planning must address how the patrol leader will communicate (both primary and alternate methods) with all the elements during each phase of the ambush.

You must determine how large an element your ambush can engage successfully. (Recall the discussion in Section 8 of the requirement for a 3-to-1 advantage in combat power.) You must be prepared to let enemy units that are too large pass by. You must report to higher headquarters any units that pass your ambush that you did not engage.

Initiating the Ambush

The PL initiates the ambush. The Claymore is the preferred method to initiate the ambush. You must also plan a backup method for initiating the ambush should the primary means fail. This should also be a device that can produce mass casualties, such as a machine gun, squad automatic weapon (SAW), or demolition that you control. You rarely use indirect fires (mortars and artillery) to initiate ambushes, however, as it is too risky to get the proper time on target (TOT). All Soldiers must understand how you will initiate the ambush, and practice for it during rehearsals.

Note:
The Claymore mine is the preferred way to initiate an ambush. It detonates instantly and produces mass casualties with an impressively loud noise. You should not initiate ambushes by whistles, yells, or small arms, as this does not provide "shock and awe" at initiation and will give the enemy time to react and defend themselves. The hand grenade is also a poor choice to initiate the ambush. The sound made by the spoon and ignitor is audible at 25 meters, and the fuse gives the enemy 8 seconds to react before the grenade detonates.

You must consider methods to engage the enemy in the kill zone during periods of limited visibility. You must balance the benefits of using tracers against the risk that doing so will help the enemy identify your positions. You may use handheld or indirect illumination flares, but must take precautions to ensure you illuminate the kill zone without illuminating yourself.

Light Discipline. When you are planning to use night vision goggles (NVGs), illumination, white light, or pointing devices (infrared or visible light) on the objective, consider the following:

- Control measures for disciplined use of pointing devices (e.g., limited to team leaders and above, machine gunners and assistant gunners, patrol leader). Your plan must consider both visible and IR pointers.

- Illumination, white light, or NVGs required by an assault element negotiating protective obstacles during movement across the objective.

- Continuous illumination, white light, or NVGs required by EPW teams to search EPWs or those killed in action (KIAs).

- The risk that enemy follow-on forces or a counterattack will be able to see you.

- Whether illumination will hinder the use of NVGs.

- "Tracers work both ways": You can use the enemy's tracers to identify his positions, but he can also use your tracers to identify your positions.

- The accuracy of illumination rounds and potential for illuminating friendly positions.

Indirect Fire

Part of your plan should include indirect fire support. You use indirect fires to neutralize, destroy, and suppress, as well as cover the flanks of the kill zone to help isolate it from follow-on forces and prevent the enemy from escaping the kill zone. They can also isolate the far side of the objective and cover and screen your unit's movement after actions on the objective. Indirect fires can also help the platoon disengage if the ambush is compromised or the platoon must depart the ambush site under pressure.

Signals

You must have a good plan to signal the advance of the assault element into the kill zone to begin its search and collection activities. The support element may not be able to see smoke. Consider using specific colors of flares or a timed event based on the initiation of the ambush. Although these are suitable signals, situations may arise where flares may not work and the timing of the mission may be off. Regardless of the signal used, all Soldiers must know the primary and alternate signals and practice relaying them during rehearsals.

Movement Speed and Security

The assault element must be prepared to move rapidly across the kill zone. The assault element uses speed as the best form of security, giving little time for any surviving enemy to recover from the initial shock of the surprise ambush. The most expeditious manner for the assault element to cross through the kill zone is to assault in a line formation. With this technique, the width of the kill zone is secured simultaneously. The line formation also reduces the chance of fratricide by keeping all Soldiers in the assault on line, not having any teams forward of another. In many cases, bounding half of the assault element through the kill zone will leave half of it unsecured, exposing the flank of the bounding half to enemy fire.

Aid and Litter Teams

Once at the LOA with the kill zone secured with a hasty perimeter, aid and litter teams assist friendly casualties first, then enemy wounded, time permitting. Search and secure all EPWs and move them out of the kill zone before searching dead enemy. Establish a location for EPWs and enemy wounded to be treated and processed in accordance with the "5 Ss" (search, silence, segregate, safeguard, and speed to the rear). Consider using the ambush release point as the EPW control point. Search from one side of the objective to the other and mark bodies that have been searched to ensure the area is thoroughly covered. (Remember to mark cleared bodies with a chalk mark or by folding arms over chest—or whatever other mark is easy to identify—so there is no duplication of effort. Include this as part of the rehearsal.)

Search Techniques

At a minimum, EPW teams will be two-Soldier teams (search and security). Adding a third Soldier as the recorder will speed up the search process. As the EPW team approaches the enemy soldier, the security Soldier positions at the enemy soldier's head and aims his or her weapon at the enemy's head. The searcher lies on top of the enemy soldier and issues the security warning "roll" or "rolling." Security acknowledges by repeating "roll" or "rolling." The searcher rolls the enemy in such a manner that security can see under the enemy. Security yells "clear" if there are no weapons, hand grenades, or clackers under the enemy. If security sees anything that could be a threat, the threat is announced ("grenade," "knife," "pistol") and the searcher reacts to the threat. For example, if security announces "grenade," the searcher rolls the enemy back onto the device in order to use the enemy body to shield the blast. If the threat under the enemy is not an exploding device, the EPW team disarms the enemy or, if the enemy resists, applies deadly force in accordance with the published rules of engagement.

The searchers then conduct a systematic search of the enemy soldier from head to toe for established commander's PIR items (maps, radio frequencies, **signal operating instructions (SOI),** orders, etc.). PIR items are recorded and retained. All other items are collected and delivered to the demolition site. The search team continues in this manner until all enemy personnel in and near the kill zone have been searched, all KIAs have been marked, and all EPWs have been secured.

Actions Before Departing

The patrol identifies and collects PIR to carry back. It also identifies and collects weapons and equipment for destruction. The demolition team prepares dual-primed explosives (C4 with two M80 fuse igniters and time fuse) and awaits the signal to ignite. This is normally the last action a patrol performs before departing the objective. The patrol also moves EPWs to the collection point and moves any wounded to the MEDEVAC pickup zone.

If a flank security team makes contact, it fights as long as possible without becoming decisively engaged. It uses a prearranged signal to let you know it is breaking contact and moving back to the release point. You may direct a portion of the support element to assist the security team in breaking contact.

Withdrawal

It is your job as platoon leader to plan the withdrawal from the ambush site. Normally, elements withdraw in the reverse order that they established their positions. This allows for the security elements to cover the main body's withdrawal. The elements may return first to the release point, then to the ORP, depending upon the distance between elements and the distance and direction to the ORP. If you leave security at the ORP, the security element at the ORP must be alert to assist the platoon's return. It maintains security for the ORP while the rest of the platoon consolidates and prepares to depart the ORP.

A thorough search of enemy EPWs and KIAs is vital to your higher headquarters' intelligence-gathering efforts. Information found on the objective will better enable commanders to plan future operations.

signal operating instructions (SOI)

unit daily frequencies, call signs, and passwords used by members in the unit

Critical Thinking

When would you not leave security in the ORP and why not?

Note:

Consider the necessary control measures for Soldiers returning to the ORP during hours of limited visibility (such as IR lights, luminous tape, etc.).

Once you have returned to the ORP, you recover rucksacks and other equipment left at the ORP during the ambush and report to higher command (CCIR, SALUTE, LACE).

Area Ambush

In an area ambush, the patrol conducts two or more related point ambushes. A platoon is the smallest unit that conducts an area ambush. Your platoon will conduct area ambushes when enemy movement is largely restricted to trails or streams (Figure 12.3). You should select one principal ambush site around which you organize outlying ambushes. These secondary sites are located along the enemy's most likely approach to and escape from the principal ambush site. Squad-sized elements are normally responsible for each ambush site. Each element establishes a point ambush as described above. Squads responsible for outlying ambushes do not initiate their ambushes until after the principal one is initiated.

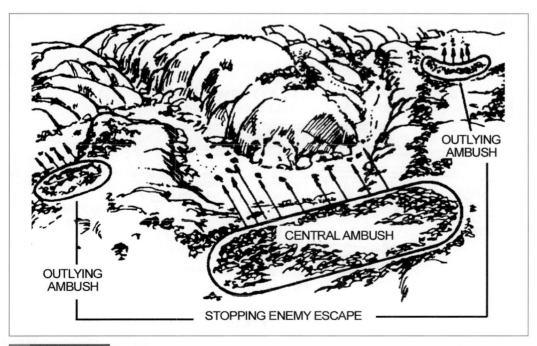

Figure 12.3 Area Ambush

Critical Thinking

Why is the platoon the smallest element that can conduct an area ambush?

They then engage to prevent enemy forces from escaping or reinforcing. You must determine the best employment of your machine guns. You normally position them both with the support element of the principal ambush site.

Ambush Formations

Units conduct ambushes using one of two formations: the *linear* formation and the *L-shaped* formation.

Linear Ambush

In an ambush using a linear formation, the assault and support elements deploy parallel to the enemy's route (Figure 12.4). This positions both elements on the long axis of the kill zone and subjects the enemy to enfilading fire. You can use this formation in close

Critical Thinking

In a linear ambush, you position both the assault and support elements parallel to the kill zone. How would you position your support element in relation to your assault element? How would you position your machine guns in order to have both interlocking and enfilading fires? Would you task organize a squad or fire team to be the support element?

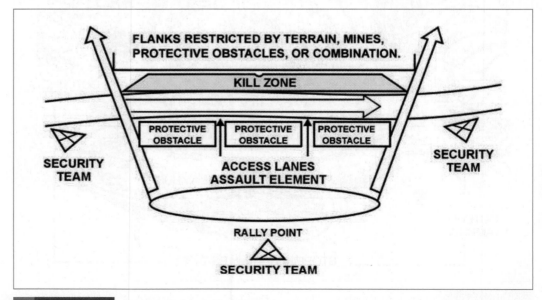

Figure 12.4 Linear Ambush Formation

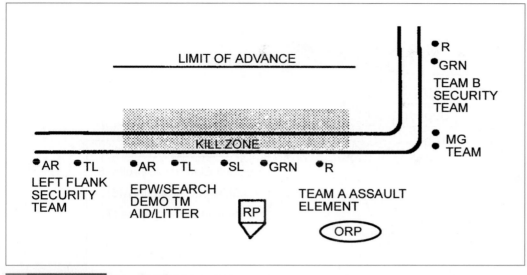

Figure 12.5 L-shaped Ambush Formation

terrain that restricts the enemy's ability to maneuver against the platoon, or in open terrain provided you have a way to keep the enemy in the kill zone.

L-Shaped

In an L-shaped ambush, the assault element forms the long leg parallel to the enemy's direction of movement along the kill zone. The support element forms the short leg at one end of and at right angles to the assault element. This provides both flanking fires (long leg) and **enfilade fires** (short leg) against the enemy. You can use the L-shaped ambush at a sharp bend in a trail, road, or stream. You should use it where the short leg would have to cross a straight road or trail (Figure 12.5).

enfilade fires

fires delivered on the broad side of a target, so that the range pattern of the fall of shot generally aligns with the long axis of the target

Leader Actions in the Ambush

The PL completes the plan for the ambush in the ORP. You prepare to conduct a leader's recon; designate the members of the leader's recon party (typically including element leaders, the surveillance team, or security element, and the RTO/FO); and issue a contingency plan to the assistant patrol leader (APL).

Critical Thinking

You are conducting a deliberate ambush on a road or trail. The leader's recon is complete and you have left and right flank security in place. You are ready to emplace the security and assault elements into the ambush site. Do you require a surveillance team to observe the kill zone while your security and assault elements move into position? Why or why not?

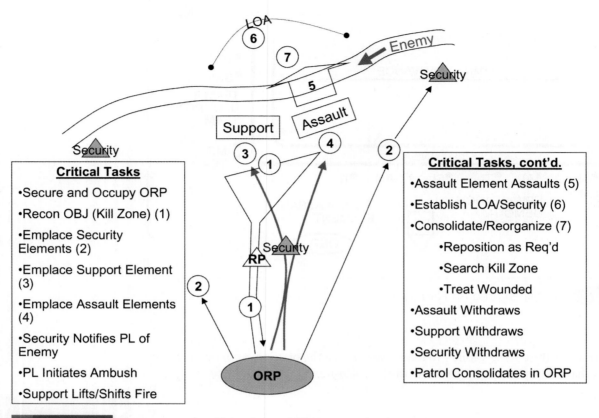

Figure 12.6 Actions on the Objective—Deliberate Ambush

You then conduct your leader's recon, ensuring that the recon party moves undetected. You confirm the objective's location and suitability for the ambush; post a surveillance team at the site, and issue a contingency plan. You also select a kill zone, and confirm the suitability of assault and support positions. You identify a release point (RP), routes from element positions to the RP, and locations for targets, mines, and collection points.

You then return to the ORP, adjust your plan, and decide on necessary control measures based on info from the recon.

At this point, you confirm the ambush formation. If you did not emplace them during the leader's recon of the objective, the security teams occupy first, securing the flanks of the ambush site provide early warning. The security element must be in position before the support and assault elements move forward from the release point. A security team remains in the ORP if the patrol plans to return to the ORP after actions on the objective. The support element leader assigns sectors of fire. Once the support element is in position, the PL leads the assault element from the RP into the assault position. The assault element uses line formation when occupying the assault position.

The security element identifies the enemy and notifies the PL, reporting the speed and direction of movement, size, any special weapons or equipment carried, positions of key leaders, traveling technique, movement formation, and dispersion. The security element must also keep you informed if any enemy forces are following the lead force. You alert other elements and determine if the enemy force is too large, or if your ambush can engage successfully. You usually do this by a preplanned code word for ambush. You initiate the ambush and conduct actions on the objective (Figure 12.6—Deliberate Ambush and Figure 12.7—Hasty Ambush).

A good SOP will help you assign and direct special teams on the objective.

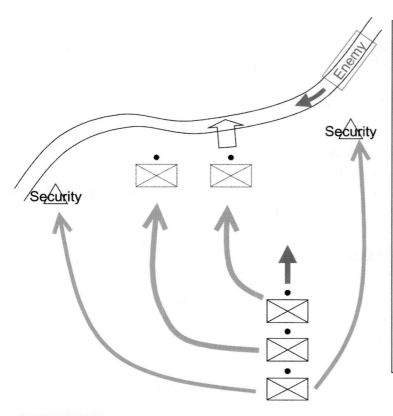

Critical Tasks

•Patrol detects an enemy unit; PL is notified

•Patrol halts and remains motionless

•PL gives signal for hasty ambush

•PL directs elements to covered and concealed positions

•Security elements move to flanks of patrol

•PL establishes control measures

•PL initiates and controls ambush

•PL directs a hasty search

•Patrol consolidates, reorganizes, withdraws, reports, and continues mission

| **Figure 12.7** | Actions on the Objective—Hasty Ambush |

After the ambush, you direct the unit's withdrawal from the ambush site. You disseminate information, or move the platoon to a safe location (no less than one kilometer or one terrain feature away from the objective) and then disseminate information. As required, the PL and forward observer (FO) execute indirect fires to cover the platoon's withdrawal from the area of operation (AO).

Critical Thinking

Recall that you must have direct control over both the primary and alternate most-casualty-producing weapons when initiating the ambush. In most cases, these are your Claymores, SAWs, or machine guns. How can you position these weapons or yourself to ensure that you have direct control when initiating the ambush?

CONCLUSION

By its very nature, an ambush is perhaps the most violent and lethal of all military operations. If properly executed, the amount of damage—physically *and* emotionally—that an ambush can do is remarkable. Understanding how to plan and execute different types of ambush will also help you survive if the tables are turned and your platoon finds itself caught in an enemy ambush.

Learning Assessment

1. Describe the terrain in which you would use a linear ambush or an L-shaped ambush.

2. What is the best method for initiating an ambush? Why? What are alternate means of initiation?

3. How do the planning considerations for an ambush differ from that of an attack? How do they differ between deliberate and hasty ambushes?

Key Words

kill zone
Claymore
isolate
limit of advance (LOA)
signal operating instructions (SOI)
enfilade fire

References

Department of the Army. (1970). *Vietnam Interview 242*. 22nd Military History Department, 101 Airborne (Airmobile). San Francisco, CA. Retrieved 18 April 2005 from http://www.army.mil/cmh-pg/documents/vietnam/vni/242.htm

Field Manual 3-21.8, *The Infantry Rifle Platoon and Squad*. 28 March 2007.

Field Manual 5-0, *Army Planning and Order Production*. 20 January 2005.

Field Manual 7-85, *Ranger Unit Operations*. 9 June 1987.

SH 21-76, *US Army Ranger Handbook*. July 2006.

SQUAD TACTICS: ATTACK

Key Points

Go forward until the last round is fired and the last drop of gas is expended . . . then go forward on foot!

GEN George S. Patton

Introduction

Successful attack depends on concentrating as much shock and violence against the enemy force as possible. The objective is to shatter the enemy unit's nerve, ruin its synchronization, unravel its plan, and destroy the unit's cohesion and the willingness of its soldiers to fight. A successful attack combines a scheme of maneuver with a coordinated plan of direct and indirect fire support. The focus of an attacking platoon's fire and maneuver is an enemy's weak point, a vulnerable flank, or rear. Once you as a platoon leader have identified the point of attack, you establish a base of fire to kill, fix, or suppress the enemy at that point. You then maneuver the rest of your force to a position from which it can assault.

CPT Arlo L. Olson Leads the Way in Italy

CPT Arlo L. Olson served with the US Army's 15th Infantry, 3rd Infantry Division. On 13 October 1943, his company spearheaded the advance across the Volturno River, south of Rome, Italy, driving 30 miles through mountainous enemy territory in 13 days.

Placing himself at the head of his men, CPT Olson waded into the chest-deep water of the raging Volturno River, and despite pointblank machine-gun fire aimed directly at him, made his way to the opposite bank and threw two hand grenades into the gun position, killing the crew. When an enemy machine gun 150 yards away opened fire on his company, CPT Olson advanced upon the position in a slow, deliberate walk. Although five German Soldiers threw hand grenades at him from a range of five yards, Capt. Olson dispatched them all, picked up a machine pistol, and continued toward the enemy. Advancing to within 15 yards of the position he shot it out with the foe, killing nine and seizing the post.

Throughout the next 13 days CPT Olson led combat patrols, acted as the company's No. 1 scout, and maintained unbroken contact with the enemy. On 27 October 1943, CPT Olson conducted a platoon in attack on a strongpoint, crawling to within 25 yards of the enemy and then charging the position. Despite continuous machine gun fire that barely missed him, CPT Olson made his way to the gun and killed the crew with his pistol. When the men saw their leader make this desperate attack, they followed him and overran the position. Continuing the advance, CPT Olson led his company to the next objective at the summit of Monte San Nicola. Although the company to his right was forced to take cover from the furious automatic and small arms fire, which was directed upon him and his men with equal intensity, CPT Olson waved his company into a skirmish line, and despite the fire of a machine gun that singled him out as its sole target, led the assault which drove the enemy away. While making a reconnaissance for defensive positions, CPT Olson was fatally wounded. Ignoring his severe pain, this intrepid officer completed his reconnaissance, supervised the location of his men in the best defense positions, refused medical aid until all of his men had been cared for, and died as he was being carried down the mountain.

For conspicuous gallantry and intrepidity at the risk of his life above and beyond the call of duty, CPT Olson was awarded the Medal of Honor.

Hyperwar

Types of Attack

An attack is an offensive operation that destroys or defeats enemy forces, seizes and secures terrain, or both. It can be a decisive operation or one that shapes the battlefield for later operations. Attacks incorporate coordinated movement supported by direct and indirect fires. They may be *hasty* or *deliberate,* depending on the time available for assessing the situation, planning, and preparing. Commanders execute hasty attacks when the situation calls for immediate action with available forces and minimal preparation. They conduct deliberate attacks when there is time to develop plans and coordinate preparations. The same fundamentals of the offense—surprise, concentration, tempo, and audacity—apply to each type of attack. Success depends on skillfully massing the effects of combat power.

Hasty Attack

Commanders order hasty attacks to seize opportunities to destroy the enemy or take the initiative. These opportunities are fleeting. They usually occur during movement to contact and defensive operations. In a hasty attack, commanders intentionally trade the advantages of thorough preparation and full synchronization for those of immediate execution. In a movement to contact, commanders launch hasty attacks to destroy enemy forces before they concentrate or establish a defense. In the defense, commanders direct hasty attacks to destroy an exposed or overextended attacker.

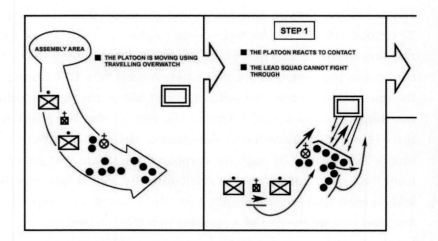

Critical Thinking

Compare the principles of the offense with the desired outcome of the defender.

Once they decide to attack, commanders execute as quickly as possible. While hasty attacks maximize the effects of agility and surprise, they incur the risk of losing some synchronization. To minimize this risk, commanders make maximum use of standing operating procedures (SOPs) that include standard formations and well-understood and rehearsed battle drills.

Deliberate Attack

In contrast to hasty attacks, deliberate attacks are highly synchronized operations characterized by detailed planning and preparation. Deliberate attacks use simultaneous operations throughout the area of operations (AO), planned fires, shaping operations, and forward positioning of resources needed to sustain the attack's momentum. Commanders take the time necessary to position forces and develop sufficient intelligence to strike the enemy with bold maneuver and accurate, annihilating fires. Because of the time required to plan and prepare deliberate attacks, commanders often begin them from a defensive posture. Time spent preparing a deliberate attack may allow the enemy to improve defenses, retire, or launch a spoiling attack. Therefore, commanders direct deliberate attacks only when they cannot bypass or overcome the enemy with a hasty attack.

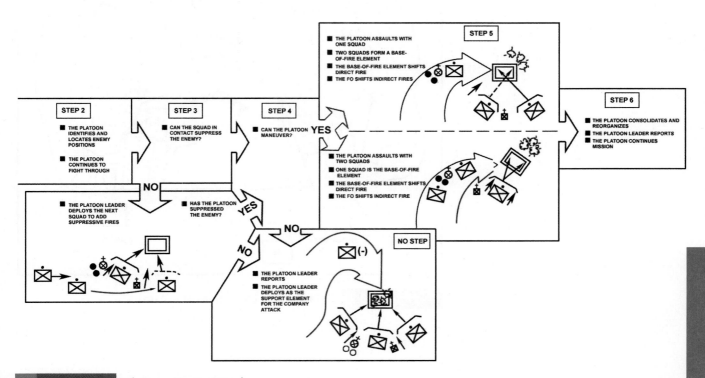

Figure 13.1   Platoon Hasty Attack

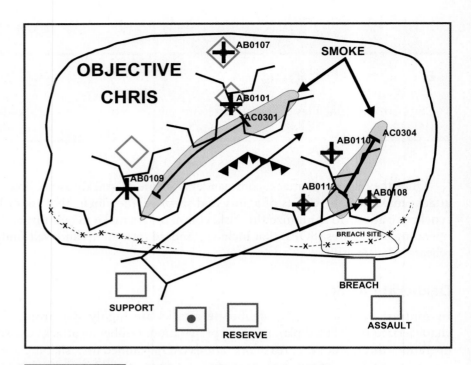

Figure 13.2 Attack of an Objective: The Breach

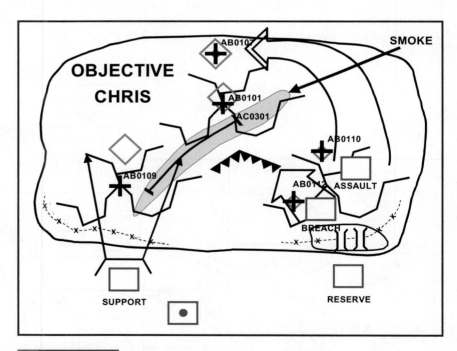

Figure 13.3 Attack of an Objective: The Assault

Initial Considerations

When the commander decides to attack or the opportunity to attack occurs during combat operations, the execution of that attack must mass the effects of overwhelming combat power against selected portions of the enemy force with a tempo and intensity that the enemy cannot match. The resulting combat should *not* be a contest between near equals. The attackers must be determined to seek decision on the ground of their choosing through the deliberate synchronization and employment of their combined-arms team. Platoons consider an attack most favorable when they enjoy a 3-to-1 advantage—not in terms of Soldiers, but in total combat power. Due to the technological and tactical superiority that the US military has over its enemies, an element smaller than a platoon can often achieve a 3-to-1 combat power advantage over a larger enemy force.

Planning Considerations

Platoons and squads conduct deliberate attacks as part of a larger force. You as a platoon leader use the troop leading procedures and the estimate of the situation to develop a plan.

Task Organizing for the Deliberate Attack

The platoon attack has three elements: the *assault* element, the *support* element, and the *breach* element. Larger units can also designate a *reserve* element. The support element provides supportive fires onto the objective to destroy or suppress the enemy and allow the breach element and the assault element freedom to maneuver. The assault element maneuvers to the enemy in order to destroy enemy personnel and/or equipment. If used or required, the reserve element gives the maneuver commander flexibility and freedom of movement during the attack. The reserve element can be used to support or reinforce either the support or assault element.

In a company attack, the company commander will task organize the platoons into assault, support, and reserve elements based on mission analysis and METT-TC. In a platoon attack, the platoon leader will task organize the squads in the same manner. As a general planning consideration, more forces are needed to assault than to conduct the **support by fire** (SBF) mission. It is generally best to assault with light weapons rather than with crew-served weapons and machine guns. Your final decision on how to task organize for the attack, however, is ultimately based on your mission analysis and METT-TC.

Consider a scenario in which your platoon is conducting a platoon deliberate attack on two enemy squads defending high ground. Your platoon has its three **organic** squads and two company M240 machine guns (MG TMs) assigned to your platoon for the mission. You have several options for task organizing your squads:

Assault: 1st Squad, 2nd Squad
Breach: 3rd Squad
Support: MG Team 1 and Team 2

Assault: 1st Squad, 2nd Squad
Breach: A Team, 3rd Squad
Support: B Team, 3rd Squad; MG Team 1 and Team 2

In addition to the above possible task organization options, you can also consider **cross attaching** your assault element's squad automatic weapons (SAW) gunners to the support element to give the support element more supporting fires. Likewise, you could cross attach your riflemen from the support element to the assault element to give the assault element more agility.

> **support by fire (SBF)**
>
> *a tactical mission task in which a maneuver force moves to a position where it can engage the enemy by direct fire in support of another maneuvering force*

> **organic**
>
> *personnel or equipment assigned to and forming an essential part of a military organization— Soldiers and equipment that are organic to a unit belong to that unit and are not attached or detailed from another unit*

> **cross attach**
>
> *the exchange of personnel, weapon systems, or units between units for a temporary period*

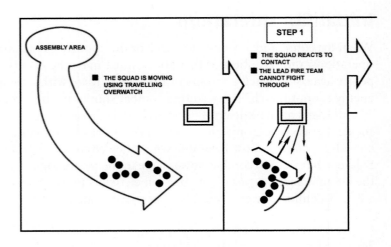

If the company commander's concept calls for decentralized execution to platoon level, you must consider your objective, the enemy's vulnerable flank or exploitable weakness, routes, movement, fire-control measures, and formations and movement techniques. The platoon leader considers these along with METT-TC and the commander's intent to develop a scheme of maneuver and a fire-support plan.

Movement to the Objective

Platoons and squads use the appropriate formations and movement techniques to avoid contact with the enemy and achieve surprise. The enemy must not detect your platoon. If the enemy detects you early, your platoon concentrates direct and indirect fires, establishes a base of fire, and maneuvers to regain the initiative.

Movement from the FOB or AA to LD

line of departure (LD)

a line designated to coordinate the departure of attack elements; a phase line crossed at a prescribed time by troops initiating an offensive operation

attack position

the last position occupied by the assault echelon before crossing the line of departure

In a company attack, the platoon moves under company control. If the platoon leader is forward with the company commander (such as on a leader's recon, or coordinating departure and reentry of friendly lines), the platoon sergeant will move the platoon forward to the **line of departure** (LD). During the leader's recon or rehearsal, leaders time the move from the forward operating base (FOB) or assembly area (AA) to the LD to ensure the lead element crosses the LD at the correct time and location. In order to maintain speed and tempo, it is best to try to cross the LD without stopping in an attack position. If you must make last-minute checks or coordination, then plan to do so while in the **attack position**, before you cross the LD. From the attack position, you will deploy to your formation and maneuver technique and cross the LD quickly using the best covered and concealed route you identified during your recon and terrain analysis.

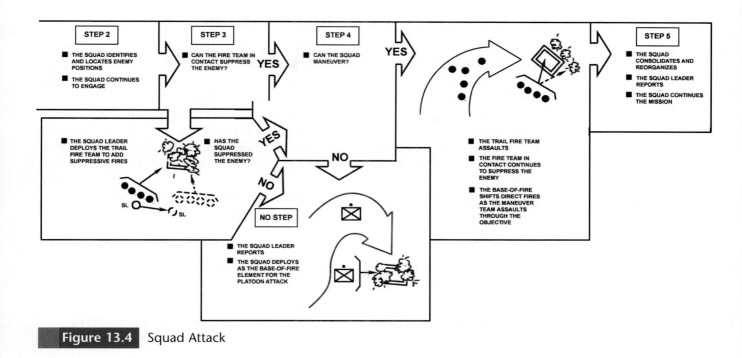

Figure 13.4 Squad Attack

Movement from the LD to the Assault and Support Positions

You will move along your selected route to your pre-designated operation rally point (ORP). Depending on METT-TC, you will probably need to establish an ORP and conduct a leader's recon to emplace a surveillance team, security teams, identify the release point (RP), the SBF position, and the **assault position**. Establishing the ORP allows you to return from the leader's recon and distribute any changes to your original plan. In some cases, your intelligence, planning, recon, and rehearsals may result in simply hitting a pre-determined release point and deploying each element to its respective security, SBF, and assault positions. This technique can also be used if you are running late. One of the most important things you must confirm is the assault element's route to the objective. It is critical that you identify any existing or reinforcing obstacles that will increase the time it takes to cross the distance between the assault position and the objective. Knowing what obstacles you will encounter also helps you decide whether it is necessary to identify and use a **breach** element and what breaching equipment to take with you for actions on the objectives.

You must also consider when to initiate your supporting fires:

- **Surprise.** If the attack is not detected, the SBF position may hold fires until the assault element approaches the assault position. This will enhance surprise. The SBF position may also initiate fires early to keep the enemy's attention off the assault element as it moves to a flanking or ready position.

- **Suppression.** You must consider the length of time needed to suppress the enemy position and destroy as many of his weapons and bunkers as possible before beginning the assault.

assault position

a covered and concealed position short of the objective, from which final preparations are made to assault the objective

breach

a tactical mission task in which the unit employs all available means to break through or secure a passage through an enemy defense, obstacle, minefield, or fortification

Movement from the Assault Position to the Objective

You must coordinate the movement of your support and assault elements so that the support element is in place and has good observation and fields of fire onto the objective before the assault element reaches its assault position. This is important in the event the assault element encounters an enemy LP/OP or enemy R&S team on patrol. If the assault element makes contact before the attack is initiated, chances are you will execute the attack as planned. For this reason, the support element must be in position to lay down suppressive fires on the objective. You as platoon leader will always lead the assault element; the platoon sergeant (APL) controls the support element. You place the assault element in a line formation (not on line) and await the pre-planned time to begin, or give the platoon sergeant the signal to initiate fires on the objective. Upon hearing the support element's fires, you move the assault element toward the objective.

Note:

If you are conducting the attack during limited visibility or using smoke, and the cover and concealment to the objective benefits the assault element, there is no need to immediately begin individual maneuvering techniques (IMT) or buddy team or team bounding as you move toward the objective. It is best to move quickly, maintaining the line formation in order to maintain surprise and speed.

Once the enemy identifies the assault element, or the assault element begins to receive aimed or effective fires, then the assault element must begin bounding by fire teams and individual movement techniques (IMT).

How do you plan for how much ammo the support element will need for the attack? The amount the support element requires depends on several factors. But only one of these factors directly relates to the support element itself—controlling its rate of fire. The other factors concern the assault element. These include the effects of OAKOC on the assault element's approach to the objective and the technical and physical capabilities of the Soldiers in the assault element and the speed and effectiveness of the breaching team. During the leader's recon, you must gather as much information as possible on the objective, terrain and existing and reinforcing obstacles. Then you must plan, rehearse, and time the assault element's ability to cross the terrain and obstacles. It is one thing for your assault element to make it to the objective; it is another for them to have enough stamina left to fight through to the LOA. Do not select an assault position that is so far from the objective that your Soldiers are exhausted upon reaching the objective. After you gain an understanding of the best location for the assault position and the time it will take to breach obstacles and cross the distance to the objective, you must consider the support element's sustained rate of fire. You then calculate how much ammo the support element will require to maintain that sustained rate of fire long enough for the assault element to assault through the objective. If you do not properly analyze and plan, you risk having the support element run out of ammo before the assault element reaches the objective.

Note:

The assault and breach elements should avoid halting on the assault position, because it may cause the loss of tempo.

Assaulting the Objective

As the assault element breaches the final protective obstacles of the enemy's defenses and is prepared to move across the objective, you signal the platoon sergeant to shift the supporting fires away from the advance of the assault element and toward and beyond the limit of advance (LOA). You assault the objective using your pre-planned control measures to ensure the entire objective is secured without fratricide. You might have tasked each squad in the assault element to clear the objective using the clock method, or you might have given each squad a sector of the objective. Each squad leader must assign the team leaders specific targets or objectives within the squad's assigned sector. Teams cover each other's movement through the objective. Fires must be accurate to prevent hitting other squads or teams operating near or next to the squad's sector. Each Soldier of the assault element must actively seek and destroy any enemy on the objective who continue to fight. Soldiers will not kill those enemies attempting to surrender, but must immediately take actions to disarm and secure them. When fighting has ceased, the objective has been declared secure, or the assault element has reached the LOA, you signal for the platoon sergeant to lift fires, reposition the support element to seal the objective, and consolidate on the objective to form a hasty perimeter with the assault element.

Actions on the Objective/Consolidate and Reorganize

The platoon conducts actions on the objective, consolidates, and reorganizes in a manner nearly identical to the ambush and raid. In the attack, however, you do not immediately withdraw from the objective as in a raid or ambush—you defend the ground until you receive a FRAGO, WARNO, or OPORD ordering you otherwise. Since you will remain on the objective to defend it, you must remember to plan for and send a detail to retrieve the platoon's rucksacks and equipment left in the ORP. Your company commander's OPORD will identify your platoon's task to defend the ground you just seized by either giving you a "Be prepared to defend . . ." mission or task, or an "On order, defend . . ." mission or task. Your company commander will write this in Paragraph 3 (Mission) of the OPORD, or in Paragraph 3 (Task to Maneuver Units) of the OPORD. If your task is "Be prepared to defend . . . ," then your platoon OPORD will include detailed plans to immediately defend after the attack, to include carrying all necessary supplies and equipment to conduct a defense on the objective. If your task is "On order, defend the objective . . . ," you will only conduct a deliberate defense if you receive a FRAGO.

CONCLUSION

The pace of combat does not always allow for well-designed and perfectly rehearsed plans. Often, the nature of intelligence requires *immediate* action. Some of the best intelligence comes from informants. To wait too long will be to have missed the window of opportunity for mission success. Understanding the fundamentals of the attack will allow you and your platoon to develop a quick plan or establish routines (SOPs) that will help you conduct hasty or deliberate attacks. Additionally, in armed conflict against insurgent guerrilla forces, you must take full advantage of every opportunity to close with and destroy the enemy. You will not be able to take a defensive position against these forces and expect to remain victorious. Success will depend on how quickly you and your forces can organize and execute the attack.

Learning Assessment

1. Consider the differences between deliberate and hasty attacks. What factors distinguish the two types of attack from each other?
2. What lessons from CPT Olson's actions in Italy during World War II apply to your platoon in the nonlinear contemporary operating environment?
3. What factors of METT-TC can affect your decision on how to task organize your platoon to conduct an attack?

Key Words

support by fire (SBF)
organic
cross attach
line of departure (LD)
attack position
assault position
breach

References

Clancy, P. (Ed.) (n.d.). HyperWar: A Hypertext History of the Second World War. *World War II Medal of Honor Recipients*. HyperWar Foundation. Retrieved 15 April 2005 from http://www.ibiblio.org/hyperwar/MoH_K-O.html

Field Manual 3-0, *Operations*. 27 February 2008.

Field Manual 3-21.8, *The Infantry Rifle Platoon and Squad*. 28 March 2007.

Field Manual 3-90, *Tactics*. 4 July 2001.

SQUAD TACTICS: DEFENSE

Key Points

1 Defensive Operations

2 Conduct of the Defense

3 Preparing the Defense

4 Fire-Control Measures

The best form of defense is attack.

Karl von Clausewitz

Introduction

The US Army is an offensively oriented force. It conducts defensive operations only long enough to plan offensive operations to regain the initiative. In the current operating environment, military operations are decentralized down to the level of maneuver teams and squads. Military leaders at all levels must understand how to plan, coordinate, and execute the defense so they can quickly regroup and take the fight back to the enemy.

Rangers Defending in Mogadishu

By this time, we were receiving extremely heavy fire from the north and the west. I watched helplessly from across the street as four more of my Soldiers were wounded within four minutes. They were all pulled to safety into a courtyard directly across the street from my location. I then radioed CPT Steele and informed him that I had two critically wounded and only three able bodies left in my chalk, including myself.

CPT Steele then told me that we had become separated from the ground reaction force and that they were unable to find our location. To make matters worse, the ground reaction force was also under heavy fire and breaking contact to bring their wounded and the prisoners back to the airfield. I looked down at my watch; it was 1730 hours. We had been on the ground for two hours and it was getting dark fast. . . .

By this time, all of our forces were secure in four different locations near the crash site. We ensured that every alleyway leading to our positions was covered by someone and I felt fairly confident that we could hold out until some form of relief force could arrive to get us and help pull Chief Wolcott's body out.

LT Larry Perino

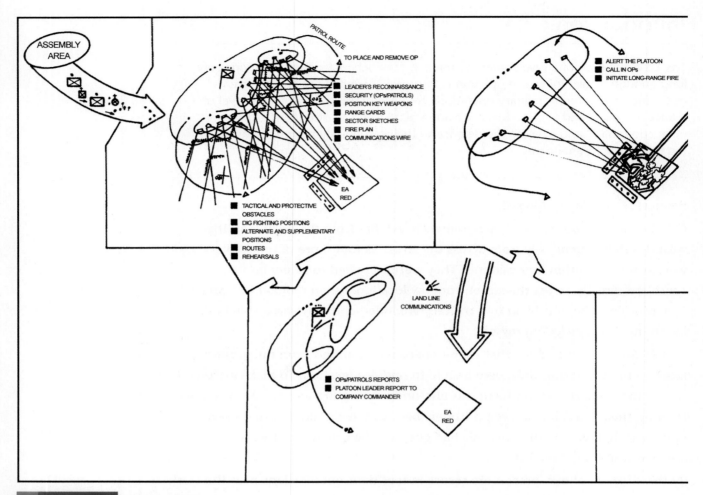

Figure 14.1 Platoon Defense

Defensive Operations

Defensive operations defeat an enemy attack, buy time, economize forces, or develop conditions favorable for offensive operations. Defensive operations alone normally cannot achieve a decision. Their purpose is to create conditions for a counteroffensive that allows friendly forces to regain the initiative. Other reasons for conducting defensive operations include:

- Retaining decisive terrain or denying a vital area to the enemy
- Attritting (i.e., destroying or thinning out) or fixing the enemy as a prelude to offensive operations
- Increasing enemies' vulnerability by forcing them to concentrate their forces.

While offense is the most decisive type of combat operation, defense is the stronger type. The inherent strengths of the defense include the defender's ability to occupy positions before the attack and use the available time to prepare defenses. Defenders constantly improve their defensive posture and end only when they decide to retreat or begin to fight. Defenders can study the ground and select defensive positions that mass the effects of their fires on likely avenues of approach. They combine existing and reinforcing obstacles to canalize (channel) the attacking force into their **engagement areas** (EAs). They can coordinate and rehearse their defensive plan while gaining familiarity with the terrain. Defenders do not wait passively for the attack. They aggressively seek ways to attrit and

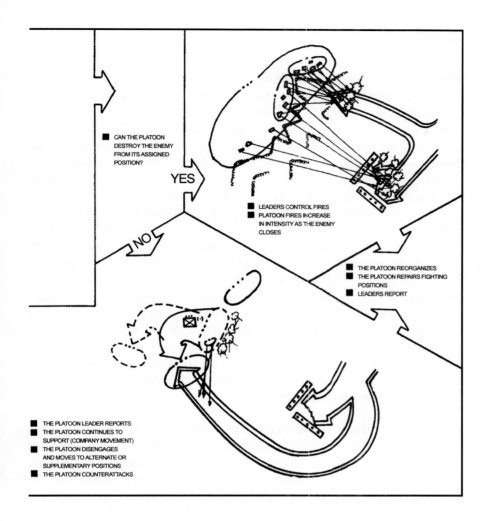

weaken attacking enemy forces before the enemy attack begins. They maneuver to place the enemy in a position of disadvantage and attack them at every opportunity, using their direct and indirect fires. They contain the enemy while seeking every opportunity to move to the offense.

Conduct of the Defense

This section will explain the steps you must consider when conducting a small-unit defense. You will recognize most of the leader steps from your previous studies of terrain analysis, troop leading procedures (TLPs), and tactical orders. The leader's critical decision points that lead to the standard sequence of actions a platoon takes in defensive operations are shown in Figure 14.1. The standard sequence of actions is:

- Prepare for combat
- Move to defensive positions
- Establish defensive positions
- Locate the enemy
- Initiate contact/actions on enemy contact
- Fight the defense
- Reorganize.

Prepare for Combat

The leader applies the same TLPs to the defense as to all military operations. But each military operation has its own unique planning and coordinating considerations. The more familiar you become with defensive operations, the more intuitive you will become about what unique considerations you must plan and coordinate for the defense. As with all TLPs, defense begins when you receive the company warning order (WARNO) or operations order (OPORD) to go to the defense. In most cases, your company commander will call the platoon leaders to a central location to issue the company order. In today's fluid contemporary operating environment (COE), it is not unusual to receive the company order over secure radio. After you receive the order, you must make a quick mission analysis (METT-TC) of the company order so you can put together and issue your own WARNO to your platoon sergeant and squad leaders. This WARNO should not be lengthy or detailed. It should give all the particular information that your platoon requires to start the necessary defensive movement. Limit the information to those things that cannot wait or must be completed before you issue the OPORD. After the WARNO, your platoon sergeant will start and supervise the necessary movement so that you can conduct your leader's reconnaissance and complete the plan. There are many different tactics, techniques, and procedures (TTPs) and unit standing operating procedures (SOPs) on how to reconnoiter your defensive position. How and when you recon the platoon's defense position will depend on many factors, but mostly on the time available and the enemy situation. Generally, there are three methods to recon and occupy the defense: *conduct the leader's recon, send an advance party, or occupy the platoon defense by force.*

Leader's Recon. If time permits, it is best that the platoon leader conduct the leader's recon. You are responsible for ensuring that the platoon's sector of fire ties in with adjacent units' sectors of fire. To accomplish this, you must confirm each squad's sectors of fire. During the leader's recon, you must also analyze the effects of terrain (OAKOC) on the platoon's defensive operation. Most importantly, you must identify enemy avenues of approach and select the best terrain for observations, fields of fire, cover and concealment, and existing obstacles. You must determine whether the terrain affords the opportunity

to emplace reinforcing obstacles. Based on this terrain analysis, you adjust the squad's positions and sectors of fire as necessary before confirming the location of the platoon defense and left and right limits of fires.

Advance Party. You are responsible for whatever the platoon's defense achieves or fails to achieve. You should retain the task of selecting the squad's positions and sectors of fire for the platoon's defense. You should delegate this task only if time is short; in that case, you should give the task to the most competent squad leader. You must be able to clearly articulate to the NCO leading the advance party the task, purpose, and what is required. In many units, sending an NCO to lead the advance party is the norm because it saves time, allows you to focus on completing the plan, and allows the platoon sergeant to focus on supervising the platoon's implied tasks and priorities of work. The advance party NCO must be technically and tactically competent and should have experience in conducting advance party operations. In short, your advance party NCO must be as capable as you in understanding the effects of terrain, weather, and light data on the platoon's defense. If not, upon arriving at the platoon defense, you may have to reposition or reassign the squads' sectors and key weapon locations, resulting in wasted time and energy.

The advance party's leader establishes local security to allow freedom of maneuver so that he or she can identify and mark the left and right limits of each squad's defensive position and the location of the platoon command post (CP). This may require posting flank security, establishing listening and observation posts (LP/OPs), sending out one or more reconnaissance and security (R&S) patrols, or any combination thereof. As soon as the advance party's leader determines the suitability of the terrain to defend and identifies the left and right limits of squads' battle positions, he or she radios the platoon leader and confirms any changes. The leader of the advance party then establishes a guide to the rear of the defense to link up and guide the platoon into the defense. While the platoon moves to the defense, the advance party leader continues to identify and mark key locations such as routes to supply caches, water points, and latrines. When the platoon reaches the guide, the advance party leader guides the squad leaders to their respective battle positions and briefs you and the platoon sergeant on the other key locations identified and marked for the platoon.

You are responsible for confirming each squad position and the platoon CP. The platoon sergeant will confirm the location and routes to the supply and services areas of the platoon defense. This is why the competence and trust that you must share with the advance party NCO are so important. The advance party NCO must be on the "same sheet of music" with you, or you risk wasting a lot of valuable time. You also risk hurting your unit's morale, trust, and cohesiveness if you must undo all the advance party's work when you arrive at the platoon defense.

Occupy by Force. If time is short, or the enemy is quickly gaining the advantage, you may not have the time to conduct a thorough leader's recon or send out an advance party to occupy and start defense preparations. In situations like this, you must move quickly on the best covered and concealed route you have selected and occupy the proposed platoon defense ground by force—that is, you move cautiously but decisively onto the terrain and set up a hasty defense while you complete those steps that you would have taken during your leader's recon, or that the advance party would have completed. When occupying by force, it is especially important that you emplace security, establishing LP/OPs and sending out R&S patrols. Constructing such a defense is the challenge of the adaptive leader in a nonlinear, fluid COE.

Move to Defensive Positions

When taking up defensive positions, the platoon applies fundamentals of movement:

- Move on covered and concealed routes
- Avoid likely ambush sites
- Enforce discipline over camouflage, noise, and light
- Maintain all-round security, including air guards
- Use formations and movement techniques based on METT-TC.

Establish Defensive Positions

Tactical wire. This concertina-wire obstacle performs a separate function from wire used as a protective obstacle. Tactical wire ties in with your direct fire planning and is used along an FPL to help defeat advancing forces. This is why you set up your tactical wire on the friendly side of your FPL.

At this point, the platoon halts short of the defensive position in a covered and concealed location and establishes local security. You, your squad leaders, and a security team (minimum of two Soldiers) move forward to link up with the advance party team that is acting as the platoon's guide. The squad leaders return to the platoon and move their squads forward. If the platoon used an advance party, you begin conferring with the leader of the advance party while the squad leaders move their squads forward. You or the advance party leader guide the squad leaders to their squad battle positions. You identify the sectors of fire and **final protective fires** (FPFs) for each crew-served weapon and emplace the weapon and crew. The platoon begins priorities of work.

Additionally, the platoon leader:

final protective fires (FPF)

an immediately available prearranged barrier of fire designed to impede enemy movement across defensive lines or areas

- Walks forward of positions, if possible, to check camouflage and confirm dead space. The most important aspect of fighting positions is that the enemy cannot observe them until it is too late.
- Checks on wire and mine teams. The platoon leader ensures that protective wire is outside of hand-grenade range from the fighting positions and *tactical wire* lies along the friendly side of the **final protective line** (FPL).
- Confers with the platoon sergeant on the logistics plan (including resupply and casualty-evacuation routes).

final protective line (FPL)

a selected line of fire where an enemy assault is to be checked by interlocking fire from all available weapons and obstacles

- Issues the finalized platoon order and checks Soldiers' knowledge and understanding. (All Soldiers must be aware of friendly units forward of the position—for example, patrols or scouts—and their return routes. They must also know the signals or conditions to initiate fire, shift fire, fire FPF, and cease fires, and to move to alternate and supplementary positions.)
- Compiles squad sector sketches and crew-served weapons' range cards and constructs a platoon sector sketch to give to the company commander.

Locate the Enemy

listening post/ observation post

a position from which military observations are made, or fire directed and adjusted, and which possesses appropriate communications—it may be airborne

The platoon establishes and maintains **listening posts/observation posts** (LP/OP) and conducts security patrols as the company commander directs. Patrols, OPs, and individual Soldiers look and listen. They use both day and night optics to detect the enemy's approach.

Action on Enemy Contact

Once the enemy is detected, you alert the squad leaders, platoon sergeant, and your forward observer and send a SALUTE (size, activity, location, unit, time, and equipment) report to your company commander. You call in any security patrols and must decide whether to leave the LP/OPs out or bring them into the defensive perimeter. If the LP/OPs will be protected from the platoon's direct and indirect fires, and can still effectively report on the enemy situation, you may decide to leave them in place.

Fight the Defense

The platoon leader engages the enemy as far out as possible using close air support (CAS) and the maximum effective range of indirect fires. You determine if the platoon can destroy the enemy from its assigned positions. If yes, the platoon continues to fight the defense. You mass fires and initiate them simultaneously to achieve surprise. Long-range fires tied in with obstacles will disrupt the enemy's tempo and attack formation. The platoon's obstacle plan will **canalize** the enemy into the platoon's organic-weapons engagement areas as the enemy advances. The obstacles will also prevent, or severely limit, the enemy's ability to observe the location of the platoon's defense. The platoon masses fires in order to destroy the enemy in the engagement area as the enemy attempts to breach or bypass the tactical obstacles.

The platoon uses pre-planned and rehearsed fire-control measures and signals such as standard commands, pyrotechnics, and other signals. The platoon increases the intensity of fires as the enemy closes within range of organic weapon systems. Squad leaders work to achieve a sustained rate of fire from their positions by having buddy teams fire their weapons so that both are not reloading them at the same time. Leaders control fires by determining the enemy's range, assigning priority targets (what to fire at, when to fire, and why), engaging the nearest or most dangerous targets first, shifting and concentrating their own fires in the absence of direction from higher command, ensuring the platoon engages the enemy with **grazing** or enfilading **fires**, and engaging enemy's flanks or rear.

If it appears that the enemy will breach your platoon's protective wire, you initiate final protective fires (FPF). When you call for FPF, machine gunners will move to and fire at their FPL and all other Soldiers will turn to and fire in their principal direction of fire (PDF). Grenadiers will cover the predesignated dead space along the platoon's FPL. Soldiers must blow all command-detonated mines that support your FPL. You must also remember to call for any and all pre-arranged CAS or indirect fires that support your FPL. Since you would only initiate the platoon's FPF if you were about to be overrun, you must call for all available fire assets. When the enemy is within hand-grenade range, Soldiers begin to throw hand grenades. If the enemy continues to gain ground, you must order "fix bayonets" and prepare to engage the enemy in hand-to-hand combat. The platoon continues to defend until the enemy is repelled or the platoon is ordered to disengage.

If you determine that the platoon cannot defeat the attacking enemy, you must report the situation to your company commander. Your commander will order you to initiate one or more actions, such as:

- Engage the enemy in the engagement area
- Reposition the platoon (or squads of the platoon) to occupy supplementary positions
- Fire or maneuver to reinforce other platoons in the company
- Counterattack locally to retake lost fighting positions
- Withdraw from an untenable position using fire and movement to break contact

You cannot move your platoon out of position without prior approval, or it will destroy the integrity of the entire company's defense.

Note:
In any movement out of a defensive position, the platoon MUST employ all direct and indirect fire available to suppress the enemy long enough for the unit to move. You must rehearse all movements and actions to reposition squads and platoons.

---

canalize

a tactical task used to restrict enemy operations to a narrow zone by the use of obstacles, fires, or unit maneuvering or positioning

grazing fire

fire approximately parallel to the ground, where the center of the cone of fire does not rise higher than one meter from the ground

***Smoke in the withdrawal.** If you must withdraw from your battle position under fire, your actions will be similar to the Break Contact battle drill. Consider the use of smoke and smoke operations from indirect fires to aid your withdrawal.*

Critical Thinking

Compare and contrast the characteristics of the defense with those characteristics of the offense.

Consolidate and Reorganize

When your platoon destroys the enemy or enemy resistance ceases as the result of a successful defense or platoon counterattack, you must first reestablish security, reman key weapons, and redistribute ammo. You must send out aid and litter teams to tend first to your wounded Soldiers and then to enemy casualties. You must also send out enemy-prisoner-of-war (EPW) teams to secure EPWs and record information on captured enemy and equipment. If you are to remain in the defense, you begin to reconstruct your defense as you did before the fight. You repair damaged obstacles; replace mines and booby traps; relocate key weapons if any were damaged; consider relocating selected weapons to alternate positions if you believe the enemy may have pinpointed them during the attack; adjust other positions to maintain mutual support; and reestablish communications. As with the conclusion of all actions, you must collect and forward ammunition, casualty, and equipment (LACE) and SALUTE reports to your commander. If you MEDEVAC a leader, you must reestablish the platoon chain of command. Your platoon sergeant will coordinate for resupply and supervise evacuation of casualties and EPWs. Your platoon continues to improve positions. The platoon quickly reestablishes OPs and resumes R&S patrolling as directed.

Preparing the Defense

Priority of Work

The platoon's *priority of work* is a list of tasks that you as the leader use to control who does what and in what order in preparing the defense. These tasks are normally set forth in the SOP. You adjust the priority of work based on your consideration of the factors of METT-TC and on your and your higher commander's intent. The platoon's normal priority of work is:

- Establish local security
- Position antiarmor weapons, machine guns, and squads, and assign sectors of fire
- Position other assets attached to the platoon
- Establish the CP and wire communications
- Designate FPLs and FPFs
- Clear fields of fire and prepare range cards and sector sketches
- Coordinate with adjacent units—left, right, forward, and to the rear
- Prepare primary fighting positions
- Emplace obstacles (such as concertina wire and ditches) and mines
- Mark or improve marking for target reference points (TRPs) and other fire-control measures
- Improve primary fighting positions such as overhead cover

- Prepare alternate positions, then supplementary positions
- Establish a sleep-and-rest plan
- Reconnoiter routes
- Rehearse engagements, disengagements, and any counterattack plans
- Adjust positions or control measures as required
- Stockpile ammunition, food, and water
- Dig trenches to connect positions
- Continue to improve positions

Coordination

Coordination between adjacent platoons/squads normally goes from left to right and from front to rear. The platoons exchange the following information:

- Locations of leaders
- Locations of primary, alternate, and supplementary positions and sectors of fire of machine guns, anti-armor weapons, and subunits
- Routes to alternate and supplementary positions
- Locations of dead space between platoons and squads and how to cover it
- Locations of OPs and their withdrawal routes to the platoon's or squad's position
- Locations and types of obstacles and how to cover them
- Patrols the platoon will conduct, including their size, type, lines of departure and return, and routes
- Locations, activities, and passage plans for scouts and other units forward of the platoon's position
- Signals for fire and cease-fire, and any other signals that may be observed
- Engagement and disengagement criteria

Weapons Emplacement

The success of the defense depends on where you position Soldiers and weapons. To position weapons effectively, you must know their characteristics, capabilities, and limitations, the effects of terrain and weather on them, and the enemy's tactics. You should position weapons where they have cover and concealment. Place them where they can avoid detection and surprise the enemy with accurate, lethal fires. In order to position the weapon, you must know where you want to destroy the enemy (engagement area) and what effect you want the weapon to achieve (suppress, attrit or destroy the enemy). Additionally, you must consider whether your primary threat will be armored vehicles or dismounted infantry. When the platoon must fight armored vehicles, you first position anti-armor weapons along the most likely armor avenue of approach. You must place the anti-armor weapons so the gunner has fields of fire on the enemy armor's flank or rear. You should also place the anti-armor weapon where the blast signature is hidden from enemy observation and there is enough backblast area to protect the gunner. When the primary threat is from dismounted troops, you should first position your machine guns on the most likely dismounted avenue of approach. Squad leaders position all other weapons to support these key weapons, cover dead space, and provide security. You must reflect back to the company intelligence officer's (S2's) intelligence on the enemy's most probable course of action and the enemy's most dangerous course of action, and apply these to your terrain analysis of your defense. You must then plan a defense that will defeat the enemy's most probable and dangerous courses of action.

Machine Guns

M240B (7.62-mm) and M249 (5.56-mm) machine guns are the platoon's primary weapons against a dismounted enemy. They provide a high volume of lethal, accurate fires to break up enemy assaults. They also provide limited effects against lightly armored vehicles and cause vehicle crews to button-up and operate with reduced effectiveness. You position machine guns to:

- Concentrate fires where you want to kill the enemy
- Fire across the platoon front
- Cover obstacles by fire
- Tie in sectors of fire with adjacent units' sectors of fire.

The following definitions apply to the use of machine guns:

- *Grazing fire.* Grazing fire occurs when the center of the cone of fire does not rise more than one meter (about waist high) above the ground. When a gun is firing over level or uniformly sloping terrain, it can obtain at most 600 meters of grazing fire.

- *Enfilading fire.* Enfilading fire is a type of engagement in which the beaten zone of the firing weapon (where the cone of fire falls) is on the long axis of the target being engaged. This usually occurs when the machine gunner engages the enemy from the oblique or flank.

- *Dead space.* Dead space is any area within the maximum effective range of a weapon, surveillance device, or observer that direct or indirect fire cannot observe or cover because of masking obstacles, the nature of the ground, the characteristics of ammo trajectory, or the limitations of the systems' pointing abilities. You must identify the dead space in your sector and determine how to use it to your advantage, deny its use to the enemy, or cover it with mines, booby traps, or pre-planned fires. You can emplace reinforcing obstacles to block or turn the enemy from entering the dead space, or to trap the enemy in the dead space to enable your direct and indirect fires or command-detonated mines to engage and destroy them. You must observe all dead space and obstacles and cover them with fires to be effective. If you place an OP or FO to observe an obstacle or dead space for another weapon or weapon system, you must plan for communication between the observer and the weapon system that will engage the obstacle or dead space.

- *Final protective line.* A final protective line (FPL) is a predetermined line along which you place grazing or enfilading fire to stop an enemy assault. Where terrain allows, you assign a machine gun an FPL. Once the gun is in position, one Soldier from the machine-gun team walks the FPL to identify both dead space and grazing fire along its length. The FPL and dead space are recorded on the machine gun's range card.

- *Principal direction of fire.* A principal direction of fire (PDF) is a priority direction of fire you assign to cover an area that provides good fields of fire or contains a likely avenue of approach. It is also used to provide mutual support to an adjacent unit. Weapons are laid on the PDF if an FPL cannot be assigned due to terrain. When other targets are not being engaged, weapons are laid on the PDF (if one is assigned).

Each weapon has a primary and secondary sector of fire. Their sectors of fire should overlap each other and those of adjacent units. Soldiers fire in their secondary sector only if there are no targets in the primary sector, or when a leader orders them to do so. Each weapon's primary sector includes an FPL or a PDF. The weapon is laid on the FPL or PDF unless it is engaging other targets. When FPFs are called for, the Soldier shifts to and engages on the FPL or PDF.

Antiarmor Weapons

The AT4 or Javelin are direct-fire, fire-and-forget antiarmor weapons that are organic to the rifle platoon—they are part of the platoon's normal armament. In some units these weapons are organic to weapons platoons at the company level. At times, the platoon may be supported by TOW (tube-launched, optically-tracked, wire-guided) antiarmor missiles. The gunner must track the TOW to target until impact. During antiarmor planning, you as the platoon leader consider the enemy vehicle threat and position antiarmor weapons accordingly to cover armor avenues of approach. You also consider each weapon's fields of fire, tracking time, and minimum arming ranges. You select a primary position and a sector of fire for each antiarmor weapon. You also pick supplementary positions for them. The antiarmor leader selects alternate positions. Each position should allow flank or rear fire and have cover and concealment. The leader can integrate the Javelin and TOW's thermal sights into a limited-visibility security-and-observation plan.

Grenade Launchers

The platoon's only organic indirect fire capability is the M203 grenade launcher. The squad leader identifies the dead space in the squad's sector and positions the M203 grenadier to cover the dead space. During the FPF, the M203's PDF is the dead space along the machine gun's FPL. The high-explosive, dual-purpose (HEDP) round is very effective against dismounted troops and can destroy light armored wheeled vehicles. The HEDP round can also diminish the abilities of armored attacks by destroying optics and forcing the driver, gunner, and tank commander to close their hatches.

The platoon leader should not rely on the M203 to attrit or interdict an armor attack.

photo credit to come

Rifles

Squad leaders assign positions and sectors of fire to each rifleman in the squad. Normally, they position the riflemen to support the machine guns and antiarmor weapons. They also position riflemen to cover obstacles, provide security, cover gaps between units, or observe. During the FPF, riflemen turn their weapons to their assigned PDF.

Defensive Positions

Classification of Defensive Positions

Defensive positions fall into three classifications: *primary, alternate,* or *supplementary.* All positions should provide observation and fields of fire within the weapon's or platoon's assigned sector. They should take advantage of natural cover and concealment even before Soldiers begin to camouflage them. Soldiers improve their ability to move to alternate or supplementary positions by using covered routes and communications trenches; by employing smoke; or by planning and rehearsing the repositioning by fire and maneuver (one team or squad providing covering fire while the other team or squad moves).

- *Primary.* A primary position is one that provides Soldiers, weapon crews, or units the best means to accomplish the assigned mission.

- *Alternate.* Alternate positions are those that allow Soldiers, weapon crews, or units to cover the same sector of fire as they do from the primary position. Soldiers occupy alternate positions when the primary position becomes untenable or unsuitable for carrying out their tasks. Soldiers may occupy alternate positions before an attack to rest, to perform maintenance, or to add the element of surprise to the defense.

- *Supplementary.* Supplementary positions are those that provide the best means to accomplish a task that cannot be accomplished from the primary or alternate positions. Platoon leaders normally locate supplementary positions to cover additional enemy avenues of approach and to protect the platoon's flanks and rear from enemy attacks.

Battle Positions

A *battle position* is a defensive location oriented on a likely enemy avenue of approach or engagement area. The battle position is a graphic that depicts the location and general orientation of most of the defending forces. A commander's use of a battle position does not direct the position of the subordinate's entire force within its bounds, since it is not an area of operation (AO). Units as large as battalion task forces and as small as squads or sections use battle positions. They may occupy the topographical crest of a hill, a forward slope, a **reverse slope,** or a combination of these areas. Your company commander will select platoon battle positions after conducting a detailed analysis of the enemy and the terrain. The commander identifies the enemy's most likely, probable, and dangerous avenues of approach and identifies engagement areas to destroy the enemy. The commander then selects the terrain that offers the best observations and fields of fires into the engagement areas. As a platoon leader, you will confirm the feasibility of your assigned platoon battle position and report any necessary changes of your platoon battle position to your commander for approval.

The battle position is indicated as a "goose egg" on the operation overlay and the perimeter of the "goose egg" is not exact. As a platoon leader, you have some latitude in determining the final location of your platoon's battle position. If, during your leader's

Reverse slope defense. This technique provides an additional element of surprise. An advancing enemy force would be unable to observe friendly battle positions until it is too late. The attackers, however, would have the benefit of attacking downhill.

reverse slope

any slope that descends away from the enemy

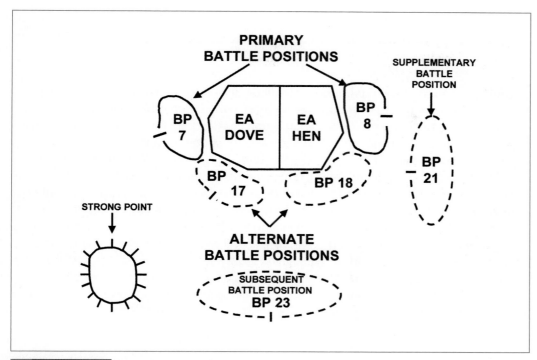

Figure 14.2 Defensive Battle Positions

recon, you must shift the "goose egg" left, right, forward, or back in order to meet your mission and the commander's intent, then you report this to your company commander for approval. Reflecting back on the Squad Tactics: Ambush (Section 12), recall that the "goose egg" objective given to you in the OPORD was further refined to a kill zone that you determine during the leader's recon. Your platoon battle position for the defense is similar in that you must confirm the "goose egg" that your commander assigns you once you are on the ground. If necessary, you should adjust it to tie in to the unit on your left or right, or readjust it in order to kill the enemy in the engagement area.

Squad Positions

As a guideline, a squad can occupy a front of about 100 meters. From this position, it can defend from 200 to 250 meters of frontage. The frontage distance between two-man fighting positions should be about 20 meters (in a "lazy W" configuration on the ground, fighting positions would be about 25 meters apart). Every position should be observed and supported by the fires of at least two other positions. One-man fighting positions may be located closer together to occupy the same platoon frontage.

The distance between fighting positions depends on the leader's analysis of the factors of METT-TC. In determining the best distance between fighting positions, the squad leader must consider:

- The requirement to cover the squad's assigned sector by fire
- The need for security to prevent enemy infiltrations of the squad position
- The requirement to prevent enemy fighters from using hand grenades effectively to assault adjacent positions, should they seize a fighting position.

Critical Thinking

One- and two-Soldier fighting positions will result in more fighting positions, which results in a larger defensive front covering more terrain. But at best they offer only 50 percent security during priorities of work (preparing and improving fighting positions; walking dead space; conducting LP/OP or security patrols, weapons maintenance, or personal hygiene; eating; and resting). The three-Soldier fighting position has fewer fighting positions, and therefore will typically cover a smaller defensive front than two-Soldier fighting positions. It will afford up to 66 percent security during priorities of work. The platoon and squad leader must balance the requirement to cover a wide front with multiple two-Soldier fighting positions with the desirability of emplacing three-Soldier fighting positions that will allow Soldiers the opportunity to conduct priorities of work while maintaining higher security. What tactics, techniques, and procedures can you implement to achieve priorities of work when defending with two-Soldier fighting positions? How do you maintain security and cover key weapons, dead space, and engagement areas if you must also operate LP/OPs or security patrols?

Platoon Positions

As the platoon leader, you assign primary positions and sectors of fire to your machine guns and anti-armor weapons, even if those weapons are task organized to one of your squad leaders. You must personally check the sectors of fire and FPL of each machine gun and anti-tank weapon. You assign primary positions and sectors of fire to your squads. The squad leader normally assigns the alternate positions for the squad and has you approve them. Each squad's sector must cover its own sector of fire and overlap into that of the adjacent squad. The sectors of flank squads should overlap those of adjacent platoons. You also assign supplementary positions if required. You may choose to position your squads in depth to gain or enhance mutual support.

Fighting Positions

Soldiers must construct fighting positions that protect them and allow them to fire into their assigned sectors.

In sandy soil, do not drive vehicles within six feet of the positions or the sides of the fighting position—it can collapse inward, crushing Soldiers.

Protection. Fighting positions protect Soldiers by providing *cover* through sturdy construction and by providing *concealment* through positioning and proper camouflage. The enemy must not be able to identify the position until they are already in the platoon or squad's engagement area. When possible, Soldiers should site positions in places that are not obvious, behind natural cover, and in locations that are easy to camouflage. The most important step in preparing a fighting position is to make sure the enemy cannot see it. In constructing fighting positions, Soldiers should always:

- Dig the positions armpit deep
- Fill sandbags about 75 percent full
- Check to make sure wall bases are stable
- Inspect and test the structural soundness of the fighting position daily, after heavy rain, and after receiving direct or indirect fires
- Maintain, repair, and improve positions as required
- Use appropriate construction materials and techniques. The weight of a sandbagged overhead cover can exceed several hundred pounds. The fighting position must be able to maintain this load or Soldiers can be crushed to death if the structure fails.

Observations and Fields of Fire. Soldiers must be able to engage the enemy within their assigned sectors of fire. They should be able to fire out to the maximum effective range of their weapons with the most grazing fire possible and the least possible dead space. Soldiers and leaders must be able to identify the best locations for their positions that meet these criteria. Leaders must also ensure that fighting positions provide interlocking fires. This allows them to cover the platoon's sector from several positions and provides a basis for FPFs.

Prepare by Stages. Leaders must ensure that their Soldiers understand when and how to prepare fighting positions based on the situation. Soldiers normally prepare hasty fighting positions whenever the platoon makes an extended halt, such as in a patrol base, whereas occupying a hasty or deliberate defensive position would require more than a hasty fighting position. Remember, only half your Soldiers will be digging while the other half maintains security. Soldiers prepare positions in stages; a leader must inspect the position before Soldiers move on to the next stage.

Types of Fighting Positions

There are many different types of fighting positions. The number of Soldiers, types of weapons, the time available, and the terrain are the main factors that dictate the type of position.

Initial Fighting Position. (Figure 14.3) Soldiers prepare this type of position when there is little or no time to prepare fighting positions. They dig in behind whatever cover is available where they can cover their assigned sector of fire. The position should give frontal protection from direct fire while allowing fire to the front and oblique.

An initial position may consist simply of a rucksack placed beside a tree or large rock. For protection from indirect fire, an initial fighting position should be in a small depression or hole at least 18 inches deep. The term *initial position* does not mean no digging. Even if there are only a few minutes, a Soldier can scrape out prone shelter to provide some protection. This type of position is well suited for ambushes or for protecting overwatching elements during raids and attacks. Initial positions can also be the first step in building more-elaborate positions.

Figure 14.3 Initial Fighting Position

Figure 14.4   One-Soldier Fighting Position

One-Soldier Fighting Position. (Figure 14.4) This type of position allows choice in the use of cover. The hole only needs to be large enough for one Soldier with gear.

This position does not have the security of a two-Soldier position (remember that you must give each Soldier time to conduct priorities of work). The one-Soldier fighting position must allow a Soldier to fire to the front or to the oblique from behind frontal cover. When the Soldier in a one-Soldier position is conducting priorities of work, an adjacent one-Soldier fighting position must cover both their sectors of fire.

Two-Soldier Fighting Position. (Figure 14.5) A two-Soldier fighting position can be prepared in close terrain. Soldiers can use it where grazing fire and mutual support extend no farther than to an adjacent position. It can be used to cover dead space just in front of the position. One or both ends of the fighting position extend around the sides of the frontal cover. Configuring the fighting position in this way lets both Soldiers see better and have greater sectors of fire to the front. Also, one Soldier can watch the entire sector while the other sleeps or eats. If they receive fire from their front, they can move back to gain the protection of the frontal cover. By moving about one meter, the Soldiers can continue to find and hit targets to the front during lulls in enemy fire. This type of position requires more digging and is harder to camouflage. It is also a better target for enemy hand grenades.

Machine Gun Position. (Figure 14.6) The primary sector of fire is usually to the oblique so that the gun can fire across the platoon's front. The gunner uses the tripod on the side that covers the primary sector of fire and the FPL. The biped legs are used on the side that covers the secondary sector of fire. When changing from primary to secondary sectors, the gunner moves only the machine gun, not the tripod. Occasionally, a leader assigns a sector of fire that allows firing directly to the front, but this can reduce the frontal cover for the crew when firing to the oblique.

After you position the machine gun, you mark the position of the tripod legs and the limits of the sectors of fire. The crew then traces the outline of the hole and the frontal cover (if it must be improved). The crew digs the firing platforms for the bipod and tripod first to lessen their exposure in case they have to fire before they complete the position. The platforms must not be so low that the gunners cannot swivel the gun across its entire sector of fire. This reduces gunners' profiles when they are firing and reduces the height of the frontal cover.

Figure 14.5 Two-Soldier Fighting Position

Figure 14.6 Machine Gun Position

After digging the firing platforms, the crew digs the fighting position. They first place the dirt where frontal cover is needed. They dig the fighting position deep enough to protect them from direct and indirect weapon effects, while still allowing the gunner to fire the gun with comfort—usually about armpit deep. When the frontal cover is high and thick enough, the crew uses the rest of the dirt to build flank and rear cover. They dig trench-shaped grenade sumps at various points so that either Soldier can kick a grenade into one if needed. In some positions, a machine gun might not have a secondary sector of fire; so the Soldiers need prepare only half the position. The crew builds an overhead cover for a machine gun position the same as they would for a two-Soldier position.

When a machine gun has a three-Soldier crew, the ammunition bearer may construct a one-Soldier fighting position to the flank of the machine gun's position both to see and to fire to the front and oblique of the machine gun's position. If the machine gun is on a flank, you should always emplace a fighting position on the flank to prevent the enemy from flanking and overrunning the machine gun. The ammunition bearer can also protect the machine gun's flank, or you can place the ammo bearer to the side of the machine gun's FPL or PDF. This allows the Soldier to see and fire a rifle into the machine gun's secondary sector, and to maintain eye contact with the gunner and assistant gunner. The ammunition bearer's position is connected to the gun position by a crawl trench so the bearer can deliver more ammo or, if needed, become the assistant gunner in the event the gunner or AG becomes a casualty.

Antiarmor Weapon Position. (Figure 14.7) Soldiers can fire the AT4 and Javelin from dismounted fighting positions if the fighting positions are properly constructed to account for the weapon's backblast area. If the gunner is to fire the missile from a two-Soldier position, the gunner must ensure that the other Soldier is not in the backblast area.

DANGER

When Soldiers use antiarmor weapon systems from a dismounted fighting position, they must take care to ensure that no injuries to friendly Soldiers result. SOLDIERS MUST BE CLEAR OF THE BACKBLAST AREA. Do not locate other fighting positions in the backblast area. The gunner must ensure there is nothing (walls, trees, or other objects) to the rear of the weapon to deflect the backblast back toward the gunner.

Figure 14.7 Antiarmor Weapon Position

Fire-Control Measures

Responsibility for Fire Control

Normally, in a company or battalion defense, all antiarmor fires (except AT4s) are part of the battalion or company fire plan (Javelins and TOWs are organic to the company antitank section and TOWs are organic to the battalion antitank section or platoon). One leader controls all antiarmor weapons firing from a single position or into a single engagement area. Platoon leaders normally control the fires of machine guns and organic, attached, or operational-control (OPCON) antitank weapons. Squad leaders and team leaders control automatic rifles, grenade launchers, and rifle fire. The platoon leader can call for or adjust pre-planned indirect fires or close air support (CAS), but remember that the battalion will have established the priorities of indirect fires and CAS in the battalion fire-support plan. So you may or may not have indirect fire or CAS support available to you. If your company is the battalion's main effort, and your platoon is the company's main effort, you may have a **fire support team** (FIST) OPCON attached to your platoon who can best control indirect fire and CAS in your engagement area. If your battalion is the brigade main effort, you may have a **combat observation and lasing team** (COLT) located in your platoon battle position. The COLT may control CAS and indirect fires into your engagement area.

Control Measures

Platoon and squad leaders use the following fire-control measures to concentrate, distribute, and shift fires. (Figure 14.8 depicts fire-control measures.)

Sectors. You use *sectors of fire* to assign responsibility and ensure distribution of fires across the platoon and squad front. Sectors should always overlap with adjacent sectors.

Engagement Areas. You use *engagement areas* (EA) to concentrate all available fires into an area where you intend to kill the enemy.

Target Reference Point. A *target reference point* (TRP) is an easily recognizable point on the ground, such as a building or a road junction, used with engagement areas and sectors of fire to initiate, distribute, and control direct and indirect fires. A TRP may be a natural terrain feature, a building, or a marker the unit has emplaced.

Trigger. Triggers are either:

- Event-oriented or time-oriented criteria used to initiate planned actions directed toward achieving surprise and destroying as much of the enemy force as possible; or
- A designated point or points (selected along identifiable terrain) in an engagement area used to mass fires at a predetermined range.

Waiting for the main body of the attacking force to enter the engagement area before engaging would be an example of an *event-oriented trigger* in the defense. Waiting three minutes after spotting the advance guard before calling for pre-planned indirect fires would be an example of a *time-oriented trigger*. During low visibility, you can use *trigger points* in the defense by placing thermal pads (facing away from the enemy) in the engagement area at your weapons' maximum effective range and observing the engagement area with thermal optics. This will let you know (trigger) when you can engage the enemy and with which weapons. A trigger point may be an easily identifiable natural or man-made feature in the engagement area, such as a rock outcropping, water tower, building, intersection, etc. You select triggers that are at or near the maximum effective range of your weapons and direct the fires of those weapons when the attacker reaches the trigger points.

---

fire support team (FIST)

an Army team provided by the field artillery component to each maneuver company and troop to plan and coordinate all indirect fire means available to the unit, including mortars, field artillery, close air support, and naval gunfire

combat observation and lasing team (COLT)

a fire support team controlled at the brigade level that can locate targets under reduced-visibility conditions and has both laser-range-finding and laser-designating abilities

phase line

a line used for control and coordination of military operations, usually an easily identified terrain feature extending across the area of operation

Trigger Line. A *trigger line* is a **phase line** you use to initiate and mass fires into an engagement area or an objective at a predetermined range. It is located on identifiable terrain that crosses an EA. PLs can designate one trigger line for all weapon systems or separate trigger lines for each weapon or type of weapon to control fires in depth. The PL specifies the engagement criteria for each trigger line. Examples of trigger lines may be a hedgerow, trail, stream, or roads that cross the engagement area. You can also place thermal devices on or along trigger lines for use during limited visibility.

Note:

Burn barrels, tires, and oil pots can be used as thermal markers if your platoon does not have thermal pads or blankets. The MRE heater can also be used for short periods.

Fire Patterns. These include *frontal, crossfire,* and *fires in depth.* These patterns describe the relationship between the weapons and the targets. The intent is to ensure that weapons do not waste ammunition firing on the same target while other targets remain unengaged.

Engagement Priorities. These designate the priority for engaging key targets, including leaders, RTOs, crew-served weapons, and engineers.

Rate of Fire. Each weapon's technical manual will specify the weapon's rate of fire. You and your Soldiers must know and understand each weapon's rate of fire to avoid overheating the barrel. If short on ammo, you must establish lower rates of fire to prevent wasting it. For example, you may direct that riflemen only engage with semi-automatic fire rather than burst fire.

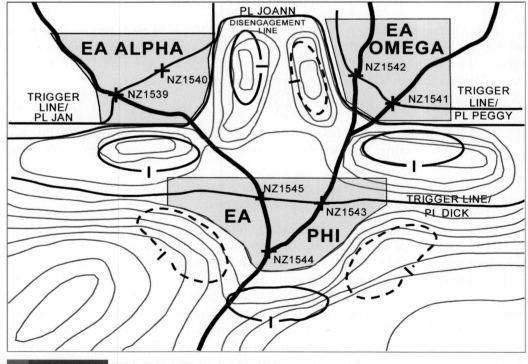

Figure 14.8 Direct Fire Control Measures

Sector Sketches

You prepare sector sketches based on y⟋ ⟋fensive plan. You use the range card for each crew-served weapon (the gunners pre⟋ and their squad leader or supervisor checks it first).

Squad Sector Sketch

Each squad leader prepares a sector sketch to help plan the defense and control fire (Figure 14.9). The squad leader prepares two copies of the sector sketch, giving one to you and keeping the second for use at the position. The SOP should state how soon after occupying the position leaders must forward sketches. The sketch shows the following:

- Squad and platoon identification
- Date/time group
- Magnetic north
- The main terrain features in the sector of fire and the ranges to them
- Each primary fighting position
- Alternate and supplementary positions
- The primary and secondary sectors of fire of each position
- **Maximum engagement line (MEL)**
- Machine gun FPLs or PDF
- AT4/Javelin positions with sectors of fire
- The type of weapon in each position
- Observation posts and the squad leader's position
- Dead space, including coverage by grenade launchers
- Obstacles, mines, and booby traps.

maximum engagement line

graphic representation of the maximum effective range of a weapon system—in the defense, you do not engage the enemy force until it has closed within this line

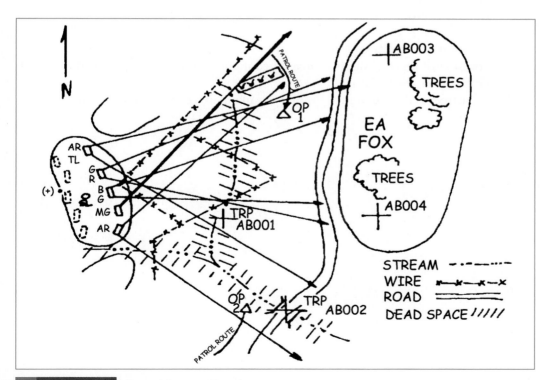

Figure 14.9 Squad Sector Sketch

Critical Thinking

Explain how the elements of planning and coordination serve critical roles in the various stages of defensive operations.

Platoon Sector Sketch

As a platoon leader, you check range cards and squad sector sketches. If you find gaps or other flaws in the fire plan, you adjust the weapons or sectors as needed. If you find any dead space, you take steps to cover it with mines, grenade-launcher fire, or indirect fire. You then make two copies of your platoon-sector sketch (one for your use; the other for your company commander) (Figure 14.10). Your sketch shows the following:

- Squad sectors of fire
- Machine gun and antiarmor weapon positions and their sectors of fire, including FPLs and PDFs of the automatic rifles/machine guns and TRPs for the antiarmor weapons
- Maximum engagement lines for antiarmor weapons
- Mines (Claymores) and obstacles
- Indirect fire planned in the platoon's sector of fire (targets and FPF)
- OPs and patrol routes, if any
- Platoon CP
- Platoon/company identification
- Date/time group
- Magnetic north
- Location of casualty collection point
- Location of thermal sights or magnified night optics that are part of the limited-visibility security plan
- Adjustments during limited visibility to maintain coverage of assigned TRPs.

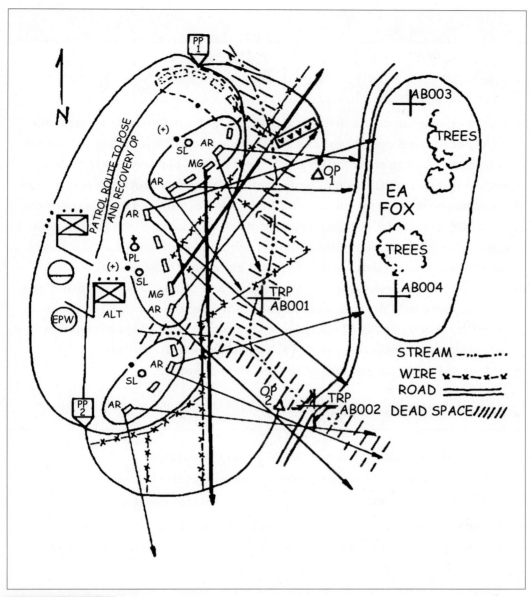

Figure 14.10 Platoon Sector Sketch

CONCLUSION

Your platoon may conduct a defense as part of a larger defense, for an assembly area (AA) or forward operations base (FOB). Or, you may be tasked to defend key infrastructure or some other facility or compound. Your platoon may need to defend its own patrol base while conducting combat patrols outside the FOB. Your platoon may be defending a platoon battle position as part of a battalion defense in sector. Or, as with the historical vignette at the beginning of this section, you may be conducting a decentralized platoon offensive operation when the enemy surprises you—thus, squads, teams, and even individuals must execute a hasty defense in order to survive, regain the initiative, and counterattack to destroy the enemy that once held the tactical advantage. Knowing the principles of the defense; the characteristics of the defense; and the standard steps in planning, coordinating, and conducting the defense will allow you to successfully defend, regardless of the enemy you face or the terrain you fight on.

Learning Assessment

1. What is the standard sequence of actions in the defense?
2. List and define eight fire-control measures used in the defense.
3. What do you look for when you review squad sector sketches?
4. Compare and contrast the characteristics of the offense and defense. Explain how the defender's addressing the characteristics of the offense can result in a successful defense.
5. What similarities exist between defensive operations and patrol base operations?
6. What does the Rangers' experience in Mogadishu illustrate about the need for US forces to be proficient in defensive operations?

Key Words

engagement area
final protective fires
final protective line
listening post/observation post (LP/OP)
canalize
grazing fire

reverse slope

fire support team

combat observation and lasing team

phase line

maximum engagement line

References

Field Manual 1-02, *Operational Terms and Graphics*. 21 September 2004.

Field Manual 3-21.8, *The Infantry Rifle Platoon and Squad*. 28 March 2007.

Field Manual 3-90, *Tactics*. 4 July 2001.

Perino, L. D. (1994). *Battle of the Black Sea: Mogadishu, Somalia*. US Army Infantry School. Fort Benning, GA. Retrieved February 18, 2005, from http://donovanlibrary.cdm.oclc.org/cgibin/docviewer.exe?CISOROOT=/coll8&CISOPTR=680

INDEX